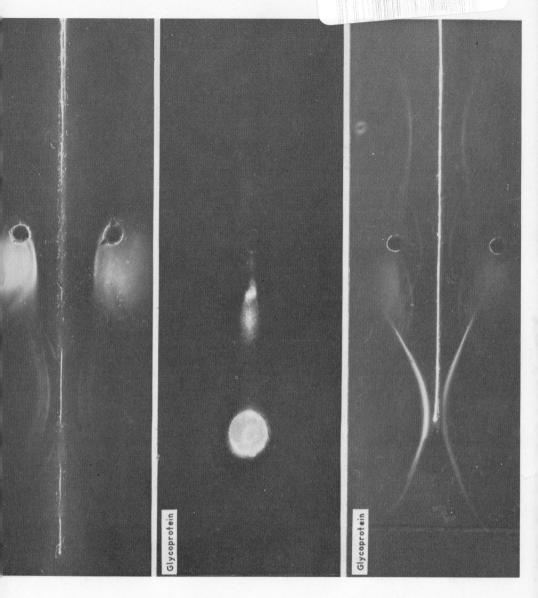

agar containing electrophoresed fractions. A double light green SF-thiazine red R stain was used for the first slide (top), thiazine red R alone for the second, oil red O for the third and fourth slides, and α-naphthol-paraphenylenediamine for the bottom two. Photographic projection prints were made with the slides themselves used as negatives in an enlarger. Chemical nature of fractions stained on each slide is indicated in each print frame.

Immunodiffusion

Immunodiffusion

ALFRED J. CROWLE

Webb Institute for Medical Research
University of Colorado Medical Center
Denver, Colorado

1961

ACADEMIC PRESS
New York and London

DEDICATED TO

J. OUDIN, O. OUCHTERLONY, S. D. ELEK, and P. GRABAR

PIONEERS IN THE PERFECTION AND POPULARIZATION
OF SEMI-SOLID MEDIUM SEROLOGIC TECHNIQUES

Preface

In the past decade immunology has enjoyed an obvious rise in popular medical and biochemical thinking, growing from a subject regarded with only moderate interest by the average physician and biochemist of a few years ago to one now often occupying their foremost thoughts. In the author's opinion, there are two reasons for this rise. The first is that allergy is being implicated as a complicating or causative factor in increasing numbers of human diseases, most interestingly those of auto- or isohypersensitization. The second, and that directly relating to the subject of this book, is that by the recent prodigious developments of immunodiffusion serologic techniques, biological research has been provided with a type of analytic tool the like of which in specificity, resolution, and simplicity has never before been known; with it researchers are performing serologic analyses which would have astounded the immunologist of a decade ago. Immunodiffusion as an analytic method has developed from something of a laboratory curiosity, misunderstood and mistrusted, into a well accepted technique now more often employed by non-serologists than by those who rightly can think of it as a proud development of their own field. Believing that its infancy is passing away and its maturation is beginning, the author thinks that the time has arrived to document basic knowledge of immunodiffusion, formally record the history of its development, demonstrate how usefully it has been employed, introduce its techniques to potential new users, and gather into one reference work various sorts of knowledge on these techniques, often obscure and overlooked, which will aid those who already utilize immunodiffusion.

The theory of antigen-antibody reactions in semi-solid media still is rather poorly developed, and its mathematical details will not interest most users of immunodiffusion. Moreover, a discussion of the mathematics of this theory would be excessively lengthy for a book of this size. Hence, theory is approached in Chapters II and III in a general, non-mathematical manner. In Chapter IV, the writer has striven to prepare a compendium of uses to which immunodiffusion has been put, but this summary must be acknowledged incomplete: immunodiffusion now is being applied in so many different fields, often being mentioned only obscurely, that completeness in any such survey is impossible. Chapter V describes in detail principal and accessory immunodiffusion techniques which in the author's opinion will best serve the reader. For those who are already users of immunodiffusion, this chapter includes descriptions of the latest improvements on established techniques. For the novice, it presents not only general methods but also details on subjects related to immunodiffusion techniques so often hard to find, such as how to photograph or stain antigen-antibody precipitin bands. Appendixes have been composed to supplement this chapter as a handy formulary, and a glossary is appended of terms commonly used in connection with immunodiffusion which might confuse the uninitiated.

The author wishes to thank several of his associates who have contributed to him their most valued assistance in preparing this book: Mrs. Lyle B. McMurry and Mrs. Peggy Braun for their secretarial work; Mr. David C. Lueker who with patience and enthusiasm has set up numerous experiments used to prepare photographic illustrations and to help answer a multitude of technical and theoretical questions which have arisen during preparation of this manuscript; the author's wife Clarice M. Crowle for her encouragement and her faithful help in many particulars, large and small; Dr. James J. Waring for his helpful suggestions on composition. To several others who have participated in lesser extent also goes the author's sincere thanks.

Preparation of this handbook has been greatly facilitated by financial assistance given to the author by the United States Department of Health, Education, and Welfare (Grants E-2283 and E-3697), the National Science Foundation (Grant G-4025), and the New York Tuberculosis and Health Association (James Alexander Miller Fellowship awarded the author, 1959–1960).

ALFRED J. CROWLE

Webb Institute for Medical Research
University of Colorado Medical Center
Denver, Colorado
July, 1961

Contents

CHAPTER I

History

Although a form of immunodiffusion test first was described in 1905 (Bechhold), in practice this technique received only passing attention for the next 40 years, to become popularly employed only after its rediscovery in 1946. The history of immunodiffusion, then, is divisible into a period of blind infancy before 1946 and a period of phenomenal maturation in following years. Its first period is interesting particularly for the examples it gives of great opportunities lost through misinterpretation and of how a technique may fail general acceptance until an atmosphere favoring its utilization has developed.

The first immunodiffusion test appears to have been described by a chemist, H. Bechhold, interested more in colloidal precipitation in gels than in antigen-antibody reactions. In his paper of 1905, he describes an experiment in which he incorporated rabbit antiserum to goat serum in 1% gelatin, poured this mixture into test tubes, gelled it in an ice box, and then overlaid this gel with goat serum for the purpose of studying a type of precipitation differing from that he could obtain with inorganic chemicals. After a time, two heavy but distinct precipitate bands appeared in his tubes, but the possibility that each might have been formed by independent goat serum antigens did not occur to him. A later paper (Bechhold and Ziegler, 1906) shows that his interest still rested in the physics of diffusion and precipitation; in this paper he reported the effects that various additives to gelatin and to agar had upon the diffusion rate of such substances as methylene blue through the gelatin and agar.

Arrhenius in 1907 saw the possibilities of using diffusion through gels to fractionate complex mixtures of antigens, but he did not use his ideas to develop any form of immunodiffusion test. He and Madsen allowed diphtheria or tetanus toxins, or their respective antibodies, to diffuse into gelatin gels in test tubes for 1 to 4 weeks. Then, they removed these gels, sectioned them, and analyzed them at various levels for separated reactants. These workers did not in any instance report using antigen and antibody together for reaction in one tube. In 1920, a primitive simple diffusion tube test was devised by Nicolle et al. for quantitating antitoxin against tetanus or diphtheria toxins. After in-

1

corporating toxin in gelatin in a series of tubes, they overlaid the gelatin in each tube with samples from a serial dilution of the antiserum to be tested and then observed whether or not a precipitate formed near the interface within 2 hours. This test was devised, simply, as a possible improvement on similar tests in aqueous media then also being developed. In 1927, Reiner and Kopp made observations similar to those of Bechhold.

The early 1930's saw the first significant practical use of immunodiffusion tests and foreshadowed, although unrecognizably to contemporaries, the developments to come a decade later which would establish this technique as a potent analytic tool. During this period, the simple diffusion plate test was employed successfully in several laboratories as a method for identifying bacteria. The unknown microorganism was cultured on agar containing antiserum specific for a known bacterial genus, species, group, or type. If a halo or band of precipitate formed around a colony planted on such agar by reaction of antiserum with antigen diffusing from the colony, then the inoculated bacterium was similar to that against which the antiserum had been prepared. G. F. Petrie must be given credit for originating this technique which he described in a paper published in 1932. Although this paper shows that he understood some of the mechanisms of antigen-antibody precipitation in agar gels, as in his predecessors, the idea that multiple halos might indicate multiple independent precipitates apparently remained dormant. He fully realized the specificity of the halos, for he showed that pneumococci and meningococci could be typed serologically with this technique. Associated with reaction specificity, and equally important in making immunodiffusion tests useful, is the so-called "reaction of identity" which is seen between precipitate bands formed by identical antigens. Petrie (1932) observed in his simple diffusion plates that if the areas of antigen diffusion from two adjacent bacterial colonies of the same serologic type (and therefore producing the same antigen) overlapped, the normally closed halos that should form around each colony now remained open where they faced each other and coalesced to form a "figure 8" (Fig. I-1). He understood that this mutual halo interference indicated serologic identity of the involved precipitating systems. Unfortunately, more than a dozen years passed before this basic observation was exploited again. Petrie described differences in the types of halos that were produced by rabbit and horse antisera, and stated that because it formed very broad halos, the former was unsatisfactory for analytic work in his plate technique. He came close to explaining this difference in type of precipitate, perhaps foreseeing that later simple diffusion tests would be used to differentiate precipitating-type from flocculating-type antibodies. A much briefer paper was published by Sia and Chung in the same year. They had developed independently the same simple diffusion plate method and also found it reliable for identifying pneumococcal types.

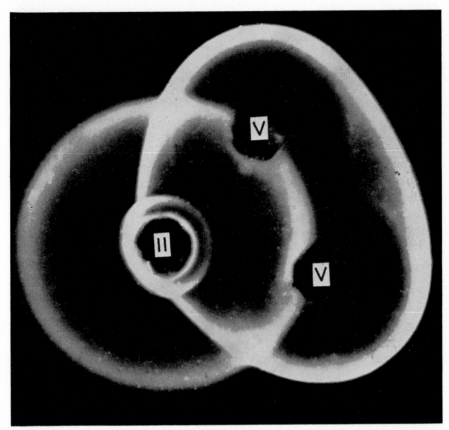

FIG. I-1. A single diffusion microscope slide test in which horse antiserum to human serum was used in the agar at a 1:10 dilution, 0.5% human serum Cohn Fraction V was used to fill two wells, and 1.0% human serum Cohn Fraction II was employed to fill the third. A single halo is formed by human serum albumin antigen in Fraction V, and the serologic identity of this antigen in the two wells charged with V is evident from the mutual interference and fusion of halos formed by each well into a flat oval of precipitate. Since neither the inner nor the outer of the two halos originating from the well charged with Fraction II is affected by the albumin halo, they are antigenically dissimilar.

Papers published in the following years by other experimenters confirmed Petrie's findings and recorded successful applications of this technique. In 1933, Maegraith used it to detect rough variants of meningococcus strains, variants which lacked capsular type-specific antigen. In the same year, Kirkbride and Cohen described before the national meeting of the Society of American Bacteriologists how they employed Petrie's method successfully to categorize bacteria, particularly meningococci and gonococci. In 1934, Maegraith and Adelaide reported that this technique enabled them both to detect and type meningococci in spinal fluid, a development of considerable practical importance in the days when, for lack of an effective therapeutic drug, meningitis was treated with type-specific antiserum. Pittman and co-workers (1938) confirmed that Petrie's test could be used to type meningococci. They also found it a useful method for quantitating antibody content in antiserum by the intensity of the precipitin halos that appeared, and reported that titers obtained by this simple diffusion test correlated well with protective antibody titers determined by mouse protection tests.

Three years before Oudin began publishing descriptions of his work with simple diffusion tube tests in which, at last, multiple precipitin bands were recognized and shown due to multiple simultaneously precipitating antigen-antibody systems, Petrie, in collaboration with Steabben (1943), used his simple diffusion plate to help identify a number of bacteria antigenically, among these members of the genus *Clostridium*. When these workers observed multiple halos forming in their plates, they still interpreted them as probably a form of periodic or Liesegang precipitation. Although they may very well have been partly correct in this interpretation, the important point is that even by 1942 no one seemed to recognize as a possibility the simultaneous occurrence of multiple antigen-antibody precipitates in a single test; Arrhenius' early idea of fractionating antigen and antibody mixtures by differential diffusion through semi-solid media still remained dormant.

Hanks in 1935 applied the type of test devised by Nicolle *et al.* (1920) to test the potency of small quantities of guinea pig antisera, but he did not attempt to use the simple diffusion tube test for qualitative analyses, nor did he impute to it any essential properties lacking in the usual tests with aqueous medium. In 1940, Brown might have stumbled upon the qualitative utility of simple diffusion tube tests had she not been interested primarily in Liesegang precipitation and assumed that any multiple precipitates which she saw in her experiments were of this type. She set up tests in which horse and rabbit antiserum were incorporated in 3% gelatin, and corresponding SSS and C substance antigens obtained from pneumococci were layered above. Photographs that she took of her tubes leave no doubt that she was observing in a given tube simultaneous formation of different specific precipitates corresponding to distinct antigen-antibody systems, but she overlooked this interpretation, rather stating that these tubes showed examples of rhythmic precipitation similar to the Liesegang phenomenon, which she originally had set out to study.

This then prevalent dogmatic idea that multiple precipitate bands merely were rhythmic precipitates formed by one antigen-antibody system all at once was challenged and overthrown by Jacques Oudin (1946) employing the same type of simple diffusion tube test which previous experimenters had used but with different notions. Thus, although his technique was not new, his fresh and deeper interpretations led him to establish immunodiffusion in its present standing and form, an analytic technique for mixed antigen-antibody systems of unsurpassed resolution and specificity, and of great reliability. From his initial observations he developed the basic tenets of immunodiffusion reactions which still hold true. Thus, he showed that concentrated antigen, layered over dilute agar-gelled antiserum in a tube, will diffuse into the antibody column forming a precipitin band which appears to migrate down the column in proportion to the antigen's initial concentration, to its diffusion coefficient, and inversely to the antibody concentration. A crude antigen used against its antiserum, he found, forms multiple lines corresponding to its multiple precipitating systems which precipitate and move independently of each other, unless one of the antigens tends to cross-react with the other. He showed that in this situation formation of precipitin bands and their interpretation becomes somewhat more complex.

Having published preliminary evidence on the utility of simple diffusion tests, Oudin set out over succeeding years in the 1940's to verify and elaborate his original findings, in particular, to develop theoretical bases for interpreting simple diffusion tube test results. He noted such points as (1) the positive correlation between precipitate intensity and antibody concentration in the lower agar layer, (2) the fact that sudden incubation temperature changes may cause appearance of artifacts (e.g., formation of secondary precipitates by a single antigen-antibody system) —and that these usually have distinguishing characteristics differentiating them from primary precipitates, (3) the fact that in tests set up by his method Liesegang bands never formed, and (4) how the presence of a cross-reacting antigen can influence the formation of precipitate by the homologous antigen (Oudin, 1947, 1948a,b, 1949).

These published experiments of Oudin employed only simple diffusion. Agar double diffusion precipitin techniques were being developed independently in Sweden and in England by Ouchterlony and Elek, respectively, who both published their first findings in 1948 (Ouchterlony, 1948a,b; Elek, 1948). Interestingly, both experimenters developed their methods largely as tests for diphtheria bacillus toxigenicity. The following year, Elek (1949a) elaborated on his previous account of his technique which was based on the principle that if antigen and antibody are allowed to diffuse into a common meeting ground from sources set at right angles to each other (e.g., impregnated filter paper strips in the form of an L), each antigen-antibody precipitating system will flocculate in an individual plane to form a precipitate band uninfluenced by any bands formed by other systems. In this paper, he described some of the technique's applications, and discussed how it functioned relative to contemporary theoretical understanding of classic precipitin tests in aqueous media; he pointed out particular advantages it had over these. Elek published one more paper in 1949 on diphtheria bacillus virulence (1949b) and two in 1950 (1950a,b) on staphylococcus antigens, but then he turned to other problems not connected with double diffusion tests or their mechanisms. Establishment of basic theories for double diffusion plate tests, aside from Elek's first 1949 paper, must be acknowledged as Ouchterlony's accomplishment. In addition to two reports in 1949 on using double diffusion precipitin techniques for toxigenicity tests (1949a,b), he also published a series of three papers on the mechanisms and theory of these precipitin tests in agar gel (1949c,d,e). Moreover, his interest in immunodiffusion has continued in succeeding years. In 1953 he published a fourth in his series, and recently he composed a review on immunodiffusion techniques (Ouchterlony, 1958).

Once the reliability and amazing analytic acuity of immunodiffusion tests had been established by Oudin, Ouchterlony, and Elek, other experimenters were quick to begin applying them to their own problems, to adapt and refine them, and to use them for studying the mechanisms of antigen-antibody reaction. The initial few scattered publications mentioning use of immunodiffusion since has swelled to a volume published yearly which defies complete survey, particularly because the technique has become so well accepted that it is increasingly employed without mention in a paper's title. The art of using immunodiffusion tests has not yet matured enough to give historical perspective to most developments in it, but a few seem sufficiently outstanding to warrant their mention as part of immunodiffusion history, even though some are very recent.

Indubitably, the most significant advance in immunodiffusion techniques since their original popularization has been their development into a new method, *immunoelectrophoresis*, in which one of the reactants is fractionated electrophoretically before it is allowed to react with the other. Thus, the advantages of electrophoretic resolution and definition are added to those already existing in the double diffusion test. Mixtures of substances antigenically identical and unresolvable in single and double diffusion tests can be distinguished from each other by immunoelectrophoresis if they have different electrophoretic mobilities. Moreover, in addition to providing serological identification of a single antigen in what may be a very complex mixture of antigens immunoelectrophoresis can indicate its electrophoretic mobility. An early form of immunoelectrophoresis was described in 1952 by M. D. Poulik who electrophoresed purified diphtheria toxoid on filter paper, embedded the toxoid under a layer of agar, and then laid upon the gelled agar a second piece of filter paper soaked with antiserum so that precipitin arcs formed between the paper strips in the agar gel. In 1953, Grabar and Williams described a method for immunoelectrophoresis in which electrophoresis and subsequent double diffusion precipitin reactions were carried out in a single slab of agar. Extensive use of this method in Grabar's laboratory by his various collaborators, as reported in numerous subsequent publications, has established its values and limitations and has been a prime force in its popularization. The word *immunoelectrophoresis* was used first in technical papers by Williams and Grabar (1955a) and Martin *et al.* (1955), who reported on its utility in analyzing human serum antigens. Immunoelectrophoresis has been improved technically and its value greatly extended by applying to it specific staining and indicator techniques usually adapted from known histological methods. Experiments performed by Uriel and Scheidegger, described in 1955, showed that serum constituents which were electrophoresed in agar could be stained readily, and a year later these experiments led to the classic publication by Uriel and Grabar (1956a) describing methods for detecting proteins, lipids, phospholipids, and glycoproteins in immunoelectropherograms.

This paper, however, was not the first to have described methods for staining precipitin bands in agar. Björklund had showed in 1954 (1954a,b) that polysaccharide antigens in double diffusion plate precipitates could be stained specifically either with mucicarmine or with basic fuchsin. Korngold and Lipari reported (1955a), without giving procedural details, that with current techniques for paper electropherograms, they could stain the lipids in antibody-precipitated β-lipoprotein bands of double diffusion plates using Sudan black B and oil red O.

An important advance in immunoelectrophoresis was made when it was miniatured by Scheidegger (1955). His modification for carrying it out on microscope slides simplified the equipment and techniques needed, considerably shortened the time required for all steps in the method (e.g., electrophoresis, double diffusion reaction development, staining), and instituted great savings of reactants, all at the cost of only a slight loss in resolving power.

Analogous variations in methods for setting up other immunodiffusion tests have been numerous. Some have proved to be particularly useful. Utilization of a double diffusion tube technique first was reported in 1951 by Pope *et al.* who give credit for invention of this technique to C. L. Oakley. Since this method first was fully described two years later by Oakley and Fulthorpe (1953), it often bears their names. The technique later was miniatured by J. R. Preer, Jr. (1956), whose improved method most workers now follow. In 1954, Jennings and Malone reported using a double diffusion gradient technique in which the reaction arena had a triangular shape. One of the chief advantages of their innovation was that by the shape of the reaction arena and the type of immunodiffusion cell employed, reactants could be used very effectively, being able only to diffuse toward their immunologic reaction centers. Two years after Scheidegger had miniatured immunodiffusion plates, Hartmann and Toilliez (1957) did the same for the double diffusion test. Their technique simply called for pouring melted agar on a microscope slide, punching depot holes in this agar, after it had gelled, with a small punch such as a sawed-off hypodermic needle, and charging the depots with the minute quantities of reactants required. In the same year, Wadsworth in Sweden (1957) described a more efficient semi-miniaturing of the double diffusion test in which reactants were fed into very thin sheets of agar gel on lantern slide glass plates from plastic matrixes. This technique soon afterward was adapted in this country to more convenient use on microscope slides (Crowle, 1958c).

For several years, precipitin immunodiffusion patterns could be recorded permanently only by photography or drawing. Now, the precipitin tests themselves can be preserved. P. G. H. Gell appears to have reported earliest an effort at such preservation (1955b). He showed that the gel in which the precipitin reactions had occurred could be washed, mounted on a lantern slide, dried, and finally preserved with a coating of protective plastic. In the following year, Rondle and Carman (1956) published a short communication on a method for washing, staining, drying, and preserving double diffusion precipitin tests carried out in Petri dishes. They used either a negative stain (toluidin blue) or, with better results, naphthol black or Congo red positive stains, and they preserved their dried, stained agar with clear plastic coatings or by mounting it under glass. It is the classic 1956 contribution of Uriel and Grabar mentioned above (1956a), however, which seems to have been the root of most methods now used for permanently preserving original immunodiffusion patterns.

Specific precipitates may occur in immunodiffusion tests which are so faint as to be invisible, unphotographable, and perhaps not amenable to revelation by special enhancement or staining techniques. It is in such a situation as this that autoradiography could excel, since immunologic fixation of a radioactive (tagged) antigen in agar could be detected by the ability of this antigen's invisible band of aggregate to record its own image on photo-sensitive material. Prolonged exposure of the photosensitive film and tagging with a strongly radioactive substance could extend the sensitivity of immunodiffusion considerably through autoradiography. This technique appears to have been introduced into the art of immunodiffusion by Perlmann and Hultin in 1958. Their antigen was labeled with C^{14}, and their autoradiograms compared well with photographs of similar precipitin patterns stained with protein-specific azocarmine B showing that the precipitin bands recording their own images by radioactive emanations did so by means of the tagged protein antigens partly constituting these images.

As is true of any technique, particularly in its infancy, new modifications constantly are being improvised which offer various advantages over older methods. The above discussion has been intended merely to give the reader a casual acquaintance with highlights in the development of immunodiffusion; by necessity, this discussion has been selective. Fuller details of several of these events and of other discoveries, which the future may show to figure prominently in the history of immunodiffusion but have not been included here, will unfold in chapters which follow.

CHAPTER II

Basic Considerations in Immunodiffusion Tests

Immunodiffusion tests are best applied and interpreted with a knowledge in hand of basic factors affecting them. The purpose of the present chapter is to supply this information in an elementary form, avoiding advanced theoretical considerations in the interests of simplicity and brevity, and because some of these considerations still are controversial enough to require lengthy discussion not of particular interest to the average user of immunodiffusion. The nature and mechanisms of antigen-antibody precipitin reactions, the characteristics of diffusion in semi-solid media, and the essentials of zone electrophoresis, will be discussed.

The ability of antibodies specifically to precipitate antigens from solution in a test tube has been recognized for more than six decades (Wilson and Miles, 1955). Specific agglutination had been observed occasionally before 1896 when Gruber and Durham published the first detailed paper on this phenomenon. A year later, Kraus described his serologic experiments which showed that certain substances in culture filtrates of plague or cholera bacteria were precipitated specifically by antiserum obtained from animals injected with these bacteria; he was describing antigen-antibody precipitation. Uhlenhuth showed in 1903 that the sensitivity of precipitin tests could be increased, and the range of antigen:antibody ratios yielding visible precipitation could be greatly extended if, instead of mixing antigen and antibody together all at once, he carefully layered the first upon the second and then observed their interface for appearance of a ring of precipitate. In this "ring test," original ratios of antigen to antibody used are far less critical than those in tubes in which the two are completely mixed, because mutual reactant diffusion across the interface creates locally a series of different reactant ratios some of which satisfy conditions for visible precipitation. This diffusion of one or both reactants to concentration ranges compatible with specific precipitation is one of the basic and distinctive features of immunodiffusion.

The Precipitin Reaction

The following discussion of antigen-antibody precipitation is based upon data and analyses published by various experimenters (Boyd,

11

1956; Carpenter, 1956; Cushing and Campbell, 1957; Grabar, 1957a, 1959b; Kabat, 1958; Marquevielle, 1957; Ouchterlony, 1958; Salvinien, 1957; Singer, 1957).

Antigen-antibody precipitation is the result of specific and firm, but partially or totally reversible, combination of the two reactants in which entire reactant molecules or fragments of them may combine, apparently at their respective surfaces, in two major stages, neither of which causes profound chemical change of antigen or antibody. In this reaction, antigen molecules behave like spheres, while antibody molecules have characteristics resembling ellipsoids. Precipitates, which may form at any of several antigen-to-antibody ratios, consist principally of antigen and antibody, but they also may contain other substances such as lipids and nonantibody serum proteins.

Specific precipitation begins in its first, or complexing, stage with a very rapid but invisible combination of antigen molecules with antibody molecules. It becomes visible during a second, or aggregation, stage which takes far more time, relatively, to develop and consists of formation from the initial rather small soluble antigen-antibody complexes of a growing network or lattice of these complexes, which becomes too large to remain either invisible or soluble and hence becomes the visible precipitate. The first stage is more readily reversible than the second and probably is more specific. Under certain conditions, it may fail to develop into an aggregation phase.

Antigen-antibody complexing in the first stage results from an attraction between the two reactants which is strong enough so that when two individual molecules nearly or actually happen to collide, they combine. This attraction may be one or more of five different types: (1) positive-negative chemical group attraction, (2) dipole-dipole attraction, (3) dipole-ion attraction, (4) attraction by van der Waals forces, or (5) hydrogen bonding. Since these reactions are due to certain groups on a given reacting molecule, if this molecule is disrupted into not-too-simple fractions, some of the groups may be active and able to yield a visible precipitate. If most of these fractions possess only one reactive site, however, they become incapable of forming the lattice required for visible precipitation, although they may react well enough to complete the first stage. Animals often produce antibodies, which, like these fragments, complex with antigen but do not aggregate it. The aggregation phase also may be prevented if one reactant exceeds the other, tying up its combining sites so that they are prevented from forming the lattice bridgework anchors which they would form under more nearly equivalent conditions. Incomplete precipitation, such as these instances exemplify, can be important in immunodiffusion because, although it is invisible, it can have visible effects on normal precipitation, weakening or preventing it by deviating one of the reactants. Thus, combination without precipitation can interfere with more complete reactions occurring in a mutual reaction area, since active groups on components ordinarily able to precipitate may be blocked by combination with "incomplete" antigen or antibody.

Occasionally, reactive areas on one type of antigen molecule may be spatially and electrically similar enough to cross-react with antibodies directed against a different antigen; viewed from another aspect, the spectrum of antibodies in an antiserum includes a large proportion able to react with heterologous, although similar, antigen, especially if the antiserum has been produced by hyperimmunization. For example, duck ovalbumin will precipitate an appreciable quantity of antibody from an antiserum against chicken ovalbumin. An antiserum against one antigen may cross-react with two other entirely different antigens related only to the first but suggesting by their reaction with the heterologous antiserum that they are identical. Thus, although a prime characteristic of antigen-antibody precipitation is its specificity, this characteristic is variable, and its variability must be recognized if interpretive errors are to be avoided. Augustin (1959a) has published a brief but cogent exposé of this problem (see also Fig. III-2 in Chapter III).

The first stage of the precipitin reaction is specific; and although the second stage also has specificity, its degree has not been settled. Lattice arrangement of antigen and antibody molecules in the latter stage depends upon the molecules' specific interaction, but other not directly related factors can influence antigen-antibody aggregation strongly, preventing it, modifying its form, or enhancing it. These factors may not act, as similar ones do in the first stage, upon the specific combining mechanisms of antigen and antibody, but rather, they can act upon various other physico-chemical mechanisms of aggregation in ways which are yet poorly understood.

Antigen and antibody combine in different ratios. This combination is the most susceptible to rearrangement or reversal during the earliest stages of the precipitin reaction. The proportions and sequence in which antigen and antibody are mixed in immunodiffusion tests tend to regulate what kind of reaction will appear. If either reactant, particularly antigen, greatly exceeds the amount with which the other can combine optimally, an unstable complex may form but never progress to the stage of aggregation. Consequently, the strongest precipitation will be obtained most rapidly when antigen-to-antibody proportions are best matched; that is, when both are used in the region of optimal proportions. The reversibility of antigen-antibody combination and the liability of combinant rearrangement during specific precipitation also depends upon the characteristics of the antibody and of the antigen being used. For example, horse antibodies against most proteins form readily reversible combinations with their antigens. With this kind of system, inhibition or reversal of antigen-antibody aggregation is obtained readily with either antibody or antigen excess, and visible precipitation is prevented by these conditions of excess reactant. Horse antibodies to polysaccharides, however, or rabbit antibodies to proteins or polysaccharides form less reversible combinations with their antigens. Excesses of these antibodies usually only partially inhibit visible precipitation, and they have very little dissociating effect upon already-formed aggregates. To varying degrees, excess antigens in such systems may prevent visible precipitation or dissolve formed aggregates. Antibodies of the horse antiprotein type which apparently combine with antigen rather tenuously and quite reversibly are called, popularly, "H" or "flocculating" antibodies, while the more tenacious antibodies formed typically by rabbits are known as "R" or "precipitating" antibodies (Fig. II-1). Both kinds can occur in human beings (Roitt *et al.*, 1958), and although one species of animal (e.g., the horse) may be especially prone to produce one of them, their appearance in a given species depends largely upon what kind of antigen is used in their induction and how it is administered.

Various physico-chemical factors affect the first stage of specific precipitation. Although antigen-antibody combination can occur in the absence of electrolytes, it is aided by their presence. There is an optimal pH range for such combination beyond which the reaction is inhibited, perhaps by chemical changes of the reactants themselves. Optimal electrolyte concentration and pH cannot be predicted on the basis of present information for a given, previously untested system, although generally satisfactory results will be obtained if the natural *in vivo* environment of the antibody being used is simulated. This is exemplified nicely by the influence of temperature on antigen-antibody combination. While a range of 15°C. to 40°C. permits optimal combination for most types of antisera, usually obtained from warm-blooded animals, 10°C. seems to be optimal for antibodies produced in the frog, a cold-blooded species (Boyd, 1956).

The forces which bring about the second stage of precipitation, i.e., the visible reaction, are also affected by physico-chemical factors usually in ways that are readily demonstrated but not necessarily understood. Thus, factors promoting visible aggregation have been moderately well defined, but exactly how antigen-antibody complex aggregation occurs still remains to be determined. The most widely accepted notion of precipitation is that antigen-antibody aggregates bridge together, mostly by specific interaction, to form a lattice growing large enough to precipitate. The visibility and degree of insolubility of an aggregate depends, sometimes to an important extent, on the nature and ratio of hydrophobic and hydrophilic groups that its surface displays to the fluid around it.

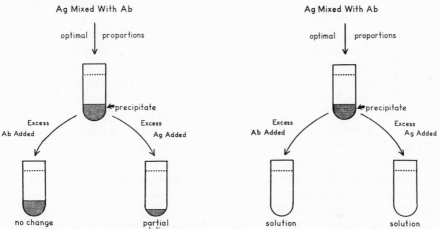

"R"-type Antibody

1. Horse ɣ Globulin Anti-protein
2. Horse Anti-polysaccharide
3. Rabbit Antibody

Ag Mixed With Ab

optimal | proportions

precipitate

Excess
Ab Added

Excess
Ag Added

no change

partial solution

"H"-type Antibody

1. Horse β Globulin Anti-protein

Ag Mixed With Ab

optimal | proportions

precipitate

Excess
Ab Added

Excess
Ag Added

solution

solution

Fig. II-1. A contrast of types and properties of the two most often used precipitins. The R-type antibody, typically produced in rabbits against various antigens, forms precipitates with antigen insoluble or poorly so in reactant excesses, particularly in antibody excess. H-type antibody, best exemplified by horse antitoxins, forms a precipitate with its antigen which is readily and usually completely soluble in either antibody or antigen excess. These differences between H and R antibodies control the type of precipitin band formed in immunodiffusion tests and often affect the significance of results.

Electrolytes usually must be present for aggregation to occur, but the quantities required by different systems can vary (see Aladjem and Lieberman, 1952). For example, while the optimal range for the horse antitoxin-diphtheria toxin system and for most other systems which have been studied is between 0.05 and 0.25 M NaCl (Ouchterlony, 1958; Boyd, 1956), chicken precipitins require NaCl more in the order of 1.5 M for optimal precipitation in liquid media (Goodman *et al.*, 1957). At this concentration, both stages of specific precipitation of pneumococcus polysaccharide by horse antibody can be reversed (Boyd, 1956). Interestingly, although chicken precipitins require high electrolyte concentrations for optimal activity in liquid media, the same sera precipitate the same antigens much better at physiologic salt concentrations in immunodiffusion tests, whether these are performed in agar or gelatin gels or in cellulose acetate (Crowle and Lueker, unpublished). The optimal electrolyte concentration for any precipitin, even one of several in a single antiserum, is not predictable and for critical experiments should be determined by trial. Some electrolytes (salts of the metals cadmium, nickel, lanthanum, and cerium) in the minute quantities found in laboratory grade agars can enhance or inhibit specific precipitation (Crowle, 1958a, 1960a); their possible influence upon observed reactions should not be overlooked.

The second stage of the precipitin reaction is affected by pH within about the same range as the first stage. At pH lower than 6.5, nonspecific precipitation (e.g., of serum proteins) is likely to occur and create artifacts in immunodiffusion tests. At the other extreme, a pH exceeding about 8.2 may impede specific precipitation and tend to dissociate some antigen-antibody complexes. This is the reason why immunoelectrophoretic serum analyses are usually carried out in a buffer at pH 8.2 rather than the pH of 8.6 generally preferred for other electrophoretic methods of serum fractionation (Grabar, 1959a).

Mention has been made above of the influence of temperature on the primary stage of antigen-antibody precipitation. This influence seems to be greater on the second stage in that, although most precipitin reactions can be carried out over a wide temperature range from refrigerator temperature to 56°C., instances of a particular temperature yielding best results are common. Some specific precipitates form only in the cold, and these may disappear on warming (cf. Rheins et al., 1956). Generally, more complete precipitation is obtained at refrigerator temperatures of 0° to 4°C. than at higher temperatures. The biggest advantage to using higher temperatures is one of accelerating precipitation and, in immunodiffusion tests, of causing more rapid reactant diffusion through a semisolid medium. In deciding what temperature to use, one must choose between this advantage and the likelihood of obtaining less precipitation and possibly missing some reactions all together as well as the possibility that precipitin bands formed at higher temperatures will be fuzzier, causing decreased resolution, than those formed in the cold. The cooler temperatures also are less likely to denature reactants. Some types of immunodiffusion tests (e.g., simple diffusion) are prone to developing confusing artifacts if their temperature fluctuates more than 2 or 3 degrees. Hence, in immunodiffusion, selecting a working temperature may be dictated partially by methods and apparatus available for best maintaining constant temperatures.

Other factors which may affect specific precipitation and, particularly in immunodiffusion tests, events leading up to it are (1) the proportions in which antigen and antibody are used, (2) the presence of lipids in the reactants, (3) the presence of proteins foreign to the reaction itself, and (4) the presence of extraneous substances.

That the nature and quantity of precipitate depend largely on antigen-antibody proportions is common knowledge among users of serologic techniques. There is an optimal range of ratios which gives the maximum, fastest, and most stable precipitate and within which can lie two optimal proportions ratios which may but usually do not exactly coincide. One is that resulting when decreasing quantities of antigen are mixed with constant quantities of antibody in a series of tubes, and the other is that obtained when decreasing quantities of antibody are mixed with constant quantities of antigen. The optimal proportions range acting in immunodiffusion tests and evidenced by precipitin band formation probably is not equivalent to either of these, but rather is more a blending of their characteristics in which at the front of a forming band, antibody predominates, and at the rear, antigen is dominant, and between these two extremes are to be found precipitating complexes with gradually varying antigen-to-antibody ratios all of which, within the area of the precipitin band, are able to precipitate (Fig. II-2). The ratio of one reactant to another becomes most important in immunodiffusion tests when it initially is highly unbalanced: under such conditions artifacts may appear, a band may develop too rapidly for study and interfere with resolution of other bands, or, a precipitate may never develop at all.

Proteins and various other substances different from the primary reactants may, in yet often unpredictable ways, influence antigen-antibody precipitation and phenomena leading up to it. Since many of these influences seem to be peculiar to immunodiffusion tests, especially the simple diffusion test, they will be discussed in more detail below in connection with this technique.

In most precipitin tests, both antibody and antigen are impure. Both reactants may be mixtures of substances of varying "avidity" and of differing specificity. Any precipitin band which forms is likely, then, to be the result of a range of antigen-antibody reactions, and in a given test more than one band may be constituted by a single reactant combining either with another single reactant or varieties of it (Crowle, 1960c). Antigens are more readily obtained "pure" than antibodies, but problems of serologic heterogeneity even among these highly purified

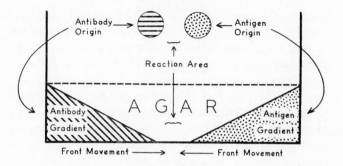

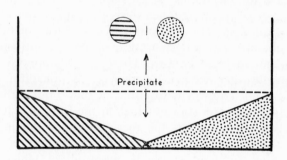

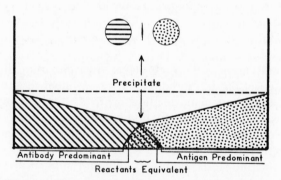

FIG. II-2. A diagrammatic representation of how precipitin bands develop in agar and of their composition. In the first drawing at the top of the figure, antigen and antibody diffusing from their respective origins toward the reaction area in agar have set up concentration gradients, the tips of which have not yet met but continue with time to move toward each other. Both reactants are assumed to be present in proportions which are optimal for this hypothetical double diffusion test. In the second, these tips have just met and have formed a thin band of precipitate which is slightly thicker at its center than at its extremities. In the third drawing

substances, or apparent but false serologic homogeneity, continually are being encountered. For example, chemically and physically apparently identical antigen molecules may show marked serologic differences by one precipitin test and not by another. It is possible to obtain γ-globulins, which, by immunodiffusion tests with antisera to them are identical, and yet it is possible to find among these clear evidence, with other immunodiffusion tests, that several serologically distinctly different species of molecules are present as evidenced by their respective abilities to react as different antibodies against different antigens. Molecular homogeneity falsely may be concluded if polymers of a given antigen are studied, since although they truly differ, they can have the same serologic specificity. On the other hand, an antigen also may depolymerize so that what originally appeared to be serologically a homogeneous antigen, becomes a mixture of different antigens (Bartel and Campbell, 1959). Analyses are complicated further by the extent to which an animal vaccinated with a given antigen yields antiserum responsive to a whole antigen, portions of it, or both; this introduces the inescapable problem of great antibody heterogeneity.

Ideas of the nature of antibody have become more complex as more has been learned about it. Most antibodies used in precipitin tests are γ-globulins, but these themselves are heterogeneous. β- and even α-globulin precipitins may be employed. Antibodies produced by a single animal against one antigen may have widely differing characteristics which affect immunodiffusion results (Crowle, 1960c). A toxoid injected into a horse, for example, may elicit (1) antibodies able to combine with the antigen but not to precipitate it, (2) R-type γ-globulin antibodies which form aggregates with the antigen not later readily soluble in reactant excesses, and (3) H-type β-globulin antibodies which form precipitates with antigen easily soluble in reactant excesses. Weak immunization may provoke an animal to form antiserum to an antigen which cross-reacts little or not at all with very similar antigens, while hyperimmunization tends to induce production of a range of antibodies which make the antiserum likely to cross-react even with distantly related antigens. The hyperimmune animal produces a mixture of anti-

---

the precipitin band is well developed but still has its spindle cross-sectional shape, and the precipitate represented graphically in the reaction area is shown to consist of antigen-antibody complexes mostly formed in or near equivalent reactant ratios but also partly, at the precipitin zone's respective edges, formed under conditions of either antibody or antigen excess. The type of reaction illustrated here would occur between human serum γ-globulin and its rabbit antibody, but it would be different in some details if horse antiserum were used, or if the antigen were human serum albumin.

bodies against one antigen differing widely in specificity and in avidity, and even the weakly immunized animal's antibodies will not be homogeneous in these two respects, although they may tend to be more so.

Antibody production to a single antigen in several individual animals receiving identical immunization varies unpredictably. Some individuals fail to manufacture antibody to an antigen even on prolonged immunization; some respond with much antibody of a single kind; some yield smaller amounts of more than one kind. Differences in response are far greater among different animal species. Again, responses may vary from none to heavy. Antibodies of strikingly differing characteristics (molecular weight, electrophoretic mobility, mode of precipitation, and conditions required for it) will be produced. Comparison to one antigen of two antisera which have been obtained from different animals or, sometimes, from different bleedings of the same animal is likely to produce a reaction only of partial identity in immunodiffusion tests.

Immunodiffusion tests by their greater versatility and resolution represent more effective analytic tools than classic precipitin techniques in aqueous media, but they also force one to recognize and take into account a correspondingly greater variety of factors which influence them, some of which would be negligible in the classic tests.

Gels and Diffusion

Gels

One of the most obvious differences between classic and immunodiffusion techniques is that the second is carried out in semisolid media and is more noticeably affected by factors influencing diffusion and mixture through these media.

Several types of semisolid media have been used for immunodiffusion: agar, gelatin, pectin, cellulose acetate, paper, and chemicals which polymerize to gel when catalysts are added to their aqueous solutions. Undoubtedly, many other media could be used, since precipitin tests can be carried out in or on any substance through which antigen and antibody can diffuse in aqueous solution. The supporting medium should not substantially interfere physically or chemically with uniform antigen and antibody diffusion or specific precipitation, but it should prevent convection currents. The substance should be uncharged or negatively charged, it should have a cohesive structure, and its "pores" (whatever form these may be imagined to take) must not be too small.

Partly because it has been used successfully for so many years to solidify bacteriologic media, and partly because no substance so far has seriously rivaled its versatility and availability, agar has been, and probably will be for many years, the most commonly utilized gelling agent for immunodiffusion tests. Although surprisingly little is understood about its gels, this is sufficient to provide a practical working knowledge for the serologist and a basis from which information for other semisolid media can be extrapolated.

Two kinds of semisolid media prepared from aqueous solutions could be used for immunodiffusion. In one category are the gels, and in the other and not yet utilized are the pastes. A gel consists of a hydrophilic substance which forms a stationary structure holding water. The gelling agent usually is employed at a concentration of less than 10%. A paste, on the other hand, rather than being a solution of gelling agent is a dispersion of fine solid particles in a liquid continuum (Alexander and Johnson, 1949). Under certain conditions a paste may become what properly is called a gel. Gels can be formed by dissolving the gelling substance in water and then treating the solution in some way to lower that substance's solubility so that it undergoes a process similar to crystallization. Thus, agar and gelatin are dissolved in water with heat and then are gelled by cooling; they form so-called thermal gels. Pectin gels can be prepared in two ways, neither thermal. One appears to depend upon a partial dehydration of pectin in solution to lower its solubility and is accomplished by adding large quantities of alcohol, sugar, or glycerine to it. Another method depends upon the action of an enzyme, which, added in small quantities together with calcium ions to a pectin solution, will gel the solution at room temperature (Grabar et al., 1956b). Gels can be prepared from inorganic salts by dissolving them and then changing them into their insoluble forms (e.g., silica gel). Certain substances, when made into a thick paste upon standing, will form a thixotropic gel. This is the kind of gel which results when a slurry of starch in water is allowed to stand, and it differs from the gel which forms when a much lighter suspension of starch in water is heated to form a thermal gel. Thixotropic gels generally are not transparent and so have not been used for precipitin reactions.

Gels such as are formed by agar, gelatin, and pectin, probably have a fibrillar or mesh-like rather than cellular structure (Hartman, 1947). This kind of structure would not have a uniform "pore" size but must have some average pore size which regulates the rate of molecular diffusion and a minimum pore size setting an upper limit to the size of molecules which can diffuse through it. Both average and minimal pore sizes are inversely proportional to a gel's concentration. For example, 5% gelatin gels are said to have pores no larger than 5.5 mμ; those of a 10% gel are about 1.7 mμ and of a 15% gel about 0.8 mμ. The mesh space width in 2% agar is from 3.0 to 6.0 mμ (Wunderly, 1958a). The greater a gelling agent's concentration, the slower will molecules diffuse through the gel; some gelling agents can be used concentrated enough to prevent selectively the diffusion of certain molecules (Allison and Humphrey, 1959). An obvious extension of this idea is that if molecules combine growing to sufficiently large complexes in a gel they will become unable to diffuse and, as happens to antigen-antibody aggregates in precipitin bands, the molecules will be trapped in the gel so that they cannot even be washed out.

Aside from average pore size, increased viscosity caused by a gelling material's soluble substances may retard diffusion. From 25% to 30% of an ordinary laboratory agar may be soluble in cold water and have this effect (Belicetta *et al.*, 1949). Thoroughly washing the agar before it is used removes most of these materials.

Many types of gels swell or shrink. This depends upon several factors such as the amount of water held in the gel, the ambient temperature, the nature of the gelling substance, and what salts are dissolved in it (Hartman, 1947). A film of dried agar, for example, will swell considerably in proportion to its original thickness upon being soaked in water. On the other hand, freshly prepared neutral agar or gelatin gels kept below 30°C. do not imbibe water or swell. Acids and bases increase the swelling capacity of organic gels; gelatin gels tend to swell progressively more as a pH increasingly distant from the isoelectric point of gelatin is employed. If it occurs, maximum swelling of saccharocolloids, such as agar and pectin, will be at about pH 7, since these substances have no isoelectric point. Some anions promote swelling and others promote shrinkage. Citrate, tartrate, and phosphate, in decreasing order, depress swelling; univalent anions are the least effective in this respect. Most gels will synerese if left standing long enough regardless of the surrounding vapor pressure. For some, such as silica gel, this tendency for syneresis increases with the concentration of the gelling medium; for others, including starch, agar, and cellulose acetate, increasing the gelling concentration decreases this tendency. Practically, however, syneresis sems to be negligible with both agar and gelatin gels even over long periods of standing (Alexander and Johnson, 1949).

Often, the temperature of gel liquefaction is important practically. One reason that gelatin is used less often than agar in bacteriology and immunodiffusion is its tendency to liquefy at or below body temperature. However, it is worth noting that gel melting points can be altered by various additives. For example, 10% gelatin made up in 32% glycerine in water will remain a gel up to 44°C. The longer this gel stands, the more heat is required to melt it again (Kruyt, 1949). The same additives do not necessarily have equivalent effects on other gels. Thus, contrary to raising the melting point of agar gel, glycerine lowers it. Sodium chloride raises the melting point of agar gel but lowers that of gelatin gel. A form of agar (carrageenan or "K-agar" marketed by Baltimore Biological Laboratory) has various melting and gelling points ranging between 35°C. to 66°C. depending upon its concentration and whether, and in what concentrations and proportions, sodium chloride and potassium chloride are used in the water employed to dissolve it (Baltimore Biological Laboratory, 1960).

Diffusion

Antigen-antibody reactions in semisolid media occur only when the two reactants have made contact after having diffused through the medium. The nature and rate of this diffusion generally can be described and predicted using theories contrived to characterize other forms of diffusion. The fact that diffusion rates for a reactant, usually antigen, are determined by measuring the apparent rate of precipitin band movement introduces complexities connected with such factors as the time which must be allowed for antigen-antibody precipitation to occur and the possibility of dissociation and reassociation of antigen and antibody in the trailing edge of such a band and above it. Calculation of general solutions for these difficulties is extremely difficult and is not yet completed, although progress in this direction is being made. However, these subtleties need not concern the average user of immunodiffusion tests for whom this book is intended; generalities should suffice. The reader wishing to acquaint himself with the mathematical niceties of immunodiffusion tests is referred to original papers (Augustin *et al.*, 1958; Becker *et al.*, 1951; Becker and Neff, 1958, 1959; Engelberg, 1959; Neff and Becker, 1956; Ouchterlony, 1958; Oudin, 1952; Preer and Telfer, 1957; Spiers and Augustin, 1958).

Practically, diffusion through agar gels and diffusion through water can be comprehended according to the same basic rules of diffusion. Diffusion itself is a tendency for any substance to spread uniformly throughout the space available to it (Glasstone, 1950). Diffusion occurs because the diffusing molecules are in constant agitation, and there is an over-all tendency for entropy to increase, that is, a tendency for these concentrated molecules to become randomly distributed. Hence, net movement of a species of molecules will be from an area of high concentration to one of lower concentration (Randall, 1958).

Diffusion rates are influenced by various factors such as a substance's initial concentration, the system's temperature, or gravitational field. The presence of nonspecific substances may either accelerate or retard reactant diffusion rate.

Diffusion rates of large molecules (e.g., proteins) through an agar gel are lower than they are in water, because, although they can pass through gel meshes, the latter retard large molecules mechanically. Only molecules with weights of less than 500 are not likely to be retarded. Hence, differences between diffusion constants of small and large molecules are distorted in gels as opposed to liquids (Duclaux, 1936). The degree of diffusion retardation in a gel depends upon its concentration, for as this increases, the average "pore" size decreases causing higher resistance to diffusion. Decreases in rate of diffusion with increases in gel concentration are linear for gelatin, but their relationship in agar is apparently more complex (Ouchterlony, 1958). Conversely, at one gel concentration, smaller molecules generally will diffuse faster than large ones, although since molecular shape also affects diffusion rates (Ouchterlony, 1958), this relationship does not always hold. Even in well washed agar or in other gels, an equilibrium may be established between the gelling substance and its solvent in which surfaces of the gel phase are bounded by enough gelling substance in solution so that through increased viscosity, diffusion is impeded (Ouchterlony, 1958). Since the primary resistance to diffusion in gels is a result of their mesh-like structure, anything favoring swelling of the gel (expansion of spaces in the mesh) will increase diffusion rates.

Diffusion of any substance through a gel can be influenced by its reacting with the gel. At slightly alkaline pH, this is no problem with many proteins in either gelatin or agar, since at this pH both gel and protein have a net negative charge and repel rather than attract each other (Belicetta et al., 1949). However, if the pH is lowered so that the substance diffusing through an agar gel becomes basic, it will be attracted to the oppositely charged agar and will tend to be immobilized, probably forming a salt with the agar. This has been demonstrated with tryptophan, for example, and is the reason that basic dyes do not diffuse through agar at alkaline pH and are difficult to wash from it, while acid dyes do diffuse and are washed out readily. The same principle holds for other gels, whence it is important to know what kind of charge, if any, a gel's molecules carry in solution.

The characteristics of diffusion through gels can be summarized as follows. The rate at which a substance diffuses increases with its initial concentration, with an increase in temperature, and with a decrease in its molecular weight, and vice versa. However, the diffusion rate can be altered by such influences as the nature and viscosity of the supporting medium and by the strength of a field of gravity applied to the diffusing area. Diffusion rate is defined by Fick's equation:

$$\text{diffusion rate} = -D \cdot A \frac{dC}{dx}$$

where D is the diffusion coefficient, A is the area of contact between the substance diffusing and the substance into which it diffuses, and dC/dx is the concentration gradient, or the rate of change of concentration with respect to distance. The negative sign indicates that the rate of diffusion decreases with increasing distance from an origin (Randall, 1958). The distance that a substance diffuses from a given boundary is in linear proportion to the square root of time (Ouchterlony, 1958). This is expressed by the equation

$$h = k \sqrt{t}$$

in which h is the distance traveled by the diffusing substance over a period of time t, and k is a constant equivalent to the slope of a line in a graph plotting h vs. $\sqrt{t}$ (Fig. II-3). Other ways have been used to

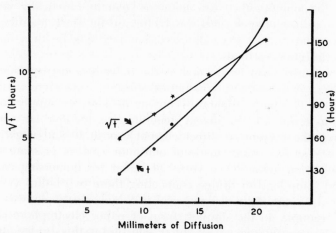

FIG. II-3. Data obtained from the experiments of Augustin and co-workers (1958) with the bovine serum albumin-rabbit antiserum system in single diffusion tube tests have been plotted here to illustrate the linear relationship between millimeters of diffusion of a protein antigen (as detected by movement of its precipitin band front) and the square root of the time ($\sqrt{t}$) at which measurements were made. For comparison and to illustrate that this relationship means that with increasing time the antigen front moves progressively more slowly, a plot also has been made from the same data of distance vs. time (t).

express these basic characteristics of diffusion and formulas have been developed for special purposes and situations, particularly to compensate for effects that the antigen-antibody reactions themselves have on apparent diffusion. When exactness is required, as in determining diffusion coefficients for a given antigen or in studying the characteristics of antigen-antibody reactions and their effects upon diffusion coefficients, these formulas must compensate for such minutiae as the effects of meniscus curvature at the interface between antigen and antibody layers, and the effects of using the antigen in solution as opposed to using it gelled. Some of these points will be discussed more fully in the next chapter.

Electrophoresis

Electrophoresis is one of the most powerful analytic tools in biochemical research. Its scope of application has been broadened enormously in recent years by simplification of the apparatus required for its use, and particularly by popularization of paper electrophoresis. Recently, the resolution and sensitivity of electrophoresis has been greatly extended at no marked decrease in simplicity by combining it with immunodiffusion into an analytic procedure known as *immunoelectrophoresis*. So long as they are antigens, electrophoretically separated fractions can be detected with this technique by antigen-antibody precipitin reactions which are more sensitive and specific than optical or chemical detection methods.

Electrophoresis can be defined as the movement of particles or ions by direct current through a conducting solvent (electrolyte), using buffered water. The basic apparatus consists of a power supply for direct current (batteries, direct current generator, or rectifier for converting alternating line current to direct current), positive and negative nonpolarizing electrodes (e.g., made of platinum, carbon, or some similarly inert conducting material), a vessel of buffer for immersing each electrode, and some kind of bridge connecting these two buffer vessels and acting as the support for the material in which electrophoresis will occur. For example, in the simplest form of paper electrophoresis a strip of paper previously soaked in buffer constitutes this bridge. Immunoelectrophoresis generally is carried out in agar gel. In this instance, the bridge can consist of a glass microscope slide covered with a layer of the gel and connected with each electrode vessel by a strip of moistened filter paper (Fig. II-4).

A simple visible demonstration of electrophoresis also illustrates its principles. Any of a number of acid dyes (e.g., thiazine red R) can be the substance to be electrophoresed. In preparation for the experiment, 1% agar is dissolved by boiling in an alkaline buffer such as one of the barbital buffers used for fractionating serum. The hot solution is poured onto a microscope slide to a quantity which nearly runs off, and it is permitted to solidify. Then, the slide is used as a bridge between the two buffer vessels as in Fig. II-4. A hole is punched in the agar at the cathode end of the slide and filled with thiazine red R solution dissolved in buffer, and the current is switched on (e.g., 100 volts using a buffer of pH 8.2 and ionicity 0.05). Across this slide the spot of dye can be seen to migrate away from its origin toward the anode at a constant

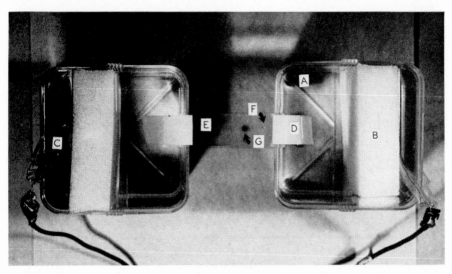

Fig. II-4. A simple form of agar electrophoresis commonly adapted to immuno-electrophoresis. Buffer vessels (A) contain sponge baffles (B) to prevent electrolysis products from the electrodes (C) changing the pH of buffer in contact with the paper connecting wicks (D). The glass slide (E) has been covered with agar about 2 mm. thick, and the origin (F) punched in this agar was charged with thiazine red R solution which by electrophoresis at pH 8.2 has moved away from the origin toward the anode and was located at G when this photograph was made.

rate of movement directly proportional to voltage applied to the agar and the dye's electronegativity, and inversely proportional to the buffer's ionicity, the opposing force of electroosmosis, the length of the agar bridge, and the agar's viscosity (Fig. II-5). With some modifications, the same findings will result if a serum protein is used in place of the dye. Factors affecting zone electrophoresis, particularly in semisolid media, include buffer pH, ionicity, and composition, electric current and voltage, supporting medium charge, temperature, and the nature of the substances being electrophoresed.

The pH of the buffer employed controls, chiefly, the direction and rate of fraction movement. Since, in immunoelectrophoresis, proteins or their derivatives are the most frequent subjects for investigation, pH and other factors will be discussed in relation to them. A protein, being composed of amino acids with both acidic and basic groups exposed to the environmental solvent, can have a positive charge, a negative charge,

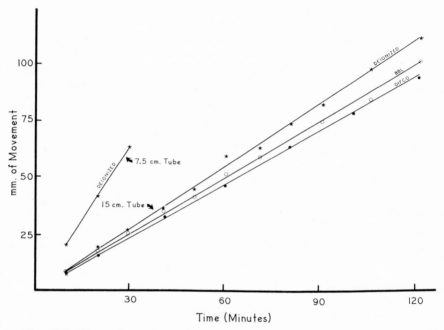

Fig. II-5. Electrophoretic migration of the acid dye thiazine red R at 100 volts in barbital buffer of pH 8.2, ionicity 0.05, through three different lots of agar in a 15 cm. long glass tube and through one of only 7.5 cm. length. This figure illustrates that a given substance can have different migration rates in different batches of agar, the rate usually being the highest in the purest agar (ash for "deionized" agar 0.01%; for Difco agar 3.0%). It also illustrates that in electrophoresis if the path of current flow is shortened while other conditions remain the same, the voltage field strength increases proportionally causing faster fraction movement. In this experiment, the volume of agar gel was decreased as well as the path of current flow, and this also can be seen to have caused an increase in migration rate which superimposed upon that simply due to increase in field strength. Hence, halving the length of a migration chamber without affecting its other dimensions more than doubles the rate of electrophoretic movement of substances in it.

or can be electrically neutral. The net charge of a protein molecule will vary in kind and intensity with variations in pH of the surrounding medium. At its isoelectric point (pI), the pH at which the protein is electrically neutral, it may be imagined to have an equal number of negatively charged carboxyl and positively charged amino groups at its surface. As pH is raised, the positive charge on increasing numbers of the amino groups is neutralized by whatever alkali is being used, and the protein molecule becomes increasingly negative as the unaffected carboxyl groups become dominant. Conversely, if pH is lowered below the protein's pI, amino groups remain unaffected while increasing numbers of negatively charged carboxyl groups are neutralized, and the protein becomes positively charged. Hence, a serum protein such as γ-globulin with pI of about 7.2 dissolved in buffer of pH 8.2 will be mildly negative, while another serum protein with a lower pI, such as albumin with a pI 4.7, will have a strong net negative charge. A mixture of these two proteins electrophoresed at pH 8.2 theoretically would separate into the γ-globulin, tending to move slowly from cathode to anode, with albumin moving more rapidly in the same direction. In practice, separation occurs as predicted, but the γ-globulin may not appear to move away from the cathode for reasons mentioned below. The two proteins separate at this pH because, although their directions of movement are the same, their rates of movement differ. If the buffer pH were lower than γ-globulin pI, assuming that this protein remained soluble, but higher than that of the albumin, then these two proteins would separate electrophoretically by moving in opposite directions. In agar electrophoresis this kind of separation occurs at pH values well above the γ-globulin pI because of electroosmosis (see below).

The ionic strength, or ionicity [a convenient term used by Wieme, (1959a)], of a buffer affects electrophoretic resolution, apparently because, by increasing it, one can minimize reactions between the substance being separated and its supporting medium and between the substance being separated and other substances in solution with it. However, ionicity also controls the rate of fraction movement, the buffering capacity of the medium, and the amount of current passing through the medium. If ionic strength is low, current carried by the medium will be low, and high voltage can be applied to it without excessive heating. Movement of fractions then will be very rapid for two reasons. The first is that at a given ionic strength and pH an increase in voltage or, more precisely, field strength increases the net differences in charge between the substance being electrophoresed and the similarly charged electrode, and, therefore, their net mutual repulsion. The second is that the migrating ion is surrounded by an atmosphere of electrolyte ions of opposite charge so that there is a tendency for fluid around it to move in the opposite direction and against it thus decreasing its mobility. Since this is proportional to the ionic strength (that is, the electrolyte ions available for forming this atmosphere), the lower the ionicity, the less will this effect prevail upon the migrating fraction. The advantage offered by low ionicity of rapid fraction movement (and therefore a minimum time during which it can diffuse) in a medium carrying little current may be offset by poor fraction resolution and by reduced buffering capacity, a condition incompatible with production of consistent results. In immunoelectrophoresis, the best practice generally is to use an ionicity which will permit the most rapid separation (to minimize fraction diffusion) at constant pH with good resolution and lack of trailing. The ionicity of commonly employed buffers ranges between 0.1 and 0.02.

A formula can be employed to calculate buffer ionicity, providing that all ions composing the buffer are completely ionized:

$$\mu = \tfrac{1}{2}\Sigma(i \cdot n^2)$$

in which μ is the symbol for ionic strength or ionicity, i is the molal concentration of an ion, and n is the valence of the ion. Since in electrophoresis ionicity is used as an indication of the electric current carrying capacity (conductivity) of the buffer, casual reference to it can be misleading. In the first place, the ionic strength calculated for a given solution does not accurately reflect its conductivity, and in the second place, the conductivity of one type of buffer with a certain calculated ionic strength may be quite different from that of another type of buffer with the same calculated ionicity. For example, the calculated ionicity of a sodium barbital-hydrochloric acid buffer and of sodium chloride solution will be equal at 0.15, and both usually are presumed to be completely ionized. Yet, the conductivity of the buffer is less than that of the sodium chloride solution. This, along with some other interesting points, is shown in Fig. II-6. Fortunately, since this buffer is used so often, in the ionicity range employed for immunoelectrophoresis, it has essentially the same conductance as sodium chloride solution, and the calculated ionic strength for both, therefore, will be the same. This trend for greater relative conductivity (i.e., degree of ionization) with decreasing salt concentration is quite obvious from Fig. II-6 which shows that eventually the lines drawn for four different electrolyte solutions will converge. Nevertheless, some buffers are made with constituents ionizing so poorly that the calculated ionicity will never agree with that estimated by conductivity in concentration ranges practical for immunoelectrophoresis. This is illustrated by the TRIS buffer shown in Fig. II-6 as well as by barbital buffer made up with acetic rather than hydrochloric acid and occasionally used for immunoelectrophoresis. For example, while calculated and actual ionicities of a barbital-hydrochloric acid buffer at pH 8.6 and ionicity 0.05 are equal, for a barbital-acetate buffer to attain equivalent conductivity, it must be made up at a calculated 0.079 ionic strength. If it were prepared at an estimated ionicity of 0.05, its true ionicity would be only 0.032. For the very weakly dissociating buffer sodium borate-boric acid to attain conductivity equivalent to that of completely dissociated sodium chloride at ionicity 0.05, it would have to be made up at a calculated ionicity of 0.228 at pH 8.6.

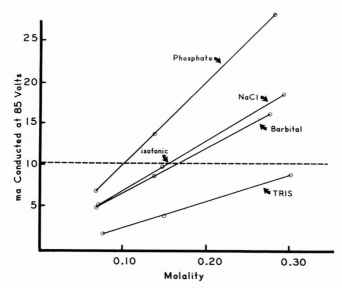

FIG. II-6. A comparison of the conductivity (ma) under standardized conditions of four different electrolyte solutions at different molalities showing that salts made up at identical calculated ionicities (e.g., 0.15 molal sodium chloride and 0.15 molal sodium barbital-hydrochloric acid) will not necessarily conduct equal quantities of electric current, that as the electrolytes are used in progressively lower concentrations they ionize more completely and therefore conduct more efficiently, and that some buffer constituents ionize so weakly (e.g., TRIS) that within concentration ranges employed for immunoelectrophoresis their calculated ionicities invariably will be higher than their ionicities determined by actual conductivity studies.

True ionic strength (i.e., a value equivalent to the current-carrying capacity of dissolved electrolytes) can be calculated only if one takes into account such factors as electrolyte dissociation constants, pH, actual salt concentrations, temperature, and the influence of one kind of ion upon the dissociation of another. This is neither simple nor practical for most users of immunoelectrophoresis.

It would seem, then, that the best way to report the electrolyte "strength" of a buffer used in electrophoresis experiments would be to record its ability to conduct a certain amount of current at a given voltage (under conditions resembling those used for electrophoresis) and to relate this to the conductivity of a known concentration of some standard electrolyte such as sodium chloride solution. For example, one may determine how much current is conducted by a 0.05 N ($\mu = 0.05$) sodium chloride solution at a given voltage, make up a barbital buffer at a desired pH somewhat more concentrated than this, measure its conductivity at three or more different dilutions, and from values so obtained and graphed, determine exactly what dilution of the original barbital mixture at that particular pH will conduct the same amount of current at the selected voltage as the standard 0.05 N sodium chloride solution. Then the electrolyte strength of the barbital could be reported as "conductivity equivalent to 0.05 N sodium chloride solution"; or it could be reported as some multiple or fraction of this conductivity. With these data available, any other buffer made up at that pH could be concentrated or diluted to the same conductivity under given conditions for directly comparable use in electrophoresis, in which the only variable would be that this buffer contained different ions. Some of the formulas for electrophoretic buffers given in an appendix of this book have been composed in this manner. Conductivity measurements satisfactory for this purpose can be made simply by filling two beakers with the buffer, connecting them with an inverted glass U-tube filled with the same buffer (Fig. II-7), and measuring the milliamperes of current passed through this bridge at a convenient voltage.

The importance of a buffer's composition is obvious from what has just been discussed, i.e., that conductivity varies among different buffer salts. Aside from this, however, certain buffers used under more or less equivalent conditions may give strikingly different results, some permitting separations not possible with others. Examples of this are given in the discussion of immunoelectrophoresis in the chapter on techniques.

In a sense, electric current is a villain in immunoelectrophoresis. Other factors such as ionicity, buffering capacity, pH, and voltage must be regulated so that the most rapid possible separation of components can be achieved without inducing excessive flow of current, because several complications will arise if this precaution is not taken. One product of excessive current is excessive heat. Heat can lead to local drying on the bridge connecting the buffer vessels, rapid dehydration of the agar which simply leads to a flow of even more current as electrolytes become more concentrated, and sometimes to local "hot spots," such as at the origin if the sample being electrophoresed has not previously been dialyzed against the buffer being used for electrophoresis and exceeds its ionic strength. Another product of excessive current is pH change caused by electrolysis of buffer salts. Normally, this is low enough or baffled well enough to be insignificant, but excessive current together with insufficient baffles, small buffer volume, and poor buffering

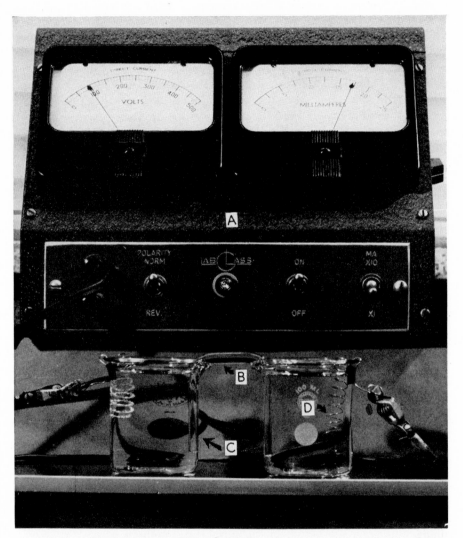

FIG. II-7. Apparatus required for simplified conductivity measurements on electrolyte solutions employed for immunoelectrophoresis. This consists of a direct current power supply (A), a glass tube bridge (B) filled with electrolyte solution and dipping into two small beaker buffer vessels (C), and a nonpolarizing wire coil electrode (D) in each buffer vessel. The greater the dissociation or actual ionicity of an electrolyte, the greater amount of current will be carried by the bridge (as registered by the milliampere gauge) at a given voltage.

capacity can cause significant pH change. The amount of current passing across the bridge can be diminished by lowering the voltage, the ionicity, or the temperature. It also can be lowered while the same ionicity and voltage are maintained by increasing the length of the agar bridge in which electrophoresis is taking place. Thus, the shorter bridge in Fig. II-5 conducted slightly more than twice the current as the longer bridge which was just twice its length but otherwise was used under identical conditions. Actually, however, although the voltage registered as being put out by the power supply remained the same, the shorter bridge was under the influence of twice the voltage field strength as the longer bridge, causing the electrophoresed dye to move at greater velocity in it.

The term "field strength" has been used somewhat confusingly by various writers describing their zone electrophoretic techniques and deserves some explanation. A voltage of 100 read on the dial of an electrophoresis power source merely indicates that this is the difference in electric potential between its two electrodes. If all that separated these electrodes were a glass tube 10 cm. long filled with electrolyte solution, the field strength would be 100 volts/10 cm., or 10 volts/cm. In practice, some types of zone electrophoresis apparatus offer too much resistance to permit realization of full voltage potential across the actual electrophoretic zone. Paper wick connectors (Fig. II-4, D) exemplify this electrical bottleneck. Ideally, then, to determine the true field strength being applied to an agar strip, one should place voltmeter probes at either end of the agar strip, find the voltage drop across the strip, and divide this drop by the length of the strip. This would be the only field strength figure valuable to anyone attempting to duplicate electrophoretic conditions reported in another laboratory unless his apparatus were identical with that originally used. Practically, it may be better to report the movement rate under the conditions used of some standard easily available substance, such as serum albumin, since this also reflects the influences of many other agents affecting immunoelectrophoretic separation such as electroosmosis, a factor, in turn, dependent upon the nature of the supporting medium used.

That the kind of supporting medium in immunoelectrophoresis partly controls the type of result which will be obtained is illustrated by Fig. II-5, which shows that the rates of movement of thiazine red R differ in three different batches of agar used under identical conditions. A prime cause for such differences is the phenomenon of electroosmosis which is greater in crude than in purified agar. Electroosmosis, the transport of water through an agar gel toward the cathode, is due to the negative electrical charge of the agar gel itself. Since the gel is fixed and unable to move, its tendency to move away from the cathode is counterbalanced by an equivalent actual movement of the water, which it holds, toward this electrode. All substances dissolved or suspended in the water will be affected by this flow to a degree inversely proportional to their own tendency to move toward the anode under the influence of electrophoresis. This is the reason that γ-globulin migrates toward the cathode in agar electrophoresis. In a hypothetical uncharged agar gel it would move slightly toward the anode (cf. Fig. V-3), but in practice it is carried backward at a rate nearly proportional to the intensity of electroosmosis and therefore to the electronegativity of the batch of agar utilized. The practical effects of electroosmosis on the variability of results is shown in Table II-1. Although human serum fractions are distributed similarly in the same type of agar used in different laboratories,

TABLE II-1

POSITION OF ORIGINS IN RESPECT TO HUMAN SERUM COMPONENTS AFTER THEIR ELECTROPHORESIS IN DIFFERENT AGAR PREPARATIONS[a]

Experimenter	Agar	Origin	pH
Wieme	Difco special agar-Noble	Between α_2 and β_1	8.4
Wieme	Behring Rein-agar	At β_1	8.4
Wieme	Difco Bacto-agar	At α_2	8.4
Crowle	Difco Bacto-agar	At α_2	8.2
Crowle	Deionized Difco Bacto-agar	Between β_2 and γ	8.2
Williams and Grabar	Washed Difco Bacto-agar	At β_1	8.2

[a] These data obtained from the following sources: Wieme, 1959a; Crowle, 1956; Crowle and Lueker, unpublished; Williams and Grabar, 1955a.

there are major differences among different batches of agar used in the same laboratory (cf. Fig. V-1; also see Götz and Scheiffarth, 1957). Among other media likely to be used in immunoelectrophoresis, five of these media, showing little electroosmosis, are filter paper, cellulose acetate strips, starch gel, gelatin, and a synthetic polymer, Cyanogum 41®, about which more will be said later. Yet, results obtained with one may differ considerably from those yielded by another (cf. Moretti et al., 1959).

Another medium factor which may affect zone electrophoresis is viscosity, which is lowest in the most refined agars. It rises as temperature drops, and as it rises apparent fraction movement is decelerated. Viscosity probably was lower in the short bridge of Fig. II-5 than in the long one, because it carried more current and was warmer and hence permitted faster dye migration. Viscosity probably also was lowest in the deionized agar, partially accounting for its difference from the other two shown in Fig. II-5. Interestingly, when the experiment described in this figure was repeated at lower voltage so that temperature was better controlled in the short bridge, the dye migration was just twice as rapid as in the long bridge rather than 2.5 times shown for comparisons made with the higher voltage.

All conditions set up for an immunoelectrophoretic experiment are aimed, of course, at providing optimal fractionation of some mixture of substances and consequently depend upon their nature. Knowledge of the mechanisms of electrophoresis in semisolid media is so incomplete that how to electrophorese a given substance must be largely determined empirically, and any improvements which one wishes to make on an already studied system, or any original investigation one attempts, must be based mostly on empirical knowledge and trial and error experimentation.

The above discussion on electrophoresis has been composed from information available from several sources. The reader is referred for more detailed information to monographs on zone electrophoresis and paper electrophoresis (Abramson et al., 1942; Block et al., 1955; Kunkel, 1954; Lederer, 1955; McDonald, 1955; Wolstenholme and Millar, 1956) and particularly to a recent monograph on agar electrophoresis by Wieme (1959a).

CHAPTER III

Dynamics of Immunodiffusion Tests

Chapter II has dealt with the basic concepts on which various types of immunodiffusion tests are set up. The present chapter explains how these concepts operate in the three fundamental types of immuno-diffusion technique: (1) simple or single diffusion, in which one reactant diffuses actively into the stabilizing medium containing the other, (2) double diffusion, in which both reactants diffuse toward or across each other in the medium originally containing neither, and (3) immunoelec-trophoresis, in which one reactant is electrophoresed before being ex-posed to reaction with the other (indicator) reactant, and which itself may be either a single or double diffusion test.

Single Diffusion

As it is known today, this type of test originally was used by Oudin (1946) who, in subsequent publications, called this technique *diffusion simple* (e.g., Oudin, 1955, 1958a). This term can be translated from French into English either as *simple diffusion* or as *single diffusion*. Although the former name has been used more often, the latter is a better counterpart to the other basic immunodiffusion technique, double diffusion (Augustin, 1957). Usage has made either term acceptable.

Operation

Single diffusion tests are carried out either in tubes or on flat surfaces such as glass plates or Petri dishes. The single diffusion tube test has proved the more popular because it is simpler to observe and to com-prehend in such studies as on the mechanisms of antigen-antibody precipitation and on antigen diffusion rates to which the single diffusion test has been so well suited. Hence, most of the following discussion applies to the operation of tube tests from experiments with which, also, the most data are available. The basic principles considered apply equally well to plate tests, however, since these two types of test con-trast mainly in that diffusion in one is radial and in the other linear.

The single diffusion tube test is set up as shown in Fig. III-1, the nondiffusing (internal) reactant in a gel being overlaid by a liquid or gelled layer of the diffusing (external) reactant. The initial concentra-tion of external reactant, usually antigen, must considerably exceed

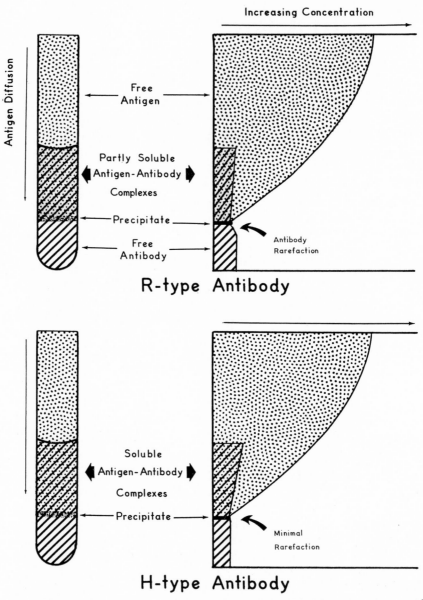

Fig. III-1. Diagrammatic comparison of single diffusion tube tests set up with R-type and H-type antibodies. In the tubes, antigen by virtue of intended original excess over antibody below it diffuses downward across the interface meniscus diluting itself by this diffusion until it forms a visible precipitate with antibody. This precipitate, a band with a flat front, appears to move slowly down the antibody-charged column. It leaves behind it a trail of specific precipitate when

being serologically equivalent with that of the internal reactant, since if it were merely equivalent it would be precipitated by the latter as fast as it was fed into the interface between the two, and nothing could be learned about its diffusion rate or antigenic complexity. When its concentration sufficiently exceeds that of the antibody, it will over-run the latter's ability to stop it and will diffuse into the antibody gel, where each of its components becomes disposed in its own individual gradient of decreasing concentration. At the far end of each such gradient, antigen has become diluted enough by diffusion to reach a precipitating ratio with the equivalent amount of antibody in the gel, and hence this end is marked by an antigen-antibody precipitin band. However, continued diffusion of antigen from its origin maintains this front continually under slight antigen excess with the effect that pre-cipitate just recently formed rapidly is overrun with antigen which tends to dissolve it and which also extends beyond the front of the previous moment, forming a new precipitate. The visible effect is one of a precipitin band moving down through the antibody layer at a rate approximately equal to that of its antigen, although actually the pre-cipitate itself does not move any more than does water through which a wave is propagated. The increasingly concentrated antigen diffusing into a given plane tends to dissolve any precipitate remaining there from previous antigen-antibody reaction, but this tendency varies de-pending upon the kind of antigen involved and particularly on the characteristics of its antibody. When R-type antibodies are utilized, the tendency is weak, and it varies with antisera yielded by different indi-viduals of one species. The tendency is strong for H-type antibodies, which form sharply defined precipitin zones in contrast to the broad bands with a sharp leading edge but only a slowly fading trailing edge produced by R-type antibodies (Fig. III-2).

The apparent movement of a precipitin band front is affected by numerous and sometimes subtle factors, and the physical appearance of

---

R-type antibody is used but little or none if H-type antibody is used. In a single diffusion tube are found (1) free antibody, (2) forming, relatively stable, and dis-solving specific precipitate, and (3) free antigen. The state of these constituents can be imagined as depicted in the diagrams to the right of their respective tubes. There are two points of particular interest. One is that large quantities of soluble antigen-antibody complexes will exist above the moving precipitin band front and below the interface when H-type antiserum is utilized. What the proportion of these is to free antigen in the same area is not known. A much smaller quantity of soluble complexes will be found in this area when R-type antibody is used. The second point is that immediately ahead of the advancing precipitin band front, the concentration of antibody is less than further on down the tube for reasons explained in the text. This will be more marked for R-type than for H-type antibody.

these bands may be a complex affair not simply explained. One can, however, make the following basic generalizations. If the antigen-to-antibody ratio is very high with respect to their equivalence ratio, and the absolute quantity of antibody is minimal, the precipitin band front moves through the antibody-charged gel at a rate governed by the dif-

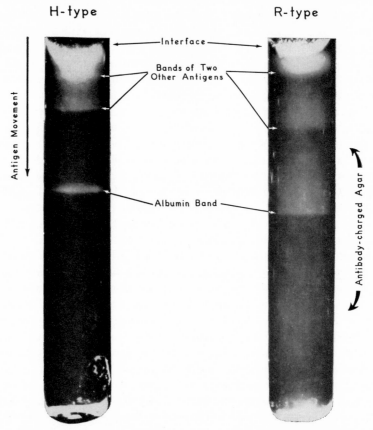

Fig. III-2. Photographs contrasting and comparing precipitin zones in single diffusion tube tests set up with H-type (horse) and R-type (goat) antisera, respectively. These were antisera against whole human serum, and Cohn Fraction V from human serum was used as antigen in both tubes.

fusion coefficient of antigen in agar, and the rules pertaining to antigen molecule diffusion described in Chapter II apply to study of this front movement and to the use of data so obtained for characterizing the antigen. One antigen-antibody precipitating system will form only one precipitin band, and this system will not affect the formation or apparent movement of bands produced by other heterologous systems also present. However, two independent precipitin systems can precipitate in the same plane, suggesting the existence of only one system. Since this results from the coincidental interplay of two major factors (antigen diffusion rate and antigen-to-antibody precipitating ratio), it can usually be detected by varying the concentration of one of the antigens so that its precipitation will be out of phase with that of the other. By and large, a precipitin band's density is proportional to the quantity of antibody available to form the band, a heavy band indicating the presence of much antibody. Hence, it follows that the sensitivity of a particular test depends on whether sufficient antibody is available to yield a visible precipitate.

Diffusion Rate

Some of the subtle factors interfering with simple interpretation of single diffusion test results based on these generalities are encountered in using this technique to measure the diffusion rate of an antigen and the two qualities of the antigen affecting this measure, diffusion coefficient and quantity. The diffusion rate of an antigen, as indicated by migration of its precipitin band front, depends upon two principal variables, its concentration and its molecular size and configuration. For most experiments in which one or the other of these two variables is studied, careful control or appropriate compensation is attempted for secondary influences such as temperature, convection currents, the presence of nonspecific substances, agar nature and viscosity, antibody concentration, and interaction between antigen and antigen-antibody complexes at the trailing edge of the precipitin band. Practically, however, such control or compensation has only in very few instances been adequate to yield absolute data, but it is sufficient to provide relative values.

The rate of precipitin band front movement is directly proportional in single diffusion tubes to the external reactant concentration and inversely proportional to the concentration of the internal reactant (Becker *et al.*, 1951). When conditions provide a large excess of antigen reacting with a low concentration of antibody, measurements over a period of time of precipitin band movement and plotted against the square root of that time ($\sqrt{t}$) will fall along a straight line (Fig. II-3) with a certain slope, k. The steepness of this slope at any single antigen concentration varies with the quantity of antibody in the gel. Thus, if k is plotted along the ordinate of a graph and antibody concentration along the abscissa, k increases in a straight line relationship with increases in antibody concentration. On the other hand, if the antibody concentration is held constant in a series of tubes in which various antigen concentrations are employed, then the steepness of the slope k is inversely proportional to antigen concentration. The value k, then, is a potential index of the concentration of either reactant (Preer and Telfer, 1957). However, a linear relationship between k and log antigen concentration at the beginning of diffusion holds only for quantities of antigen that are not too high, while a similar relationship between k and log antibody concentration exists only at antibody concentrations that are not too low (Becker *et al.*, 1951). Differing k values obtained for varying concentrations of antigen used against one antibody concentration, plotted against log concentration of the varied reactant, yield a straight line whose slope m is proportional to the square root of the true diffusion coefficient of the varied reactant, under ideal experimental conditions (Neff and Becker, 1956). However, even ideal conditions may not permit demonstration of this constant relationship with some antigens (e.g., thyroglobulin) which tend to react with agar or to dissociate or associate during an experiment (Neff and Becker, 1956).

With an otherwise satisfactory system for demonstrating the linear relationship between $\sqrt{t}$ and apparent precipitin band movement, the relationship will not be linear at the beginning of measurements when diffusion distances are very small, because k actually equals $x/(\sqrt{t} + t_0)$ rather than $x/\sqrt{t}$ (Neff and Becker, 1957b). Neither will it be linear when one of the reactants nears exhaustion. For example, if the rate of band movement is measured in the lower reaches of the antibody column where antibody concentration remains constant but antigen concentration has become very low both by dilution through diffusion and because its source is becoming exhausted, antibody just ahead of the precipitin front has time to diffuse significantly toward the zone of precipitation causing this to decelerate more rapidly than is compatible with linearity (Spiers and Augustin, 1958; see Fig. III-1). The higher the ratio of antigen to its equivalence quantity with the concentration of antibody used, the further antigen can advance into the antibody column without deviating from this linear relationship between the time it takes to travel a given distance and that distance (Spiers and Augustin, 1958). It is obvious that such deviation will occur closer to the interface as antibody concentration is increased; the distance over which linear movement of the precipitin zone (i.e., antigen) will take place will be shorter (Becker and Neff, 1958). Hence, only when antibody concentration is very low can the "back diffusion" of this reactant with its retarding effect on antigen diffusion be ignored in determining the diffusion coefficient of an antigen. Since linearity of band movement depends upon maintenance of relatively constant antigen concentration at the interface, if the antibody concentration below it is high, an insufficiently long antigen column will speed the onset of the nonlinear phase of precipitin band movement. Obviously, when low antibody concentrations are used, the length of the antigen layer can be varied over wide limits without such inconsistencies (Becker *et al.*, 1951).

Precipitin band movement will be affected by any physical characteristics of a test which affect reactant diffusion rates. Results may differ in two otherwise identical tests if in one the antigen is liquid and in the other it has been gelled. At a high antigen-to-antibody ratio, for example, penetration of the antigen into the antibody column can be significantly more rapid when it diffuses from a solution rather than a gel unless the antibody concentration is very low (Augustin *et al.*, 1958). Over a wide range of antigen-to-antibody ratios, measurements of antigen diffusion rates are more likely to scatter when a solution rather than a gel of antigen is utilized. These difficulties seem primarily due to whether or not convection currents develop in the antigen layer (Augustin *et al.*, 1958; Preer and Telfer, 1957). A liquid antigen solution with a higher specific gravity than the antibody layer on which it rests will develop convection currents, for as antigen diffuses across the interface into the antibody layer locally and at the bottom of its column, its concentration drops causing also a drop in its density. Then, as the denser upper solution descends to replace the lighter interface layer which rises, a convection current is initiated which tends by its mixing of antigen solution to maintain a constant antigen concentration at the interface. On the other hand, if the specific gravity of the antigen column is less than that of the antibody column, no convection mixing will occur, and antigen in the interface region becoming less concentrated than that above it will be replenished only by diffusion from above. In either situation, linearity between time and the diffusion rate of the antigen will hold, but the slope (k) of the linear relationship for the two will differ. The change in slope occurs rather abruptly in a transition from one condition to the other if the specific gravity of the antigen solution is varied experimentally (Preer and Telfer, 1957; Fig. III-3).

Two methods are used to overcome these potential convection current aberrations. One is to gel the antigen layer (Augustin *et al.*, 1958; Preer and Telfer, 1957). As a result, k values obtained in different tests are the same whether antigen solution density is higher, lower, or equal to that of the antibody solution; they all tend to be the same as the values derived without convection mixing of liquid antigen (Fig. III-3). The second way is to maintain antigen layer density above that of the antibody by adding appropriate amounts of salt, protein, or other solute in order purposely to induce convection current mixing (Preer and Telfer,

1957). However, this second method is susceptible to the presently
unpredictable effects upon reactant diffusion rates of various additives,
popularly called "nonspecific substances" or *n.s.s.* (Becker *et al.*, 1951;
Oudin, 1952, 1954). For example, if the same antigen used at equal concentrations is allowed to react with the same antibody in two different
tubes, the antibody being diluted with saline in one and with normal

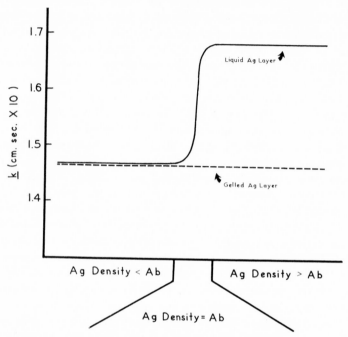

Fig. III-3. The influence of antigen layer specific gravity, when this is liquid,
upon single diffusion tube test results. When antigen layer density is less than that of
the antibody layer, there is a depletion of antigen just above the interface between
it and antibody, which is controlled only by diffusion of antigen from above it.
The result is that since there is this area of depletion, less antigen faces the antibody than immediately after the test was set up, and the diffusion rate of antigen
(*k*) is lower than if the original concentration could be maintained. It is maintained when antigen density exceeds antibody density, for then the antigen solution
is constantly mixed by convection (see text).

serum in the other, the apparent antigen diffusion rate will be greater
in the first than in the second (Oudin, 1954). Practically, this makes it
imperative that equivalent solute conditions be maintained among several tubes in which, for example, comparisons of various antigen concentrations are being made. This also holds even when convection in
the antigen column is controlled by gelling. Generally, an n.s.s. in the

antigen solution tends to increase the apparent antigen rate of diffusion. An n.s.s. in high concentration in the antibody layer usually exerts the opposite effect (Oudin, 1952). These effects again may be due partly to specific gravity differences between the two reactant layers (Oudin, 1954). Mathematical compensations for some of the effects are available (Becker *et al.*, 1951).

Unfortunately, an entire explanation for the effects of n.s.s. upon antigen diffusion rates is not available. The value k for an antigen is very sensitive to variations in the viscosity of the antibody layer (Preer and Telfer, 1957). One might expect, therefore, that increasing this layer's viscosity to a given extent by adding to it any of various n.s.s. uniformly would decrease antigen diffusion rate. However, some additives such as sucrose reduce k out of proportion with their viscosity-increasing effects. Moreover, when sucrose is added to the antigen solution to increase its viscosity, the rate of antigen diffusion does not drop as would be expected but actually rises. These unforeseen results have been explained tentatively as possibly due to some ordering effect that the sucrose molecules might have upon the random motion of antigen molecules, causing them to move more readily down a sucrose gradient rather than against it, regardless of the factor of viscosity (Preer and Telfer, 1957). The potential error of this effect is not small. The k value for bovine γ-globulin dissolved at 2.5 mg. per ml. in 0.63 M sucrose has been found to equal that of a 4.2 mg. per ml. globulin concentration made up in solution without added sucrose (Preer and Telfer, 1957).

The marked effects of viscosity on k have just been mentioned. If the diffusion rate of an antigen is being compared in some way among several single diffusion tubes, for reliability these comparisons should be in tubes having antibody columns of equal viscosity. Although viscosity is not difficult to control by addition of n.s.s., as has been explained, this remedy may create new problems in place of the one it removes, and so it must be used cautiously. Varying the viscosity by changing either the type of agar (or other gel) employed or its concentration is another remedy, but it also invites interference of unpredictable factors (Augustin *et al.*, 1958; Becker *et al.*, 1951). Differences in batches of agar may explain divergent results obtained on similar problems in different laboratories (Augustin *et al.*, 1958). Thus, the viscosity of washed agar is less than that of crude agar. Diffusion rates can differ as determined in the same batch of agar depending on how many times it is melted and gelled. For example, the diffusion rate for chicken ovalbumin in reheated agar was found to be lower than it was in agar heated only once (Neff and Becker, 1956, 1957b). Although minor variations in agar concentration usually do not much affect diffusion rates, they can if the diffusing antigen molecules are large enough for the agar gel to impede their diffusion (Becker *et al.*, 1951). Measurement of diffusion coefficients for quantitation of antigens like lysozyme which tend to combine with agar are, of course, not practical in agar; another type of gelling agent with no charge and perhaps with different chemical properties would have to be utilized. It is conceivable that a positively charged gelling agent might be useful for experiments with antigens with net positive charges at pH values harmonious with antigen-antibody precipitation, even though antibody by its net charge would be "fixed" to the gel.

The principal advantage of single diffusion tests in studies on antigen quantities or diffusion coefficients is that the front of antigen diffusion is specifically indicated with the very sensitive reagent, antibody. However, the indicator reaction (precipitation) interferes with results, since the very fact that it is precipitated prevents the antigen from diffusing entirely as it would through a column of agar gel not charged with something capable of reacting with it. The prime objective in these single diffusion tests must be, then, to minimize interference on antigen diffusion characteristics exerted by its antibody and to compensate mathematically in analyses of results for the minimal effects which cannot be eliminated technically. The following is a discussion of some of the factors with which one performing such experiments should be acquainted.

Ideally, the leading edge of diffusing antigen forming the front of the moving precipitin zone should be maintained at a constant antigen concentration corresponding serologically to an equivalent quantity of antibody which it meets in the gel (Spiers and Augustin, 1958). Hence, there should be no free antigen below the precipitin zone and no free antibody above it (Spiers and Augustin, 1958). The precipitating time for the serological system being studied must be reasonably short for this condition to hold (Ouchterlony, 1958). The extent of retardation of antigen by reaction at this front depends on how quickly it can react with and "neutralize" each new plane of antibody exposed to it. Only when antigen is used in large serological excess, then, can it be thought to migrate under conditions approaching free diffusion in the agar gel (Oudin, 1952). This also suggests that the least concentration of antibody compatible with visible precipitin band formation should be used in single diffusion tests (Oudin, 1952). Using a low antibody concentration also circumvents a tendency for it to diffuse significantly toward the advancing precipitin zone front. If the concentration happens to be high enough, it forms a gradient ahead of the front, for as the precipitate forms, antibody is removed locally from solution creating a regional rarefication (Fig. III-1) into which antibody further ahead of this band tends to diffuse; results will depend partially on the steepness of this antibody gradient and the diffusion coefficient of antibody (Crowle, 1960b,c). This condition probably always exists, but it becomes insignificant when it is suppressed by certain experimental conditions. Thus, it is minimal when antibody concentration is very low and its molecular weight is high (e.g., horse β-globulin antibody), and when a large excess of low molecular weight antigen is used against it (Fig. III-1).

The distinct effect that antibody has on antigen diffusion is evident from an experimental comparison which has been made of three assumptions: (1) that antibody has no effect on antigen diffusion; (2) that it affects antigen diffusion but itself does not diffuse; (3) that it not only affects antigen diffusion by combining with the antigen but itself also diffuses toward the antigen (Becker and Neff, 1958). When these three assumptions were tested experimentally to predict the behavior in single diffusion tests of bovine serum albumin antigen diffusing against its rabbit antibody, the last proved to be the most reliable in several experimental situations, and the first was the least reliable. However, even the third assumption used to calculate the albumin's apparent diffusion coefficient with the various k values obtained for decreasing antigen concentrations indicated an apparent rise in diffusion coefficient. This faulty product of the calculation was attributed to the erroneous assumption that the equivalence ratio of antigen and antibody in liquid medium was the same as that in agar (Becker and Neff, 1958). Other experiments showed that less antigen was required for equivalent precipitation in liquid medium than to form a nonmoving precipitin band (indicating equivalence) in agar gel against a given quantity of antibody.

Antibody not only affects diffusion of antigen at the front of and within the precipitin zone, but it also may affect it some distance behind the front as fresh antigen tends to react with already formed but not necessarily stable antigen-antibody complexes left behind the advancing precipitin zone. This is especially likely when H-type antibody is being employed. No way of measuring this very complex interaction or of handling it mathematically has yet been devised (Augustin et al., 1958; Spiers and Augustin, 1958), the problem being particularly thorny because individual sera vary in regard to how readily their precipitates redissolve in reactant excess or in how susceptible they are to rearrangement of reactant proportions. The final composition of antigen-antibody aggregate will be reached on levels well above the precipitin zone with H-type antibody (Spiers and Augustin, 1958). Under certain circum-

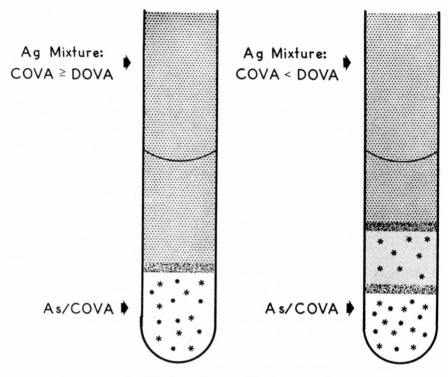

Ag Mixture:
COVA ≥ DOVA ▶

Ag Mixture:
COVA < DOVA ▶

As/COVA ▶

As/COVA ▶

✳ = Ab Specific for COVA
✹ = Ab Cross-reacting with DOVA

FIG. III-4. The influence of heterologous cross-reacting antigen (duck ovalbumin, DOVA) upon the apparent diffusion rate of homologous antigen (chicken ovalbumin, COVA), and the concentration of heterologous antigen in a mixture of it and the homologous antigen, on how many precipitin bands will form in single diffusion tubes. When the concentration of homologous antigen is such that it diffuses faster than the cross-reacting antigen, only one band is formed, since it combines with all varieties of antibody in the antiserum; it appears to migrate faster than it would were the same concentration of homologous antigen used without mixture with heterologous antigen. On the other hand, when the diffusion rate of heterologous antigen exceeds that of homologous antigen, two bands are formed because the former can combine only with antibodies of low specificity, leaving behind it a trail of uncombined specific antibodies which form the second band with homologous antigen.

stances, such rearrangement of complexes formed with this type of antibody may result in production of multiple precipitin bands by a single antigen-antibody system (Crowle, 1960c). Although the linearity of diffusion rates is not affected by this antigen-antibody interaction, an apparent diffusion coefficient is likely to be spuriously low.

Cross-reacting Antigen

The preceding discussion has been concerned with factors which may affect determination of antigen diffusion rates under ideal or nearly ideal conditions. One rather common deviation from such ideal conditions is encountered when an antigen being studied happens to be used in a mixture with another antigen able to cross-react with antibodies against the first; or possibly when one antigen dissociating or polymerizing during a test or combining with antibodies in certain proportions forms a distinct variant of the original antigen of different size but equal serological specificity so that it acts as a cross-reacting antigen (Fig. III-4). When the primary (homologous) antigen is being used in the presence of a cross-reacting heterologous antigen, and the latter diffuses faster than the former, then two precipitin bands will appear. In the converse situation only one band is formed (Ouchterlony, 1958). When two cross-reacting antigens are known to be present and two bands are formed, the upper should be due to the homologous one for the following reasons (Buchanan-Davidson and Oudin, 1958). Consider a mixture of chicken and duck ovalbumins (COVA and DOVA) diffusing against antibody to the chicken albumin (Fig. III-4). Antiserum to COVA consists of a range of antibodies with varying specificity, many capable of cross-reacting with closely related but different antigens such as DOVA. If the DOVA because of lower molecular weight, higher initial concentration, or higher relative ratio to antibody with which it can combine, diffuses ahead of the COVA, it will form a precipitin band which sweeps through the antibody-charged agar leaving behind a trail of antibody-DOVA complexes. But, also it will leave behind uncomplexed antibodies too specific to have combined with it and which can react only with the COVA, that is, the homologous antigen. On the other hand, under circumstances which favor diffusion of COVA ahead of DOVA, all available antibodies, whether highly specific or able to react with DOVA, will complex with the homologous antigen leaving none in the wake of the precipitin zone able to react with DOVA. This masking of a cross-reacting antigen in a mixture being analyzed is one of the outstanding limitations of the single diffusion technique as a qualitative test (Ouchterlony, 1958), a limitation which may not prevail in the double diffusion test and usually does not in immunoelectrophoresis. This effect may be especially deceptive when it is due to absorption to a supposedly pure antigen of minute quantities of another, as Glenn and Garner (1956) have shown in single diffusion tests to occur between γ-globulin and albumin of human serum.

An exception has been recorded to the above observation that when homologous antigen advances ahead of heterologous cross-reacting antigen only one band forms, and therefore to the general rule that if two bands are formed, that nearest the interface is due to the homologous system (Wilson, 1958). This exception, observed with bovine serum albumin antigen and an iodinated derivative of it, has been postulated due to the possibility that the heterologous antigen had a higher antigen-to-antibody combining ratio than the homologous antigen.

Quantitative as well as qualitative analysis with the single diffusion test is affected by the presence of cross-reacting antigens in a solution of primary antigen. The penetration rate of the homologous antigen precipitin band depends in such a circumstance not only upon this antigen's concentration, its molecular weight, and the concentration of antibody opposing it, but also upon the concentration of cross-reacting antigen and the degree to which this antigen can cross-react with the antibodies of lesser specificity in the antiserum being used (Buchanan-Davidson and Oudin, 1958; Jennings, 1959b; Oudin, 1952; Wilson, 1958). It follows, also, that the relative concentrations of various antibodies in an antiserum affect results, and that one antiserum may differ considerably from another in respect to this mutual interference of antigens. When two zones are formed by the COVA and the DOVA systems mentioned above, that is, when the latter diffuses faster than the former, the rate of penetration for each is greater than for either used alone against the same antiserum (Buchanan-Davidson and Oudin, 1958). This rate increase is greater for the heterologous than for the homologous antigen. The more closely a heterologous antigen resembles serologically the homologous antigen, the greater will be their mutual accelerating effects.

Reasons for this kind of interaction between homologous and cross-reacting antigen affecting their apparent diffusion rates cannot yet be clearly stated. One could suppose that by sweeping a certain concentration of antibody from ahead of the homologous precipitating zone the heterologous antigen can decrease the quantity of antibody available for reaction with homologous antigen and hence permit the latter to diffuse more rapidly, as though it had been used alone against an initially smaller antibody concentration. However, this explanation seems to have no bearing on the greater effect of heterologous band acceleration (Buchanan-Davidson and Oudin, 1958). Perhaps this effect is due to existence of antigen in more than one molecular form such as a soluble complex with antibody with combining characteristics less specific than those of the pure antigen. This hypothesis has been proposed by Jennings who also has given it some experimental support (1959b,d). In preliminary experiments testing it, Jennings (1959d) used COVA as the homologous antigen and DOVA as the cross-reacting one. "Hetero-homologous" antigen, as he calls it, was postulated to form in advance of the moving visible precipitin zone where, under the influence of great antigen excess inherent in single diffusion tests, some of the antigen was coated with specific antibody in such a way that the complex remained soluble, and antigen in this complex had some of its combining sites "masked" by the coating antibody leaving open only enough sites to combine with less specific antibodies. A front of this antigen well ahead of the precipitin zone was detected, in these experiments, by co-precipitation with DOVA supporting the hypothetical basis for explaining the mutual influence of the cross-reacting antigen and an altered form of the homologous antigen. When the antiserum used for these experiments was absorbed with DOVA, no evidence for formation of the hetero-homologous complex could any longer be obtained (Jennings, 1959d).

An alternate hypothesis explaining the effects of homologous antigen upon heterologous antigen precipitin band front movement supposes that the homologous antigen exists in two forms, one containing all the determinant groups required for combination with highly specific antibody and the other lacking some determinants and therefore unable to combine with the more highly specific antibodies but able, like the heterologous cross-reacting antigen, to complex with the less specific antibodies present in small concentrations (Jennings, 1959d). The displacement effect of COVA on DOVA precipitated by antiserum to COVA probably is serologically specific, since bovine serum albumin, an antigen physically similar to COVA but not able to cross-react with antibodies to COVA, does not have this effect (Jennings, 1959d).

Accelerating effects of one antigen on another conceivably could be due to alteration of one of the antigens by dissociation or association of its molecules during an immunodiffusion test. The same variation of antigen molecules could occur during vaccination of the animal from which antiserum is obtained so that the animal responds to form antibodies against several molecular species of the same antigen (Crowle, 1960c; Neff and Becker, 1956, 1957b). These physical changes of antigen molecules probably also would have to be accompanied by small changes in antigenic specificity, since artificial alteration of antigen molecular weights unaccompanied by changes in antigenic specificity apparently does not cause an antigen mixture to form an increased number of precipitin bands (Becker, 1953).

Precipitin Band Density

Although the quantitative single diffusion method of measuring changes in the rates of migration of precipitin zones corresponding to antigens of interest has been used, obviously it must be applied cautiously. Another quantitative single diffusion method, not yet so fully developed but promising, depends on the fact that the density of a precipitin band is proportional chiefly to the concentration of antibody available to form it (Glenn, 1958b, 1959a; Glenn and Garner, 1957; Glenn and Marable, 1957; Oudin 1952). Thus, as the quantity of the reactant is decreased, so also is the zone density. However, the relationship is not certain enough for ready determination of antibody in absolute quantities because it is affected by several other factors. For example, precipitin band density decreases in a curvilinear fashion with passage of time. This decrease is not consistent at various different antibody concentrations (Glenn and Marable, 1957). Some change albeit small, is effected on the density of precipitin zones by variations in antigen concentration (Glenn, 1958b; Glenn and Garner, 1957). A decrease in antigen concentration causes a small increase in zone density, probably because of a shift in the antigen-to-antibody combining ratio at different absolute antigen concentrations. The converse effect explains why at the beginning of a test the precipitin zones are less dense than later; they are being formed under conditions of large antigen excess, so that antigen-antibody aggregates are less efficiently composed than they are under later less unequal ratios. Since this density change influenced by antigen concentration diminishes as time passes, prolonged incubation eliminates such changes, practically, regardless of the antigen's original concentration (Glenn, 1959a).

Precipitin zone density also is influenced by interactions between the precipitate with other diffusing antigens (Glenn, 1958b; Glenn and Garner, 1957). Nonantibody serum components (e.g., albumin) can increase the density of a specific precipitate considerably; when these are removed, the density of the precipitate forming in their absence is significantly less than that of the band formed by the whole antiserum (Glenn, 1959a). This finding indicates that the use of density measurements for determining absolute quantities of antibody in whole antiserum may not be valid (Glenn, 1959a). Nonspecific substances such as sodium chloride, bovine serum albumin, dextran, and pig γ-globulin apparently affect the solubility of specific precipitates and thus increase their densities (Glenn, 1959a).

Secondary Precipitates

The movement and position of a precipitin band contribute information not only on the nature and quantity of the antigen but also on whether the band is primary or secondary. One antigen-antibody system which forms only a single (primary) band under carefully controlled conditions may form more (secondary) bands under such influences as sudden temperature changes. The differences between these two types of bands can be illustrated best by discussing how they, particularly the secondary bands, are formed.

Highly purified human serum albumin allowed to diffuse in high concentration against very dilute antibody to it at constant temperature will form only one precipitin band which moves down the antibody-charged column in the predictable fashion described above. This is the primary precipitate. However, if, during this test, the environmental temperature suddenly is decreased by a few degrees, the rate of movement of the precipitin band front will decrease. Then, this front appears to split into two precipitin bands, one continuing to move forward but the other, for most antibody systems (see below), remaining at its plane of formation (Crowle, 1960c). This is a secondary band, or *stria* (Fig. III-5), and its immobility is characteristic (Wilson, 1958). A stria also can be induced to form if the antigen concentration overlying the antibody column suddenly is lowered (Wilson, 1958). A sudden rise in temperature or increase in antigen concentration usually causes an opposite effect—the appearance of a clear area or *gap* (Fig. III-5), also usually immobile, in the ragged trail of precipitate most types of antibody leave when the advancing precipitate band does not completely dissolve immediately to its rear in antigen excess. If only one observation of a single diffusion tube is made after several hours' incubation and the temperature has varied several times, even though only a few degrees, the several secondary precipitin bands which may have been developed by the one antigen-antibody system will be misinterpreted as indicating the presence of several antigen-antibody systems. Hence, definitive single diffusion experiments require both rigidly controlled temperature and multiple observations of the number of precipitin bands and their movement.

As postulated on the basis of experimental evidence by Wilson (1958) and supported by experiments in the author's laboratory (Crowle, 1960c; Crowle and Lueker, unpublished), a gap probably is formed in the single diffusion test when at the precipitin band front there is a sudden rise in the diffusion rate of antigen (due either to increased temperature or to an artificial change in the antigen concentration at its origin), and temporarily the concentration of antigen in this area exceeds the quantity with which antibody can combine to form a visible precipitate. Beyond this gap antigen again becomes dilute enough, by diffusion and by encountering increasingly greater quantities of antibody, to resume forming visible precipitate. If conditions remain stable thereafter, this "new" precipitin band continues to migrate downward in the usual way while the gap in its trail remains stationary. A stria, on the other hand, seems to develop when a momentary slackening of antigen diffusion rate occurs, whereupon, also momentarily, antibody at the front of the precipitin zone has a chance to arrange itself with antigen with which it already has begun to react into a more stable lattice

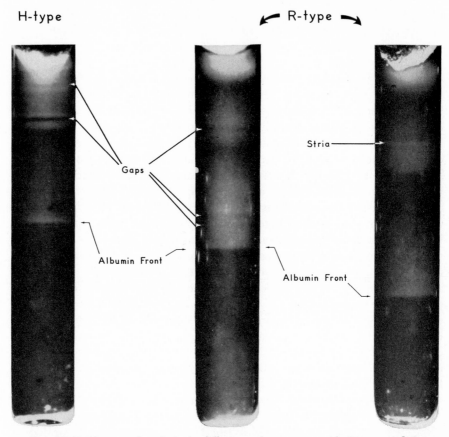

FIG. III-5. Photographs of single diffusion tubes set up with H-type and R-type antisera showing the temperature artifacts, gaps, and striae. Gaps formed when the temperature of incubation of the first two tubes suddenly was raised, while stria in third tube resulted when temperature suddenly was lowered.

under conditions closer to equivalence with the antigen than is ordinarily possible in the single diffusion test. This momentary respite for the antibody results in a precipitate which, because of its increased stability, may be heavier, and is less soluble in antigen than the primary precipitate, so that it remains conspicuously and virtually unaltered in the trail of poorly dissolving antigen-antibody complex left by the moving primary zone. It tends, therefore, to remain sharply defined and heavy.

The characteristic immobility of striae and gaps is not without exception. These artifacts, temperature-induced with H-type antiserum, have been observed to migrate (Crowle, 1960c). However, they also usually disappear after a short while, the stria dissolving and the gap merging into a background of equal clarity as precipitate trailing the primary band is completely dissolved.

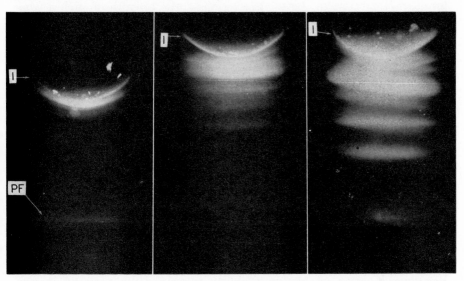

Fig. III-6. Three photographs taken at different intervals to demonstrate formation of secondary (Liesegang) precipitates in a single diffusion tube above the primary front band (PF, seen only in the first photograph) and originating from the interface (I), and to show that in this instance, when horse antiserum was employed against crystallized human serum albumin, none of these secondary bands remained stationary.

Another kind of secondary precipitate, resembling the classic Liesegang precipitation of inorganic chemistry (Stern, 1954; van Oss, 1959), has been reported several times to occur in double diffusion tests (e.g., Burtin, 1954b) and has been detected in single diffusion tests employing H-type antiserum (Fig. III-6) (Crowle, 1960c). Under the usual conditions in which it is employed, the single diffusion test is said not to develop this type of precipitate (Oudin, 1952), and to the author's knowledge no well documented proof is presently available that it does with R-type antiserum. However, there seems to be no theoretical reason why it should not; this type of precipitate would not necessarily be easy to identify. Conditions favoring the appearance of these so-called *periodic precipitates* are use of a high antibody concentration against a somewhat higher antigen concentration, and use of an antigen of low molecular weight (Crowle, 1960c). Incidentally, formation of temperature-induced artifacts is more likely with low than with high molecular weight antigens (Wilson, 1958).

Precipitin Band Characteristics

The form that a precipitin zone assumes in single diffusion tests can be instructive (Oudin, 1955). For example, the breadth of such a zone depends upon the nature of both reactants constituting it (Fig. III-2). A sharply defined band with a short trailing edge is formed by H-type antibody because its precipitates dissolve so readily in antigen excess (Augustin, 1957; Ouchterlony, 1958). On the other hand, R-type antibodies yield broad precipitin zones, rather than bands, whose leading edges may or may not be sharp but whose trailing edges tend to be long and ragged, extending into the upper reaches of the antibody-charged agar column where finally they may fade into the slight background turbidity of the agar gel. This is, of course, because these antibodies form precipitates only sparingly soluble in excess antigen.

The influence of antigens upon zone shape is illustrated by photometric comparison of zones formed by human serum components with rabbit antiserum (Glenn, 1958b; Glenn and Garner, 1957). Human serum albumin forms a zone with a sharp leading edge in which the degree of opacity of the precipitin band rises very abruptly; its trailing edge, although not so compressed as it would be were horse antiserum being used, drops off in density fairly sharply. Human serum β- and γ-globulins, on the other hand, produce a zone more symmetrical in its density distribution, the density rising gradually at its front and fading off slowly at its rear to merge with other precipitin zones behind or into the background turbidity of the agar. Precipitin bands as they are first formed are their sharpest and, with time, tend to broaden, for as a precipitin zone moves down the antibody column, its trailing edge, originally exposed to the precipitate-dissolving effect of high antigen concentration, is subject to progressively lower and less effective antigen concentrations as the gradient for this reactant broadens behind the zone (Glenn and Garner, 1957). The steepness of the optical density gradient trailing after a zone measured photometrically at different intervals during a test thus is a measure of a constantly changing antigen gradient, and potentially it is an identifying characteristic for a given antigen, since this gradient should change equally against one antiserum over a period of time.

Quantitative analyses can be performed if refined optical techniques are employed to measure a zone's density, breadth, and sharpness (Glenn, 1958b). As was mentioned above, zone density is proportional for a given antigen concentration and type mainly to antibody forming the precipitate. The sharpness of density decrease in the trailing edge of a band increases as antibody concentration increases, and consequently there also is a decrease in zone width (Glenn, 1958b). As antigen concentration is increased for use against a given quantity of antibody, these three measurements are oppositely affected, possibly because the difference between inhibitory and equivalent concentrations of antigen is increased (Glenn, 1958b).

Most protein antigens which have been studied in single diffusion tests have been observed to precipitate with either R or H antisera in bands with sharp leading edges, while polysaccharide antigens tend to form bands whose leading edges tend to be fuzzy (Becker, 1953; Oudin, 1952). However, this general difference probably is not particularly reliable, because, as more proteins are studied, several are being found which resemble polysaccharides in their precipitin band characteristics. Moreover, as Oudin has observed, antiserum from one rabbit against a protein antigen may yield a sharp band front, while antiserum from another rabbit against the same protein produces a band with a fuzzy front (Becker, 1953). This latter observation is interesting in itself as probably helping to characterize the antibodies constituting an antiserum. Thus, whether an antiserum produces a fuzzy-edged or a sharp-edged zone could depend upon whether it contains a high proportion of nonprecipitating antibodies or not, or, the nature of the antibody may be such that antigen and antibody combine in a relatively narrow range of ratios to form a sharply defined front (Becker, 1953).

Antigen-antibody Equivalence

Functionally, a rather simple quantitative aspect of single diffusion tests is their use in studies on antigen-antibody equivalence. In a series of tubes each prepared with a column of agar containing the same concentration of antibody and charged in series with decreasing concentrations of antigen solution, those with the highest antigen concentrations will develop precipitin zones migrating through the antibody column. This apparent migration is proportionally less rapid in tubes with decreasing quantities of antigen, and if this reactant's concentration is sufficiently low in some of this series of tubes, the band does not appear to move but simply forms at the interface between antigen and antibody (Fig. III-7). In the first tube in the series showing this stationary band, the diffusion rates of the two reactants and their combining ratios are equally matched, one reactant feeding into the precipitate zone no faster than the other can precipitate it. In succeeding tubes of decreasing antigen concentration, the antibody tends to become dominant, so that if the antigen in these tubes were incorporated in agar the forming precipitate band would tend to move very slowly up

Ag Added to Tubes in Decreasing Concentrations, Left to Right

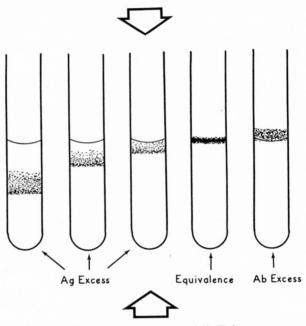

Ag Excess   Equivalence   Ab Excess

Quantity of Ab Same in All Tubes

Fig. III-7. Antigen-antibody equivalence in the single diffusion test is determined by adding decreasing concentrations of antigen solution, under otherwise standardized conditions, to equal concentrations of antibody, and observing which in the series of tubes so formed shows development of a precipitin band at the antigen-antibody interface which is compact and does not tend to move into either antigen or antibody layers. In this tube, antigen and antibody are feeding into the precipitation area at rates that are serologically equivalent for the single diffusion tube, the diffusion and reaction of each exactly counterbalancing that of the other.

into the antigen. Such a band formed by R-type antibody would be very dense, would have only a feeble tendency to migrate, and would leave behind it a very heavy trail of precipitate. The density of its precipitate would increase without passing through a maximum between its front and the interface, as it does when antigen predominates and the band is migrating through the antibody column (Oudin, 1952). However, when H-type antiserum is employed in excess to its antigen, it forms a discrete precipitin band. This band also is very dense and migrates only very slowly into the antigen layer. How exactly one can determine the ratio of antigen to antibody which is equivalent in the single diffusion test depends upon how accurately he can measure whether band movement above or below the interface occurs in a series of tubes, such as has been described, and on how closely spaced dilutions of antigen he employs. Moreover, unless molecular weights for antigen and antibody are nearly the same, the equivalence ratio obtained with one absolute quantity of antibody in this type of test may differ distinctly from that secured with another absolute quantity of antibody (Crowle, 1960b; see below).

The equivalence ratio determined by a single diffusion test will not necessarily be the same as that obtained by some form of classic precipitin test in aqueous medium; neither, then, should the latter equivalence ratios be applied directly to calculations dealing with immunodiffusion tests. Oudin (1949) has observed that in single diffusion tests with chicken egg albumin and its rabbit antibody, equivalence was attained with only 75% of the antigen needed for equivalence in a liquid system. Comparable values of 50% and 25% have been ascertained for a *Staphylococcus* enterotoxin (Bergdoll *et al.*, 1959) and bovine serum albumin (Wilson, 1958), respectively. Differences in these percentages probably depend on matching differences in the diffusion coefficients of the three antigens, for the antigens of lowest molecular weight seem to be needed in the lowest relative quantities for equivalence in these single diffusion tests (Bergdoll *et al.*, 1959). Thus, since both antigen and antibody must diffuse into the common reacting ground to form a nonmoving precipitin band characteristic of equivalence, if antigen diffuses more rapidly than antibody because of its smaller molecular weight, this "advantage" will have to be offset for no movement of the line to occur toward antibody either by a decrease in antigen concentration or an increase in antibody concentration (Crowle, 1960b). According to this notion, then, an equivalence ratio obtained in aqueous medium should agree with that in a single diffusion test if the diffusion coefficients of antigen and antibody (i.e., their molecular weights) are nearly the same, and conversely, if a heavy molecular weight antigen is employed, more antigen should be required for equivalence in the single diffusion test than in an aqueous test. Using low molecular weight antigens against high molecular weight (H-type) antibodies should yield the widest discrepancies between equivalence ratios for the two types of test.

Resolution

The value of a single diffusion test depends, in the final analysis, on the distinguishability of its precipitin bands, which with complex antigen-antibody systems often is not very good. A band must be dense enough to be visible; that is, sufficient antibody for it must be present (Oudin, 1952). Yet, to achieve this for a minor antibody by using less diluted antiserum may be impractical because coexisting stronger antibodies will form precipitin bands broad enough and dense enough to obscure the appearance of the much fainter minor system band. Concentration artifacts also may be invited by such adjustments (Crowle, 1960c). Another form of this problem is that two precipitin bands which should be resolved are not, because physical conditions cause them to precipitate and to migrate together (Munoz and Becker, 1950; Wilson, 1958). They may do so during an entire test (Munoz and Becker, 1950), or they may first form a single band which later splits into two and still later merges again into one (Wilson, 1958). Hence, the average worker will find the double diffusion test superior to the single diffusion test for studying complex antigen-antibody systems.

Single Diffusion Plate Test

The single diffusion plate test has only been mentioned. It has had sparse use, probably because theoretical experimentation, the forte of single diffusion tests, is geometrically simpler in tube tests than in plate tests. However, the potential utility of plate tests has been demonstrated by some of the earliest immunodiffusion experiments (see Chapter I), and valid uses for it at present are possible but not yet developed (Chapter V).

Double Diffusion

The essential feature of a double diffusion test is that both antigen and antibody must migrate toward a common reaction area before they begin to precipitate each other. However, if the two reactants are employed greatly out of proportion serologically, any double diffusion test becomes a form of single diffusion test governed by conditions affecting the latter (Crowle, 1960c). Usually, the balance between the two reactants initially is not exact, but moderate differences commonly encountered are compensated for soon after antigen and antibody fronts meet. Since a steep gradient of each reactant tends to form on either side of the precipitin zone, the initially stronger reactant, by forcing its way across the developing precipitate, both dilutes itself and encounters rapidly increasing quantities of the opposite reactant. As a result, the

zone of precipitation shifts slightly toward the weaker reactant and becomes stabilized as the respective reactants feed into it at equivalent
rates. If an antigen by large initial concentration or low molecular
weight diffuses much more rapidly than its antibody, in all but exceptional instances it loses its "advantage" by spreading itself across so
much gel that at its front, which meets the antibody, it has become
quite dilute, while antibody having diffused scarcely at all meets it at no
particular serologic disadvantage. Hence, by its nature the double diffusion test tends to adjust itself to balanced conditions. This balancing
effect can be overrun as mentioned above, or it can be defeated if, for
example, one of the reactants is exhausted long before the other, or one
is replenished out of proportion with the other.

Types of Double Diffusion Test

Aside from the fact that double diffusion tests can be carried out
either in tubes or on flat surfaces, they can be divided basically into
two types (Fig. III-8). In one, antigen and antibody diffuse face-to-face
(at 180 degrees) into a common reacting arena, as in the double diffusion tube technique. In the other, antigen and antibody diffuse across
each other at less than 180 degrees, usually at 90. A common form of
this method, sometimes called a double diffusion gradient test (Elek,
1949a), can be carried out in a Petri dish in which two strips of filter
paper impregnated with the two respective reactants are laid upon
agar in the plate at right angles to form an L. Several forms of double
diffusion test blend the advantages of both types (Fig. III-8). For example, if four holes are punched in agar in the form of a hollow square,
a fifth hole is punched in the center of this hollow square, and finally
the central well is charged with antibody and the outer four with
antigen, antigen and antibody approach each other at various angles,
from 180 degrees in the centers of forming precipitin bands to less than
90 in some extreme instances at band tips. Reactant convergence at
angles considerably less than 180 degrees favors identification of secondary precipitates (Liesegang bands) when they occur, for reasons
explained below.

General Considerations

The double diffusion test's principal applications have been in qualitative analyses (cf. review by Wodehouse, 1956a) for it readily resolves
many constituents of a complex antigenic mixture at one time and simultaneously can compare these with possibly identical ones in another
antigen mixture. Recently, it has been used quantitatively by a number
of experimenters, and it seems to be infringing successfully upon what

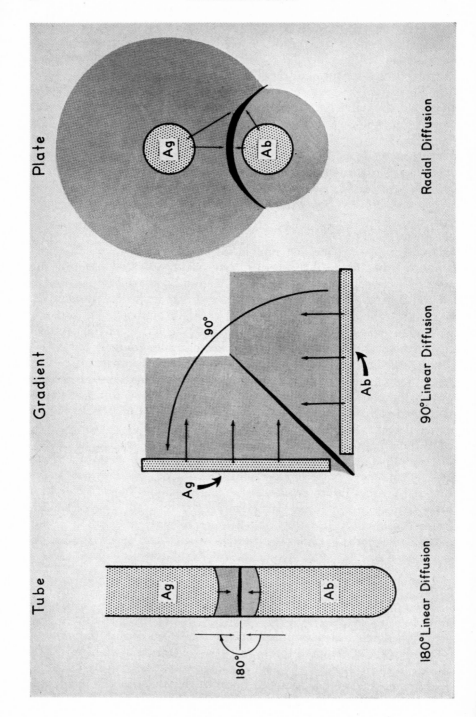

hitherto has been primarily within the domain of single diffusion tests: determination of reactant diffusion coefficients and of their molecular weights.

In the double diffusion test, as in the single diffusion test, the number of precipitin bands developing usually can be interpreted as representing the minimum number of precipitating systems present; however, they do not necessarily represent the maximum number (Fujio *et al.*, 1959; Kaminski, 1954b; Richter *et al.*, 1958; Ouchterlony, 1958). If several systems are present, the double diffusion test generally is capable of detecting more of them than the single diffusion test because its sensitivity and resolution inherently are greater (Wilson, 1958; see below). Occasionally, the number of bands appearing may exceed the number of distinct precipitating systems taking part in a double diffusion test, but these secondary precipitates are readily identified in many variations of this test, particularly the double diffusion gradient test, but not in the tube test (Crowle, 1960c).

Most factors governing the development of single diffusion tests play similar roles in the double diffusion test (Ouchterlony, 1958). However, in the latter there is no distinction between internal or external reactant; both diffuse and neither remains at a constant concentration during the test. Both edges of a precipitin zone formed in the average double diffusion test, regardless of type of antibody or antigen employed, tend to be sharp. When H-type antibody is being used marked unilateral precipitin band border diffuseness suggests that the reactant on the side of the diffuseness is excessive in respect to the other. (Ouchterlony, 1948a, 1958). However, when antibody is excessive this may be untrue, particularly with R-type antibody (Korngold and van Leeuwen, 1959b). Thus, at antigen excess against either R- or H-type antibody both edges of the precipitin line will tend to move in a situation analogous to a normal single diffusion test, but if R-type antibody is in excess, the band edge facing this reactant will remain stationary and only that facing the antigen will move, merely broadening the existing band (Oudin, 1952). Unilateral band diffuseness also may indicate that precipitation in the presence of the proximal reactant is either somewhat

FIG. III-8. Three basic types of double diffusion test are (1) the tube test, (2) the gradient test, (3) the plate test, which permit antigen and antibody to diffuse face-to-face, across each other at right angles, or both, respectively. The first hypothetically is the most sensitive test, the second is particularly useful for identifying secondary precipitation which may be confusing interpretation of antigen qualitative analyses, and the third because of its convenience is the most often used of double diffusion tests for qualitative comparisons of antigen and antibody mixtures.

unstable or that it can vary considerably in the proportions at which antigen and antibody combine. Bilateral band diffuseness hints that the particular precipitin system being studied might consist of rather wide ranges of antigen and antibody types, that is, that the antigen is not entirely homogeneous in combining ability with available antibody, and that several kinds of antibody with varying specificity and avidity are present (Lapresle, 1959). It also could suggest reaction between anti-serum prepared against one antigen with a heterologous but cross-reacting antigen (Jennings, 1959d). If the system being observed were studied in an aqueous precipitin test, it probably would have a rather broad optimal proportions range (Becker, 1953). Finally, bilateral dif-fuseness also could occur if the reactants diffuse into the reaction zone faster than they form nondiffusible aggregates and hence diffuse as growing small aggregates a short distance to either side of the middle of the precipitin zone before accumulating sufficient mass to become immobilized and visible.

Comparatively little attention is paid to band movement in double diffusion tests. Consequently, many of the factors affecting this in the single diffusion test have attracted only secondary interest in using and interpreting it. For example, results from the gradient double diffusion technique employed to ascertain an antigen's diffusion coefficient are not of band movement rate but rather of the angle at which its precipitin band forms with respect to either the antigen or the antibody source, since the tangent of this angle is determined by the ratio of the antigen diffusion coefficient to the antibody diffusion coefficient (Allison and Humphrey, 1959, 1960; Ouchterlony, 1949c). Thus, if the ratio is unity (diffusion coefficients equal) and antigen and antibody original con-centrations reasonably approach equivalence, and the reactant sources are troughs laid out at right angles to each other, the angle of the pre-cipitin band formed by the two will be 45 degrees. However, since the angle of this band depends upon relative reactant diffusion rates, factors which could affect these unequally for the two reactants could interfere with the reliability of this test just as they can by affecting the rate of only one reactant in the single diffusion test (see Fig. III-13, below).

Sensitivity

The double diffusion test has been mentioned above to be inherently more sensitive than the single diffusion test. This is because its sensi-tivity does not depend on whether sufficient antibody is present in the reaction zone initially to yield a visible precipitate, but rather on how much can be fed into this zone against an equivalent quantity of antigen arriving from the opposite direction (Aladjem *et al.*, 1959; Elek, 1949a; Ouchterlony, 1958; Oudin, 1952; Wilson and Pringle, 1954). As antigen-antibody complexes form, each of these reactants will leave solution locally, and more from the adjoining agar will diffuse into this area to replace this deficit only to be precipitated in turn. If complexes forming in this zone (where, visibly, nothing is happening at first) are not diffusible, theoretically there is almost no lower limit to the sensitivity of the double diffusion test. Practically, its sensitivity is governed by the quantity of reactants placed and maintained in their depots, assuming that conditions reasonably close to those of equivalent proportions are maintained (Aladjem *et al.*, 1959; Ouchterlony, 1958).

The time lapse preceding visible precipitation in the double diffusion test is controlled by three primary factors (Aladjem *et al.*, 1959). The first and second govern the diffusion rates of the two reactants and therefore the rapidity with which they meet. These are their respective diffusion coefficients and their absolute concentrations (Ouchterlony, 1958). The third factor is how soon after their fronts have met antigen and antibody form visible complexes (Ouchterlony, 1949e). Assuming that antigen and antibody in a hypothetical system are employed in equivalent proportions, the time passing before a visible precipitate appears is proportional, in a mathematically predictable way, to their concentrations, to the distance between their sources, and to factors mentioned in connection with single diffusion tests which govern the diffusion rates of antigen and antibody molecules such as temperature, agar concentration, and additives to the agar gel (Aladjem *et al.*, 1959; Wilson and Pringle, 1954). If the reactant sources are too far apart, antigen and antibody fronts may meet, but the concentration of antibody at this front may never accumulate sufficiently to form a visible precipitate (Aladjem *et al.*, 1959; Augustin, 1957; Wilson and Pringle, 1954). Both this fact and the predictability of the time required for a given precipitate to appear under standardized conditions have been applied to double diffusion quantitative analyses, and also for determining a reactant's diffusion coefficient since this is intimately concerned with its quantitation (Aladjem *et al.*, 1959). It is obvious from these considerations that, if other factors are held constant, the sensitivity (but not the resolution when complex antigen mixtures are being analyzed) of a double diffusion test for a given system is directly proportional to the closeness of antigen and antibody depots (Fig. III-9) (Aladjem *et al.*, 1959; Wilson and Pringle, 1954).

Since neither reactant in double diffusion tests must traverse much area charged with the opposite reactant in any way free to combine

Reactant Diffusion and Precipitation with:

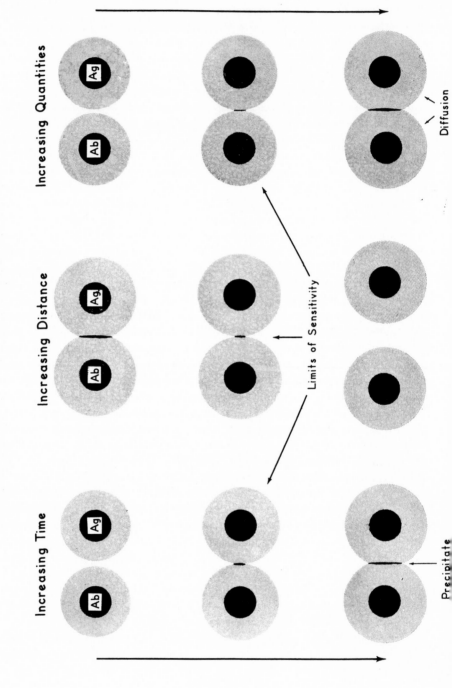

Increasing Time

Increasing Distance

Increasing Quantities

Limits of Sensitivity

Diffusion

Precipitate

Ab   Ag

with the first, one of the most knotty problems of single diffusion tests (that of how to cope in calculations with this possible interaction which may affect diffusion rates) is absent from double diffusion tests.

Cross-reacting antigens in mixture can interfere with each others' precipitation in double diffusion tests much as they do in the single diffusion test. However, the adaptability of double diffusion tests to comparison of antigen preparations, varied either qualitatively or quantitatively, makes these tests somewhat more versatile in contending with this potential problem. This is doubly true if the technique is leagued with electrophoresis in immunoelectrophoresis. Comparing reactants has been the foremost function of double diffusion tests and hence will be discussed in detail below.

Secondary Precipitation

Although double diffusion tests occasionally develop secondary precipitin bands (Crowle, 1960c; cf. Fig. V-21), they are somewhat less likely to do so than single diffusion tests, because one of the conditions favoring artifact formation is an imbalance of reactant concentrations. Wilson's classic experiments on this subject (1958) exemplify this. When he set up single and double diffusion tests with the same antigen-antibody system in very similar conditions and tubes, sudden temperature variations of only 1 to 2 degrees were sufficient to produce, invariably, artifacts in his single diffusion tubes, while sudden changes of at least 5 degrees were required to provoke such artifact formation in double diffusion columns. Changing the temperature slowly by 12 degrees caused no artifact formation in his double diffusion tubes but invariably did in the single diffusion tubes. Liesegang lines can form in double diffusion tests when the disproportion between reactants approaches that used in single diffusion tests (Crowle, 1960c). These artifacts, or secondary bands resembling them, are especially likely to form if reactant depots are recharged, although the effects of recharging also depend upon reactant concentrations originally used. Thus, recharging a depot with a lower concentration of antigen than that originally used is

---

Fig. III-9. Three factors which affect the sensitivity and resolution of double diffusion tests and which govern precipitin band formation all have in common the distance across which the reactants must diffuse before reacting. They are shown here in hypothetical double diffusion plate tests. The discs of reactant diffusion represent areas over which these have spread in quantities sufficient to form visible precipitates; if the discs of opposing reactants do not overlap, no precipitate will form. Overlapping may fail for lack of incubation time, if the distance between two reactant sources initially is too great, or if the quantities of reactants originally used is too small.

unlikely to produce noticeable changes in the existing precipitin band (Kaminski, 1954a). Recharging the depot with an equal concentration augments band density, causes a small displacement, and may cause band multiplication. Recharging with a larger quantity than originally employed provokes a marked displacement of the precipitin line and its abnormal multiplication into several more. H-type antibody is more sensitive to developing these artifacts than R-type antibody because of the more ready reversibility of antigen-antibody precipitation (Kaminski, 1954a) and perhaps also because of its much greater molecular weight. Antigen molecular weight, as in the single diffusion test, also partially controls the likelihood of secondary band formation, the heavier antigens being the least likely to form them (Kaminski, 1954a; Wilson, 1958; Salvinien and Kaminski, 1955a).

Antigen-antibody Equivalence

Equivalent proportions of antigen to antibody determined by the double diffusion test agree better with those in aqueous medium than the aqueous medium values agree with proportions obtained with the single diffusion test. Probably, this is because double diffusion reactions have a tendency to adjust themselves to equivalence and to compensate for differences in reactant diffusion coefficient (i.e., molecular weight). The lower molecular weight reactants lose their serologic advantage in double diffusion tests which they obtain from being able to diffuse more rapidly than those of higher molecular weight in single diffusion tests and which makes their equivalence values in the latter spuriously low, because by diffusing farther during a given time in the double diffusion test they become proportionally more diluted. With steep reactant concentration gradients facing each other across the reacting zone, any initial tendency, except for a very marked one, for one reactant to predominate over the other, either by diffusion coefficient or concentration, is readily neutralized as this reactant simultaneously dilutes itself by diffusion and encounters succeeding planes of the opposite reactant's gradient. However, this very tendency for self-adjustment makes band movement itself so insignificant in double diffusion tests that usually other means must be used to determine accurately when the reactants truly are being used at equivalence. When H-type antiserum is employed this is simple, since in a series of tubes with a constant quantity of one of the reactants used against varying concentrations of the other, equivalence produces a sharply defined precipitin band, while an excess of either reactant causes the band to be fuzzy on the side of the excess reactant (Boerma, 1956). For R-type antibody, however, this criterion is faulty for reasons which already have been explained, but other

criteria have been employed which yield quantitative or diffusion coefficient data of quality matching or exceeding the best obtainable by
other serologic methods (Augustin and Hayward, 1955; Hayward and
Augustin, 1957; Ouchterlony, 1958; Polson, 1958; van Regenmortel,
1959). For example, one may make very accurate measurements of the
distance between the precipitin band and the antigen meniscus and cor-
relate these either with varying antigen concentration or with antigen
diffusion coefficient, assuming that the diffusion coefficient of antibody
is known (Polson, 1958; van Regenmortel, 1959). Alternately, one can
adjust the quantity of antigen so that in a series of tubes used against a
given antibody concentration or antibody concentration gradient, previously established in the gel separating antigen from antibody, the
unmoving precipitin band forms just barely below and in contact with
the antigen meniscus (Augustin and Hayward, 1955; Hayward and
Augustin, 1957; see also Fig. III-14).

Patterns of Reactant Comparison

The type of experimentation with double diffusion tests which particularly requires discussion here, and which is used only in rudimentary
form, occasionally, in single diffusion tests, is comparison of two antigen
solutions with respect to a reference antiserum, or of two antisera with
respect to a reference antigen (cf. Wilson and Pringle, 1955). The
former is the simpler, the more common, and also the most likely to
succeed. Suppose that one solution of antigen B is being compared with
another against As/B (i.e., antiserum to B) in a double diffusion plate
with three reactant depots. If in each antigen well the antigen concentration is equal, the molecular weights of antigen and antibody are the
same, and equivalent concentrations of antigen and antibody are used
to charge their respective wells, two straight precipitin bands arching
into a chevron as shown in Fig. III-10a will be formed between the
antigen wells and the antibody well (Ouchterlony, 1958). The coalescence (*looping, fusion*) of the proximal band tips signifies a *reaction
of identity* since it implies, as in this instance is so, that the two antigens
being compared are identical serologically. Since two nonidentical antigens sometimes will give a spurious reaction of identity because of indirect relationships they may possess (Wilson and Pringle, 1955), this
precipitin band pattern might more accurately be termed *pattern of
fusion*, as has been suggested by Wilson and Pringle (1956).

In this example, if the antigen concentration in one depot is less
than that in the other, but other conditions remain unchanged, the same
type of pattern will develop (Fig. III-10b). The precipitin bands will
be straight, but the band formed by antigen in the lower concentration

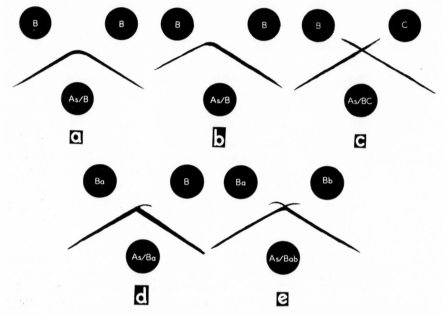

Fig. III-10. Precipitin patterns commonly observed in double diffusion plate tests and related tests in which two antigen solutions are compared using antiserum as the analytic agent. Pattern *a* (of identity or fusion) develops when the compared antigens (B) are identical serologically and are used in equal concentrations against their specific antiserum (As/B). A skewed pattern results when the same antigens are compared, but one of them is less concentrated than the other (*b*). When two serologically different antigens are compared using an antiserum which contains antibodies to both of them, each antigen-antibody system precipitates independently of the other, so that the resulting precipitin bands cross in the pattern of nonidentity or intersection (*c*). An antigen which is similar enough to another to be capable of precipitating some antibodies in the antiserum against the latter (the homologous antigen) will form a precipitin band which is arrested at its juncture with the band formed by the homologous antigen. The latter band, however, continues to grow, forming a "spur" (pattern of partial identity or partial intersection) whose length is inversely proportional to how closely related the cross-reacting antigen is to the homologous antigen and whose curvature and faintness are directly related to this relationship (*d*). A double spur forms if two antigens are compared which are different but are related to a third antigen, and antiserum to this third antigen is employed (*e*).

will not be midway between antigen and antibody wells but rather will be shifted toward the antigen depot, so that an asymmetrical chevron forms (Kaminski, 1954b; Ouchterlony, 1948a; Wilson and Pringle, 1954, 1955).

A different pattern develops when two nonidentical antigens are compared using an antiserum with antibodies against both (Fig. III-

10c). Antigen B compared with antigen C against As/BC produces a precipitin band pattern of intersection in which bands B and C cross clearly without mutual influence (Wilson and Pringle, 1956). Rarely, however, a *pattern of intersection* will be produced by identical antigens (Feinberg, 1957; Korngold, 1956a), although this only happens when the concentrations of the two antigen solutions are highly disproportionate.

In addition to patterns of fusion and of intersection, there is the intermediate pattern of *partial intersection* or, in older terminology, partial identity which is produced most commonly when cross-reacting antigens are compared with respect to antibody to one of them (Fig. III-10d). For example, if different antigens Ba and B are compared using As/Ba, then heterologous antigen B will form a precipitin band somewhat more diffuse and weaker than that produced by homologous antigen Ba. This band results from interaction between the B component of Ba and some of the less specific antibodies in the antiserum which have a particular affinity for B alone. Where the B and Ba bands meet, the B band terminates, but the Ba band extends further as a suddenly fainter band called a *spur* (Wilson and Pringle, 1956). The Ba band is formed by Ba antigen and all of the precipitating antibodies in As/Ba, but the Ba spur is the result of reaction only between Ba antigen and antibodies in As/Ba of *a* specificity, that is, antibodies which, being the most highly specific for Ba or *a* alone, have not reacted with B and have diffused through the B precipitin band, which, in its formation, precipitated all the less specific antibodies. Hence, the appearance of two precipitin bands, one interrupted at their junction and the other continuing as a weakened spur of precipitate, suggests that an antigen similar to but not identical with the homologous antigen is being studied. A common example is the serologic comparison of duck and chicken ovalbumins.

In a well controlled system, the length and the intensity of a spur is inversely proportional to the degree of antigenic similarity between two antigens being studied (Jennings, 1959c; Weigle, 1960). Double spurs sometimes form and resemble patterns of intersection, but usually they can be identified by their characteristic sudden thinning beyond the point of junction (Fig. III-10e). They also have in common with bands forming fusion patterns a tendency to bend toward each other as they come into juxtaposition (Korngold, 1956a), and the spurs themselves also tend to bend in the same direction (Wilson and Pringle, 1955, 1956).

Interpretations of spur patterns must be made carefully because spurs can form under different conditions, and, moreover, the length and intensity of a spur and even the likelihood of its appearance is governed by the type and quantity of antibodies present in an antiserum (Fig. III-11). Antiserum containing antibodies too nonspecific to differentiate two similar but not identical antigens forms no spur (e.g., hyperimmune horse antiserum to human serum reacting with serum albumins from numerous other animal species); when two antigens are compared which cross-react equally with the third against which the antibody is directed but which themselves are different, no spur forms (Crowle, 1960c). Cross-reactions between related antigens are best observed with near-optimal reactant proportions (Burtin, 1954b; Kaminski and Ouchterlony, 1951), since artifacts resembling spurs can be produced by use of grossly disproportionate reactant quantities.

Double diffusion plate patterns of intersection, partial intersection, or fusion, are the most readily interpreted if factors which affect their formation are understood. When an antigen and its antibody react in the double diffusion plate under ideal conditions, particularly when they are used in equivalent proportions, the precipitin band which they form often is said to form a "barrier" to passage of either reactant through it. However, more accurately, it (Wilson and Pringle, 1955) merely indicates the site at which antigen and antibody bar each other's passage. On one side of the precipitin zone is an ascending concentration gradient of antigen and on the other a similar one of antibody. Any antigen diffusing through this precipitin zone toward the antibody gradient statistically becomes increasingly likely to collide with antibody molecules until at the antibody edge of this zone its chances for continuing diffusion freely are nil (Feinberg, 1957). The species of antibodies in an antiserum are not uniform, some, for example, having less avidity and less specificity than others. Ordinarily, antigens are fairly homogeneous, and this antibody variation has little practical effect on formation of the precipitin band and on its barrier effect, although the band's physical appearance (i.e., sharpness or fuzziness) may be affected. The barrier gives the reaction of identity (fusion) its meaning. Antibody variation shows up, however, when a heterologous but cross-reacting antigen is employed against this antiserum. If this antigen is homogeneous, its molecules will not be able to diffuse through the zone of reaction with antibody, but on the other hand, those antibodies in the antiserum which are too specific to react with this heterologous antigen are not barred from penetration through its precipitin zone, and they diffuse freely beyond it where they are precipitated only if they encounter homologous antigen and form a spur (see Fig. III-10d). The efficiency of a heterologous antigen in barring diffusion of a range of antibodies is proportional to how closely related it is to the homologous antigen. The most closely related but still heterologous antigen will sieve out the most antibodies permitting formation of only the smallest spur across its precipitin band by the homologous antigen. The selectivity of the precipitin zone barrier is further proven by the fact that if two heterologous antigens are tested with antiserum to the homologous antigen, and one of these heterologous antigens cross-reacts more with the homologous antigen than the other (i.e., serologically is more similar), the antigen more closely resembling the homologous antigen will be the one to form a spur. This spurring by one of two heterologous cross-reacting antigens can suggest wrongly that this antigen is the homologous antigen, a mistake not readily caught when natural antigen mixtures are studied.

Purely mechanical forces can cause precipitin bands to align themselves in positions falsely indicating some relationship between them (Burtin, 1954b; Wilson and Pringle, 1955). As has been mentioned above, identical antigens from adjacent depots can form a pattern of intersection (nonidentity). This can happen if in one depot antigen is used at low enough concentration so that in the area approaching the point of line juncture it cannot precipitate all antibody diffusing against it, and this reactant penetrates to precipitate antigen diffusing from the more concentrated source behind the line formed by the weaker antigen and thereby produces a spur of precipitate (Korngold, 1956a). False spurring also can occur with H-type antibody if one antigen solution is much more concentrated than the other (Ouchterlony, 1958). In this instance, the line formed by the more concentrated antigen solution will "migrate" toward the antibody depot more rapidly than that produced by the weaker antigen solution and so break the original loop of fusion unevenly, forming a spur.

Another mechanical cause of false spurring is precipitation by two different antigen-antibody systems in one plane so that what appears to be a single line extending into a spur really is a double line, one of its components being the same as the compared antigen solution and fusing with it but the other not fusing and therefore extending beyond the point of fusion (Ouchterlony, 1953). Some particularly lucid experiments on spur formation have been performed by Wilson and Pringle (1956) and by Korngold (1956a).

False reactions of nonidentity (intersection) produced by identical antigens appear to be rare, but they can occur. In one particular instance (Feinberg, 1957), crystallized ovalbumin was used to charge small wells in serial dilution surrounding a much larger central well, charged with antibody, in a Petri dish. A pattern of intersection appeared between the wells with respectively the strongest and weakest antigen concentrations. The particular type of test being used was not designed to allow antigen to diffuse very far from its source, and so in its lower concentrations it tended to become exhausted rapidly. On the other hand, antibody in the large central well purposely was used in great abundance and was allowed to diffuse into the surrounding agar toward the potential reaction areas for some time before antigen wells were charged, to give additional physical advantage to the antibodies. Intersection resulted from the inability of exhausted antigen from one well to block antibody diffusion through its precipitate to an area behind the precipitate where it could react with antigen still diffusing from the adjacent antigen well which was originally heavily charged. Penetration of reactants through precipitin bands under such conditions as these has been well established (Korngold and van Leeuwen, 1958, 1959b).

A pattern of this kind also could be interpreted as one of double spurring, because in the photographs presented of it (Feinberg, 1957), the short bands extending beyond the point of intersection curve rather sharply toward the antibody source, a characteristic of spur formation. Double spurs can form where two unrelated antigens both able to cross-react with some antibodies against a third antigen are compared, if their sites of cross-reaction are different. This could happen, for example, if antigens Ba and Bb were compared using As/Bab (Fig. III-10e).

False reactions of identity can occur between two antigens reacting with an antiserum, usually clearly able to distinguish them, if physical conditions are such that insufficient antibody is available to foster precipitin band formation with either antigen beyond their point of intersection. The bands, growing no further than this point, then appear to coalesce.

Such spurious patterns of fusion wrongly indicating identity of antigens also are common, and in fact are difficult to avoid, even consciously, when antiserum specifically directed against the antigens being analyzed is not available (Crowle, 1960c; Korngold and Lipari, 1956b; Korngold and van Leeuwen, 1957). In practice, this is exemplified by experiments in which "abnormal" human serum γ-globulins are analyzed using some antiserum produced against pooled normal human serum or normal γ-globulins. Such an antiserum might show two abnormal globulins alike which actually differ in minor but significant aspects antigenically, or these might seem identical with a normal comparable γ-globulin. On the other hand, an antiserum prepared against these abnormal globulins themselves would demonstrate these antigenic differences since animals vaccinated with them probably would produce antibodies capable of these distinctions. Schematically, this can be exemplified if normal γ-globulin is designated Ga and two abnormal ones respectively Ga' and Ga'', the prime marks indicating minor antigenic differences (Fig. III-11). Antibody to Ga would recognize Ga' and Ga'' as identical; reactions of false identity would be rendered in double diffusion plate tests in which any two of these antigens were compared with one of the others using this antiserum (Fig. III-11a). On the other hand, if antibody produced specifically against Ga' were available, then such tests would show Ga' and Ga to be partially identical but Ga' to

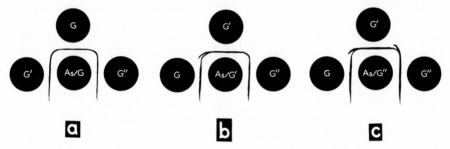

FIG. III-11. An illustration of the importance in any critical comparative study of closely related antigens of using an antiserum capable of differentiating them. Three hypothetical antigens G, G', and G'' are compared using antiserum against each, respectively. Only antiserum to G'' (c) shows that G'' has reactive sites lacking on G' and G. Although antiserum to G' cannot show this and it falsely indicates that antigens G' and G'' are identical, it does show that both of these have greater antigenic complexity than G (b). To antiserum against G, all three antigens appear to be identical (a).

have an antigenic determinant not present on Ga. Still, however, Ga' and Ga'' would appear identical to this antibody (Fig. III-11b). Only if antibody specific for Ga'' were utilized would the slight differences between Ga'', Ga', and Ga be elucidated (Fig. III-11c). The practical importance of these sometimes very elusive differences may be small in many instances; on others it may be weighty but completely overlooked. Such interpretive subtleties counsel cautious interpretation, reference to the type of antiserum employed, and, on most occasions, formation of only tentative conclusions. One is not justified in stating, for example, that a given antigen in bacterium X is identical with a comparable antigen in closely related bacterium Y if the conclusion is based solely on experiments employing antiserum prepared only against bacterium X; a mixture of antisera against both should be utilized.

Comparison of Antisera

In the discussion above, only comparison of antigens has been considered. When, in the opposite situation, two antisera are compared with respect to a given antigen, interpretations are similar, but they may be more complicated (Crowle, 1960c; Jennings, 1956). Largely, this is because no two animals vaccinated in the same manner are likely to produce exactly the same range of species of antibody against a given antigen in the same quantity or ratio, and because the specificity of antibodies produced by one animal may differ from that of another (Crowle, 1960c; Wilson and Pringle, 1956). For example, if two compared antisera, seemingly identical since they produce a pattern of fusion against an antigen, are used interchangeably in later experiments with the understanding that they truly are identical serologically, the results may be confusing. Thus, the range of antibodies in one of the antisera might show two antigens analyzed with it to be similar but not the same, while the other antiserum with a range of antibodies of narrower specificity could indicate that these two antigens were identical (see Fig. III-11).

The ephemeral value of comparing antisera as contrasted to comparing antigens in double diffusion tests is illustrated by matching the kind of results expected in each case. For example, if chicken ovalbumin and duck ovalbumin are compared using each of several different good antisera against the former antigen, precipitin patterns probably will differ in minor details, such as line intensity and spur length produced by the chicken ovalbumin, but generally from test to test they will be very similar, invariably showing the pattern of partial intersection and a spur produced by the homologous antigen. By contrast, suppose that two of these antisera are compared with each other using chicken ovalbumin, duck ovalbumin, turkey ovalbumin, pheasant ovalbumin, and other similar but not identical fowl ovalbumins. The antisera would be "identical" with reference to the chicken ovalbumin, but while one might produce a spur over the other with turkey ovalbumin, the second might produce one over the other with duck ovalbumin. There is a definite but, at first, not too obvious difference between such comparisons of antisera using antigens, and antigens using different reference antisera. In the latter instance, the antigens are being tested against reactants (antisera) formed in response to one of them. Hence, the reference reactants have induced common features. However, in the former when two antisera are tested against several different antigens there is no common denominator except the chance content of antibodies formed in response to vaccination with the original antigen which happen to be able to cross-react with the heterologous antigens. Mention hardly need be made that two antisera compared with respect to a crude antigen mixture and shown thereby to react with the same antigens similarly should not, on this basis, be used interchangeably for analyzing other similar mixtures of antigens. Compared with respect to one of these, one antiserum is likely to show content of antibodies not indicated in the first test comparison and absent from the other antiserum, or regarding an antigen not present in the first antigen mixture used for antiserum comparison, antibodies in one may differ significantly from those in the other in specificity or avidity.

Interpreting patterns of intersection, partial intersection, or fusion, is not as simple as it seemed to be during the first years that the double diffusion test was used, but on the other hand, one double diffusion test properly interpreted can yield information impossible or only very difficult to obtain by tedious use of classic precipitin techniques in aqueous media. Since the above discussion has had to be rather brief, the interested reader is referred for more details to other works (Augustin, 1959a; Crowle, 1960c; Grabar, 1957c; Ouchterlony, 1958, 1959; Wilson and Pringle, 1956).

Precipitin Band Curvature

The various applications of double diffusion tests, discussed in Chapter IV, depend upon particular characteristics of double diffusion reactions. In an example of the double diffusion plate test described above, supposing that equivalent concentrations of antigen and antibody were employed and that both had approximately the same diffusion coefficient (i.e., molecular weight), a point was made of the fact that the precipitin band which would form would be midway between antigen and antibody depots, and that it would be straight. Lowering the concentration of one or the other reactant would cause the band to shift its position toward the weaker reactant, but excepting extreme concentration differences the band would remain straight (Korngold and van Leeuwen, 1957c). The straightness or curvature of a precipitin band reflects the relative diffusion coefficients of the two reactants (Fig. III-12). Thus, if the diffusion coefficient of antigen is less than that of its antibody, the tips of the precipitin line will curve away from the lighter reactant in proportion to the difference between reactant diffusion coefficients. This effect is the most obvious in plates utilizing cylindrical reactant depots, since then the reactants diffuse radially, and any tendency toward curvature is magnified for the following reasons.

When the two reactants have equal diffusion coefficients through agar, they will diffuse into a serologically equivalent reaction plane at equal rates to form a precipitate. Since each will be diffusing radially from its cylindrical source equally rapidly, the precipitin band must grow laterally between the two depots in a straight line. If one of these reactants with equal diffusion coefficient is used in excess of the other, its diffusion rate (not diffusion coefficient) will be the greater, so that it will have moved farther from its source than the weaker reactant before it precipitates, and the precipitin band will begin to form closer to the weaker reactant. However, since serologic equilibrium is established at this plane, this equilibrium exists equally at succeeding points along

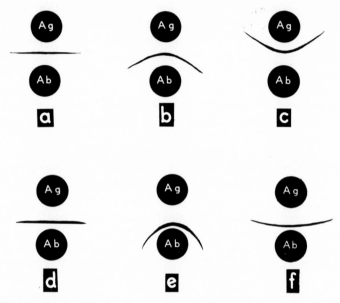

Fig. III-12. The curvature of a precipitin band between reactant sources in double diffusion plate tests depends upon the relative diffusion coefficients of antigen and antibody, even when these two are not used in exactly equivalent proportions. In diagrams *a* and *d*, antigen and antibody have equal diffusion coefficients (i.e., probably equal molecular weights), and they form straight precipitin bands. When they are used at equivalence, their band forms midway between them (*a*); when antigen concentration initially exceeds that of antibody the band is formed closer to the antibody source (*d*). The precipitin band formed by an antigen with a higher diffusion coefficient (lower molecular weight) than antibody curves toward the latter at serologic equivalence (*b*). This curvature is accented if antigen excess is employed (*e*). The opposite effects prevail when antigen has a lower diffusion coefficient than antibody (*c, f*).

this straight plane where the circles of diffusion for each reactant make first contact. This equilibrium thus exists not only for antigen and antibody at the plane of precipitation but also for their relative ratio of dilution by radial diffusion, and a straight precipitin band again will be formed (Korngold and van Leeuwen, 1957c). From this reasoning, it is easy to see that if one reactant has a greater diffusion coefficient (lower molecular weight) than the other, although the two will meet in the precipitin zone at serologically equivalent rates, the reactant of higher diffusion coefficient will increase its circle of diffusion more rapidly for a given concentration than the other, so that the serologic equivalence plane slowly shifts away from the faster diffusing reactant, curving the forming precipitin band toward the reactant of lower diffusion coefficient. As a general rule, then, a precipitin band in the double diffusion plate is concave toward the reactant of higher molecular weight; if the molecular weight of one reactant is known, then, that of the other can be estimated (Korngold and van Leeuwen, 1957c).

Double Diffusion Gradient Test Patterns

Another method for determining reactant diffusion coefficients more accurately serves also as a convenient subject for illustrating the use and mechanisms of double diffusion gradient tests, those in which reactants diffuse across each other at less than 180 degrees (Elek, 1949a; Ouchterlony, 1949c). Consider again that equivalent quantities of antigen and antibody of approximately equal molecular weights are used, and that these are placed in troughs in agar, set in respect to each other to form an "L," the antigen in the vertical trough and the antibody in the horizontal one. The diffusion front from either trough into the reaction area will be straight, and hence the reactant concentration gradients will extend outward from each trough parallel to it (Fig. III-8). Since the two troughs are not made to join where they converge but only to approach each other closely, the reactants will make first contact between these two proximal trough ends to begin forming visible precipitate there very soon (sometimes minutes) after the troughs have been charged. As time passes and each diffusion front advances farther into the reaction arena, the tip of the zone of contact will move away from the trough convergence area in a straight line exactly bisecting the 90-degree angle of the troughs (Figs. III-8 and III-13). The plane of agar traversed by this continual succession of points of contact will contain the precipitin band formed by the intermingling reactants, and under the hypothetical conditions considered here this band will be narrow and sharply defined. If large enough quantities of antigen and antibody were employed, the base of this band would be substantially broader than its very fine tip, because by their large quantities not diluted by diffusion over a considerable distance, each respective reactant will tend to diffuse through already formed and serologically inert precipitate to form additional precipitate on either side of the band's central plane. On the other hand, at the outermost actively growing end of the precipitin band, the reactants will be first encountering each other in mini-

R-type Ab; Ab Exceeds Ag

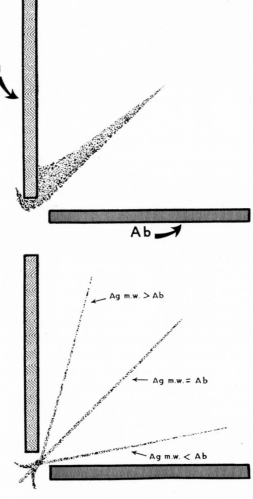

Varying Ag Mol. Weight;
Ag Equivalent to Ab

Fig. III-13. Various forms of precipitin patterns as they develop in double diffusion gradient tests. The top two patterns contrast the thin, slightly curved precipitin band formed by H-type antiserum with the broad-based, lance-shaped band formed by R-type antiserum, when both are used in excess against antigen. The lower left diagram shows how this type of test can be used to estimate antigen molecular weight when antibody of known molecular weight is used. Thus, antigen with a lower molecular weight and hence greater diffusion coefficient than antibody

H-type Ab; Ab Exceeds Ag

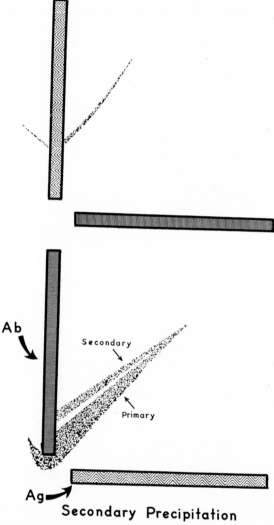

Secondary Precipitation

will form a precipitin band with a small angle between it and the antibody source, while a large molecular weight antigen forms a precipitin band with a large angle. For this type of experiment, the reactants should be used at equivalence so that band positions will be influenced solely by the relative diffusion coefficients of each reactant, and so that the tangent of the angle formed by one of these can be measured accurately for use in subsequent calculations. The lower right diagram shows how a secondary precipitate can form with R-type antiserum in the gradient double diffusion test, and how it is distinguished from the primary precipitate (see text).

mal concentrations to form the visible tip of the precipitin zone only by sufficient accumulation (Elek, 1949a). Thus, just ahead of the visibly growing precipitin line there will be a zone of antigen-antibody complexes in process of aggregating into visible quantities but not yet visible unless brought out by some auxiliary means or observed, for example, by interference microscopy.

When R-type antibodies are employed, the state of equivalence between two reactants can be ascertained by the shape of the precipitin band base formed in the double diffusion gradient test (Fig. III-13). Since the band always is formed by growth at its tip where antigen and antibody continually meet in optimal proportions for precipitation, this tip will be sharp. However, if antibody is used in excess, it will tend to diffuse through specific precipitate to form more precipitate on the antigen side of the initially sharp zone. The result is that at its base the precipitin band will broaden toward the antigen source while remaining fairly sharply defined on the side facing antibody diffusion (Fig. III-13). A relative excess of antibody has progressively less time to accumulate at increasing distance along the precipitin band from its base, so that the maximum broadness of the base gradually diminishes toward the sharp point of the precipitin zone (Elek, 1949a). The effect of using excess antigen is similar. If H-type antiserum is employed, the broadening of the precipitin band base is small, because excess reactants with this type of antiserum readily dissolve specific precipitate. Rather, there is a wholesale shift of the precipitin band up the plane of the weaker reactant, so that if only one observation is made this appears to originate not from the angle of trough convergence but rather from some point up that trough itself (Fig. III-13; Elek, 1949a). This point of insertion represents a definite ratio between the concentrations of reactants originally used, since in a given time this point will rise along the axis of the weaker reactant a distance proportional to the ratio of stronger to weaker reactant.

When equivalent antigen and antibody are utilized in this type of gradient double diffusion test, the slope of the precipitin band formed by them is proportional to the ratio of their diffusion coefficients. Hence, if this value is known for an antibody, then it can be estimated very closely for an antigen, and vice versa. When the slope is small, as, for example, when the band forms closer to the antibody source than to the antigen trough, the diffusion coefficient of antigen is greater than that of antibody, and its molecular weight is less (Fig. III-13). If the slope is steep, then the antigen has a lower diffusion coefficient than the antibody, and its molecules are larger. These data can be treated mathematically (Allison and Humphrey, 1959, 1960).

Secondary Precipitation

This type of double diffusion test has a particularly valuable definitive use, because in it the tip of antigen-antibody precipitate always is formed at equivalent antigen-antibody proportions, regardless of the original ratios of reactants (Elek, 1949a). This also tends to be true in other types of plate double diffusion tests, but it cannot be so readily observed, and in these, large reactant disproportions can prevent precipitin band formation altogether. Hence, Liesegang or secondary precipitates which sometimes appear in other types of double diffusion tests and which can be confused readily with primary precipitates, can appear in the double diffusion gradient test but are not likely to be misinterpreted (Fig. III-13) (Crowle, 1960c). In this kind of test, secondary lines form at the base of an existing precipitin band and merge at its top, thus usually revealing their true nature. Rarely, however, two lines of precipitate will merge at their tips and remain this way through several observations, and neither one will be a secondary precipitate. This could happen with the so-called hetero-homologous antigen of Jennings (1959b,d) or, even more uncommonly, such a double precipitate could be formed if the reactant diffusion rate ratios for two different antigen-antibody systems caused their precipitin bands to grow along the same plane and one of the systems was unbalanced, so that although at their forming tips precipitates from both systems were superimposed, below their common tip, one band would be shifted away from its original position by the excess reactant. The latter situation can be resolved by using different concentrations of one of the reactants, for then chances are very great that the ratios between reactants in the respective systems would change unequally and the tips of the two forming precipitin bands no longer would occupy a common space (Grabar, 1957c; Salvinien and Kaminski, 1955b). To resolve the question of whether a double line indicates Liesegang precipitation, the antigen solution should be used at a higher concentration; Liesegang lines then will intensify and probably also multiply, while double primary precipitates will be split by the unequal change in reactant diffusion ratios resulting from using more concentrated antigen solution, so that their tips no longer will converge.

Double Diffusion Tube Test Sensitivity

The double diffusion tube test has been merely mentioned so far. Yet, it has the distinction of being the most sensitive type of immunodiffusion test presently available in regard to the absolute quantities of reactants it requires for formation of visible precipitates. Hence, it is used principally for quantitation, for detection of trace antigens and antibodies, and for microimmunodiffusion experiments. Its high sensitivity is readily explained. Antigen and antibody, placed on either side of a column of agar gel in which reactions are to take place, diffuse toward each other to mingle at their fronts in any of a wide variety of ratios, one of which nearly always is compatible with precipitation. If both reactants originally are present only in very small quantities, this reaction at first will not be apparent except by special optical techniques (Easty, 1954). However, both reactants continue to feed into this zone at serologically equivalent proportions, and antigen-antibody complexes continue to form and to aggregate into increasingly larger particles until a visible precipitate finally does develop (Elek, 1949a; Ouchterlony, 1958). As it occurs, this serologic precipitation removes, from its immediate area, soluble reactants which are replaced by more reactants which are diffusing in from surrounding areas, so that in a sense, the precipitin zone has an attraction for both reactants (Allison and Humphrey, 1960; Crowle, 1960b). Consequently, quantities of reactants, too small to form a visible precipitate if they were simply mixed together, actually are concentrated in a very narrow zone of the entire volume occupied by the test to form a precipitate.

Quantitative Double Diffusion Tube Tests

Factors controlling reactions in the double diffusion tube essentially are the same as those operating in double diffusion plate tests, except that net reactant diffusion is linear rather than radial. Quantitative experiments with this method generally depend upon (a) whether a precipitin band tends to move from the plane in which it originally formed and what balance of antigen and antibody make it immobile (Fig. III-14a) (Augustin, 1957; Boerma, 1956; Polson, 1958), and (b) what quantity of a given reactant will form a precipitin band diffusing into a previously prepared increasing gradient of the other reactant at some clearly defined plane, such as at the meniscus between the uppermost reactant in a tube and the agar upon which it lies (Fig. III-14b) (Augustin, 1957; Augustin and Hayward, 1955; Hayward and Augustin, 1957). For the first method, slight movement of the band is most readily detected if R-type antiserum is employed since, for reasons already discussed, the band will be somewhat ragged on the side facing the stronger reactant (Augustin and Hayward, 1955; Hayward and Augustin, 1957). However, H-type antibody can be used if its peculiarities are recognized in advance (Boerma, 1956). When the two reactants are utilized at equivalence, each side of the zone is sharp. Since in the second method the precipitin band should remain practically immobile,

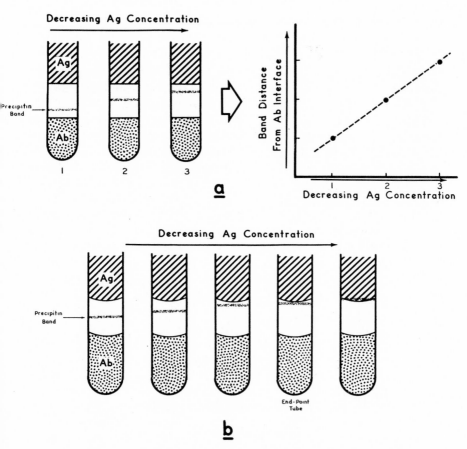

Fig. III-14. Two forms of quantitative double diffusion tube test which have been used with considerable accuracy. In the first (a), the tubes are set up with special techniques to have flat menisci, so that the distance between a precipitin band and a meniscus can be measured accurately. When decreasing antigen concentrations are used in a series of tubes containing constant quantities of antibody, the distance from the antibody meniscus to precipitin bands forming in these tubes increases in proportion to the decrease in antigen concentration as depicted in the graph. The second form of double diffusion quantitative test takes as its end-point tube in a series that in which the precipitin band forms just below and touching the upper of two menisci, the antigen meniscus in the example given (b). This test can be used, for example, to compare very accurately the quantities of an antigen in various test solutions; it also has been used to quantitate antibody.

R-type and H-type antisera can be equally well used without particular precautions.

General Considerations

Simple and double diffusion tube tests superficially appear to be similar in many respects, but they require different interpretations. For example, while the density of a precipitate in the single diffusion tube rapidly reaches a maximum and then remains essentially the same until the end of the test, and it depends primarily upon the antibody concentration initially used, the precipitin band in a double diffusion test takes considerably longer to develop, and its density continues to increase until the reactant supplies are exhausted; this density depends not only upon the amount of antibody eventually able to react but also upon the time allowed for reaction to take place (Elek, 1949a; Korngold and van Leeuwen, 1957c; Ouchterlony, 1958).

Recent findings emphasize the fact, previously known (Crowle, 1960c; Ouchterlony, 1958; Wilson and Pringle, 1956), but not too widely recognized, that invisible antigen-antibody aggregation can occur in agar gel during double diffusion tests and can influence the formation or shape of visible aggregates (Goudie et al., 1959). Sometimes the invisible aggregates are so in the sense that rather than being turbid bands in the agar, they are bands of increased clarity in the background of general slight agar gel turbidity. Some can be made visible with auxiliary methods (Crowle, 1958a, 1960; Crowle and Lueker, unpublished; Goudie et al., 1959).

Immunoelectrophoresis

Most immunoelectrophoresis tests employ the double diffusion technique in conjunction with electrophoretic separation of one of the reactants, which precedes the antigen-antibody fraction-indicating reaction. Occasionally, a single diffusion modification is used either intentionally or unintentionally. Consequently, immunoelectrophoresis tests are interpreted in the same way as double and single diffusion tests, except for some novel effects connected with the preliminary electrophoresis. Most of the following discussion on these peculiarities of immunoelectrophoresis is based upon information and ideas obtained from several informative papers and reviews (Burtin, 1954c; Grabar, 1954, 1957c, 1958, 1959a; Grabar and Burtin, 1959; Martin et al., 1954; Wieme, 1959a; Wunderly, 1957, 1958b).

General Characteristics

In a typical form of immunoelectrophoresis, a microscope slide is flooded with an even layer of agar gel in an appropriate buffer, and the ends of the gelled agar on the slide are connected with buffer vessels as described in the preceding chapter. A hole is punched in the agar and charged with antigen, and after electrophoresis slots are cut parallel to the path of electrophoretic migration on either side of it far enough away from it to permit development of precipitin arcs in the intervening agar. An antigen fraction usually has one of three shapes (Fig. III-15): it is round or symmetrically ellipsoid, it is drawn out on either side of its center equally or unequally, or it assumes the shape of a comet with a trail either before or behind it (cf. Hirschfeld, 1960a; Frontispiece). Its shape controls the shape of the precipitin arc it will form with antibody diffusing against it. After antibody (antigen sometimes also is used as the developing or indicator agent when antiserum is being studied by immunoelectrophoresis) is placed in its trough, it diffuses toward the path of electrophoresis as a straight front. Meanwhile, each fraction which has been electrophoresed expands radially by diffusion from its source, part of it moving toward the antibody as a curved front corresponding to the original curvature of the spot of electrophoresed antigen. Thus, if the final shape of the antigen spot is round, it presents a semicircular front; if it has the form of a symmetrical ellipse, its front will be symmetrically ellipsoid. An antigen spot which is asymmetrical will present a corresponding asymmetrical curved front. The acuteness of curvature also depends largely upon the relative diffusion rates of antigen and antibody (in turn depending on their respective concentrations and molecular weights), for if the antigen does not diffuse very rapidly from its origin by comparison with the rate of antibody diffusion, the precipitin arc it forms will curve around it more acutely than if opposite conditions prevail. A long arc of only moderate curvature suggests that it has been formed by an antigen which electrophoretically is heterogeneous and consists of a population of molecules with smoothly graduated differences in electrophoretic mobility. This happening is typified by serum γ-globulin which forms an elongated curve stretching evenly and thinly as far as the α-globulin area at its anodic end but curving suddenly inward at its cathodic end (Grabar, 1955c). Most γ-globulin molecules, then, have mobilities familiarly observed for γ-globulin on paper electrophoresis, but others, although serologically similar, have mobilities sometimes as great as those of the α-globulins.

There are antigens which by double diffusion tests produce only a

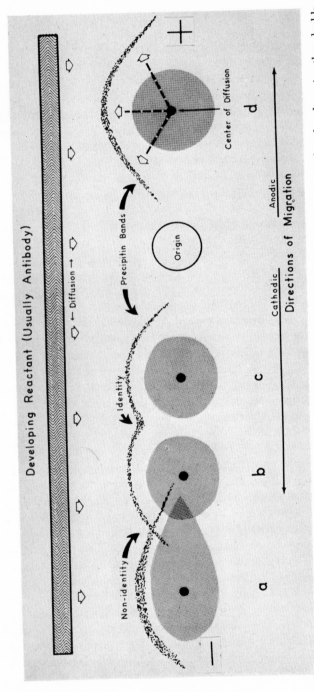

FIG. III-15. Precipitin band patterns in immunoelectrophoresis have essentially the same meaning that they have in other double diffusion tests, except that the position and curvature of each depends largely upon the electrophoretic characteristics of its electrophoresed reactant. Thus, the shape of a precipitin band reflects the shape of the spot formed by such a reactant under electrophoresis (*a* vs. *d*). The apex of a band indicates the hypothetical center of a fraction's diffusion (*d*). Two antigens which without electrophoresis never might form more than one precipitin band may be sufficiently different electrophoretically to separate and to form distinct precipitin bands, which show the relationship of the two fractions by fusing (*b* and *c*).

single precipitin band but which on immunoelectrophoresis divide into two distinctly different fractions. If these have remained close enough together during electrophoresis, each forms its own arc, but the tips of these arcs fuse (Crowle, 1960b; Fig. III-15).

Resolution

Resolution of two electrophoretically independent but closely adjacent antigens in immunoelectrophoresis theoretically depends upon whether the distance between the apexes of their respective arcs of precipitation are separated by more than twice their average precipitin band thickness (Wieme, 1959a). Best resolution of two such fractions is obtained with maximum precipitin arc curvature, minimum band thickness, and an electrophoretic path of maximum length (Fig. III-16). The last requirement is met conditionally by using a long strip of agar, the condition being that the increased time required for electrophoretic separation in the longer strip does not permit sufficient diffusion of fractions being electrophoresed to cancel its advantage. The first two are satisfied by adjusting reactant ratios and the distance between antiserum and antigen. Thus, shortening the distance between reactants diminishes the time passing before a precipitin arc forms, restricting the area of antigen diffusion, and curving the arc more acutely. Raising the antibody-to-antigen ratio has a similar effect. However, the fact that the latter also can increase band thickness and the former can flatten arcs, tending to nullify possible advantages that they offer, requires thought and experimentation in arranging the physical conditions of a given immunoelectrophoresis test.

Origin

Most antigens which are electrophoresed in agar diffuse relatively little in the time required for this process, but nevertheless the best results can be obtained if the origin charged with solution to be electrophoresed is as small as possible, if it is circular, or as narrow as possible if it is a slot. The rate of antigen diffusion away from the shape of its origin during electrophoresis is proportional to the initial concentration of antigen and is the greatest relative to origin size for the narrowest origins (Wieme, 1959a). Hence, immunoelectrophoresis carried out on the comparatively short microscope slide which will employ the smallest practical origin requires, for satisfactory resolution of complex antigen mixtures, as rapid electrophoresis as possible; that is, high voltage should be applied for a short time, and antibody should be added as developing reactant immediately after electrophoresis. In macro forms of immunoelectrophoresis using much larger origins, time

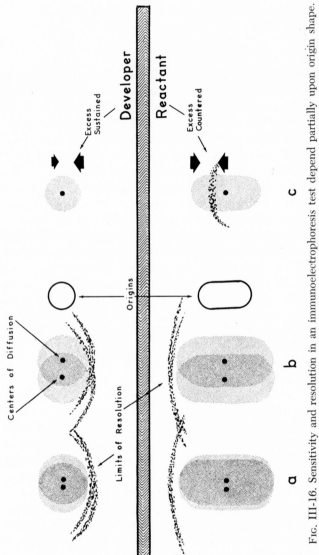

FIG. III-16. Sensitivity and resolution in an immunoelectrophoresis test depend partially upon origin shape. More reactant to be electrophoresed can be used in an oblong origin than in a circular one of the same diameter, so that while indicator reactant excess may preclude precipitin band formation by a weak fraction originating from a circular origin, it might not if an oblong origin were employed (c). On the other hand, resolution obtained with a circular origin probably is superior to that obtained with the oblong origin, because the former offers more acute curvature of precipitin bands (a and b). Immunoelectrophoresis provides fraction resolution far better than obtainable with other forms of electrophoresis, because the centers of closely overlapping fractions can be distinguished with the aid of their individual precipitin arcs. By its curvature, each arc points to a small hypothetical center of diffusion for its electrophoresed reactant.

becomes less important. Although in these, diffusion is as rapid space-wise as in micro tests, it is much smaller in proportion to the size of the origin and to the length of the electrophoretic separation. Moreover, precipitin bands in the macro test are no broader than they are in micro tests. Hence, an amount of diffusion which is critically large for a micro test usually is insufficient in macro tests to prevent resolution of two closely adjoining antigens. Not infrequently, however, precipitin bands in the thicker agar of macro tests form as slanted ribbons which overlap so that although these bands are no thicker than in micro tests, their slanted overlapping interferes with resolution. Improved forms of the micro test (Crowle, 1960b) do not have this problem.

The shape of an origin in immunoelectrophoresis can affect resolution by controlling arc curvature and the quantity of reactant which can be used. Choice between the two forms generally used (the slot and the circular well) must be established experimentally for a given antigen-antibody system and immunoelectrophoretic technique, although either type of origin will give satisfactory results in all but the most critical experiments. A larger volume of reactant can be placed in a slot of given width and depth than in a hole of equal depth and diameter (Grabar, 1959a), and consequently, minor constituents in an antigen mixture are more likely to be detected if a slot is used instead of a hole (Fig. III-16). This is true not only because more reactant is employed, but also because the electrophoresed fraction has greater depth across which antibody can diffuse, so that conditions of antibody excess which could prevent arc formation do not occur readily. On the other hand, some antigens electrophoresed from a slot tend to acquire a rectangular shape, presenting a relatively flat diffusion front by contrast with the curved one presented by similar fractions migrating from a circular origin. Hence, on some occasions the resulting, somewhat flattened precipitin lines produced by these rectangular fractions may interfere with optimal resolution by overlapping. Nevertheless, conditions minimizing diffusion of electrophoresed fractions or their trailing through the agar gel in which they migrate can favor exactly the opposite result: that fractions from the slot origin yield more acutely curved precipitin arcs than are obtainable with the circular origin. Under these conditions, the slot-shaped fraction remains slot-shaped, and the ends of the precipitin arc bend sharply around the tip of this fraction where it faces the diffusion of antibody against it. A slot origin is more likely to yield "bat wing" artifacts than a circular origin; see Fig. V-20.

Fraction Solubility

There are some problems in immunoelectrophoresis which are not often encountered in single and double diffusion tests. Electrophoresis can completely separate antigen fractions from each other, and some apparently depend for their continued solubility in agar gels upon the "protection" of others. When electrophoresis removes the protective fractions from those protected, the latter (e.g., human serum α_2-lipoprotein) become poorly soluble or actually precipitate (Uriel and Grabar, 1956b). This may result in formation of rather irregular precipitin arcs, in more or less linear precipitates, or in turbid areas in the agar which are not due to specific antigen-antibody precipitation at all (see α_2 areas, Frontispiece). No particular solution for this problem has been proposed. Changing the strength or the type of buffer or the electrophoresis medium (as from agar to gelatin; see Fig. V-2) can be helpful, or one might incorporate, in the agar gel and buffer, substances which do not interfere with electrophoretic separation or specific precipitation but which protect antigen solubility, such as gelatin or glycine.

Buffers

Optimal separation of antigens, such as those of serum, is accomplished at buffer pH values and at ionic strengths sometimes not compatible with adequate conditions for antigen-antibody precipitation. For example, some specific precipitation is inhibited or reversed at pH greater than 8.2, and nonspecific precipitation can occur below pH 6.5 (Crowle, 1960c). The low ionic strengths used in agar electrophoresis will not support specific precipitation by some antisera (Crowle, 1960c). Three solutions for this type of problem are employed. Since fraction diffusion in macroimmunoelectrophoresis is of minor importance, one can soak the agar in which electrophoresis has taken place, and in which the reactions are to occur, in a buffer of desired pH and ionicity, for several minutes before adding the indicator reactant, in order to replace the unsatisfactory buffer with one which is more amenable to precipitin reaction requirements (Grabar, 1959a). A second solution to this problem is to carry out the electrophoresis in a thin column of agar and then to embed this column in agar made up in buffer of the kind desired for the precipitin reaction and to cast troughs alongside the embedded column of agar to receive indicator reactant (Crowle, 1956). A compromise solution, particularly suited to microimmunoelectrophoresis in which plastic templates are employed (Crowle, 1960b), is to mix indicator reactant, before charging the agar trough with it, with buffer of the desired pH and high enough ionicity to supply the reaction area with adequate electrolyte.

Precipitin Band Enumeration

The maximum number of precipitin arcs for an antigen-antiserum system formed in a given immunoelectrophoresis test may not be detected by only one observation. Some bands may appear and disappear, others may merge or split, so that several observations should be made after different periods of reaction development (Wunderly, 1957). This precaution is particularly necessary when H-type antiserum is employed because of the distinct possibility that in the quantity of antiserum used to develop most of the reactions, there may be excess antibody for one particular antigen, or, when some complex mixture of antigens such as serum is being studied, the quantity of one constituent, such as albumin, may so greatly exceed that of the others that its precipitin arc is dissolved by antigen excess before the others are completely developed. With R-type antiserum, a band is not likely to dissolve, but its broadening may obscure the presence of another close to it.

✻   ✻   ✻

The dynamics of single and double diffusion tests and of immunoelectrophoresis are sufficiently complex to call for a great deal of caution in interpreting results obtained from these tests, but this very complexity contributes to their ability to yield remarkably varied information involving antigen-antibody precipitation. Consequently, efforts made by users of these tests to understand their intricacies will be rewarded with a generous return of knowledge.

CHAPTER IV

Applications of Immunodiffusion Tests

Shortly after the practicality of immunodiffusion techniques was demonstrated for analyzing such antigens as diphtheria toxin and animal serum, experimenters in various fields began to utilize them. At first, they were used only occasionally and with hesitancy for lack of knowledge of exactly how to interpret them and of conditions which affected them, but as their value repeatedly was confirmed and their versatility became more widely known they began to be used as primary rather than supplementary analytic tools. Although presently, judging from the numbers of papers published, analysis of mammalian sera (particularly human serum) is the most popular application of immunodiffusion tests, other applications have become common and are continuing to spread. For reasons mentioned previously, the following survey of such applications cannot be complete; yet, it should serve the reader as a primer on the potentialities of immunodiffusion tests, and it should suggest new uses for them.

Fluid and Cellular Constituents

Because of their great resolving power coupled with the ease with which they are applied, immunodiffusion and particularly immuno-electrophoretic techniques have seen the most use in qualitative analysis of such substances as human serum and other body fluids and of mammalian tissues and individual types of cells. A double purpose will be served by reviewing these analyses: (a) the range and applicability of immunodiffusion techniques will be illustrated, and (b) a ready reference of knowledge so far gained regarding these constituents will be made available for those who may be particularly interested in them.

Before the advent of immunoelectrophoresis, human serum was defined by methods such as paper electrophoresis, moving boundary electrophoresis, constituent solubilities, into five major fractions: albumin, α_1-globulin, α_2-globulin, β-globulin, and γ-globulin. Subfractions could be discerned by refining these techniques, but definitive identification of any given subfraction was difficult, and biochemists became aware as they did more experiments that these themselves probably were divisible [e.g., see immunodiffusion analysis of human plasma lipoproteins by Aladjem and Campbell (1957)]. The first publications on immunoelectrophoresis

95

TABLE IV-1
List of Named Immunoelectrophoretically-Defined Human Serum Antigens[a]

Name	Known Characteristics	Symbol
1. ρ_1	Tryptophan-rich glycoprotein	ρ_{1G1}
2. ρ_2-Lipoprotein	Lipoprotein	ρ_{2L}
3. Albumin	Most concentrated serum protein	Alb.
4. Acid seromucoid	Glycoprotein soluble in perchloric acid	α_{1SM}
5. α_1-Bilirubin globulin	––	α_{1Bi}
6. α_1-Lipoprotein	Heavy molecular weight lipoprotein; variable electrophoretic mobility	α_{1L}
7. α_1-Glycoprotein	Glycoprotein, sedimentation constant of 3.5 S	α_{1G1}
8. α_{1B}	—	α_{1B}
9. α_1	—	α_1
10. α_2-Haptoglobin I	Haptoglobin; binds hemoglobin; genetic marker	α_{2HI}
11. α_2-Haptoglobin II	Haptoglobin; binds hemoglobin; genetic marker	α_{2HII}
12. α_2-Macroglobulin	High molecular weight globulin	α_{2M}
13. α_2-Ceruloplasmin	Copper-binding protein	α_{2C}
14. α_2-Seromucoid	Mucoprotein	α_{2SM}
15. α_2-Glycoprotein	Low molecular weight glycoprotein	α_{2A}
16. α_2-Glycoprotein	—	α_{2G1}
17. α_2-Lipoprotein	Most concentrated serum lipoprotein, variable mobility, equivalent to β lipoprotein of paper electrophoresis	α_{2L}
18. α_2-Globulin	Binds thyroxin	α_{2J}
19. β_1-Glycoprotein	Euglobulin, glycoprotein, 9.5 S, responsible for serum complement activity; labile	β_{1C}
20. β_{1B}	—	β_{1B}
21. β_1-Transferrin	Binds iron; also known as siderophilin; may contain some lipid	β_{1S}
22. β_1-Glycoprotein	Degradation product of β_{1C} retaining no complement activity; 6.5 S	β_{1A}
23. β_1-Properdin	Fraction with activity of properdin	β_{1P}
24. β_{2X}-Globulin	Trace immunoglobulin	β_{2X}
25. β_2-Globulin	Immunoglobulin, 7 S, antigenically related to γ_A-globulin	β_{2A}
26. β_2-Macroglobulin	Macroglobulin, 19 S, antibody activity	β_{2M}
27. β_2-Globulin	Trace immunoglobulin	β_{2B}
28. γ-Globulin	Trace immunoglobulin related to β_{2A}	γ_B
29. γ-Globulin	Principal serum immunoglobulin, 7 S	γ_A

[a] Compiled from various sources available through July, 1960. The antigens are listed in order of decreasing mobility as usually observed in agar gels made up in barbital buffer at pH 8.2.

(Grabar and Williams, 1953, 1955; Williams and Grabar, 1955a,b) aimed to define human serum constituents, and this subject since has been taken up in many laboratories, particularly in Europe. Several recent reviews and papers describe contemporary knowledge of the immunoelectrophoretic components of normal human serum (Grabar and Burtin, 1959; Hirschfeld, 1960b; Moretti et al., 1959; Scheidegger, 1957; Scheiffarth and Götz, 1960).[*]

Table IV-1 lists human serum constituents so far identified by immunoelectrophoresis. The number of precipitin arcs detectable in any given test is very likely to be considerably smaller than the total in this Table (see Frontispiece), since some are demonstrable only under special conditions. For example, β_{2M}-globulin in normal serum occurs in such small quantities that unless the serum is concentrated by a factor of 5 or 6 this globulin may not be detected (Grabar et al. 1958). On the other hand, major fractions in concentrated serum may form such heavy bands that they obscure these minor components by overlapping their bands (Grabar and Burtin, 1959; Wunderly, 1957). A reactant's excess, when an H-type antiserum is used, may prevent band formation all together or rapidly dissolve an arc formed early during incubation. Finally, one antiserum is unlikely to contain antibodies to all normal human serum constituents, and a given serum will not contain all known normal constituents (Hirschfeld, 1960b; Scheidegger, 1957).

Immunoelectrophoresis of Human Serum

Human serum fractions according to available immunoelectrophoretic data can be listed in the following manner in order of decreasing mobility (i.e., distance from the cathode). This order of mobility must be understood to vary somewhat with changes in technique; below, it is based on agar electrophoresis in barbital buffer at pH 8.2. Figure IV-1 shows the major fractions diagrammatically, and Fig. IV-2 relates them to those found in paper and starch electrophoresis.

The most anodic of known antigenic serum constituents are two fractions, ρ_{1G1} and ρ_{2L}. ρ_1 forms a curvilinear precipitate, contains no lipid but much tryptophan (Grabar, 1955b; Grabar and Burtin, 1959), and has a molecular weight of about 61,000. It is the pre-albumin fraction of cerebrospinal fluid so readily demonstrated with paper electrophoresis (Scheidegger, 1957). ρ_2 is a lipoprotein accounting in agar electrophoresis

---

[*] The reader's attention is called to a manual, published after the present manuscript had been completed, edited by P. Graber and P. Burtin, entitled "Analyse Immunoelectrophorétique, ses Applications aux Liquides Biologiques Humains," and published by Masson and Co., Paris, 1960, 294 pages.

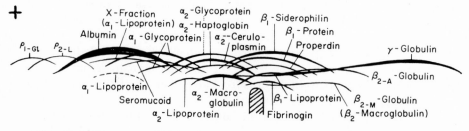

FIG. IV-1. Diagram indicating location of most of the identified human serum antigens, after immunoelectrophoresis in agar using barbital buffer at pH 8.2, and the types of precipitin arcs that they produce. (Courtesy Scheiffarth and Götz, 1960.)

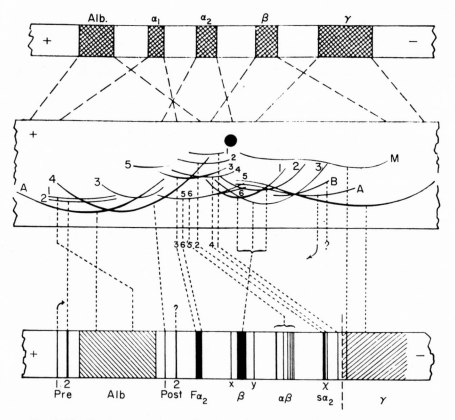

FIG. IV-2. Diagram comparing human serum electrophoretic fractions detected by common paper electrophoresis, agar immunoelectrophoresis, and starch electrophoresis (top to bottom). Note, for example, that starch electrophoresis Prealbumin 1 is immunoelectrophoresis β_{2A}. (Courtesy Moretti *et al.*, 1959.)

for 15–20% of total bound serum lipids (Scheidegger, 1957; Uriel and Grabar, 1956b).

The most easily identified fraction in serum is its albumin, characterized by a very strong and usually broad band at the anodic end of the separation area. A portion of this albumin may have lipid attached to it and so properly be called lipoalbumin (Uriel and Grabar, 1956b), although this lipid also might be an α_1-lipoprotein with a mobility equal to that of albumin (Scanu et al., 1958).

Within the albumin area is found a fraction called acid seromucoid (also orosomucoid) which has a sedimentation constant of 2.9 S, is a glycoprotein, and is soluble in trichloracetic acid or perchloric acid. By starch gel electrophoresis this fraction is "pre-albumin II." Sometimes before it, and seemingly part of the albumin (Scanu et al., 1958), and sometimes slightly behind it, is the α_1-lipoprotein, perhaps depending for its position upon the freshness of the serum being tested, since its apparent mobility seems to increase as the serum ages (Grabar and Burtin, 1959). This is a heavy molecular weight lipoprotein probably the same as the α-lipoprotein of paper electrophoresis (Grabar and Burtin, 1959; Scanu et al., 1958) and to be found in the albumin area in starch gel electrophoresis (Moretti et al., 1959). Following these two constituents are at least four α_1-fractions. One of these is a glycoprotein unrelated to seromucoid and having a sedimentation constant of 3.5 S (Grabar and Burtin, 1959; Scheidegger, 1957). What seems to be another, but perhaps might really be the same one, is known as "post albumin I" in starch gel electrophoresis (Moretti et al., 1959) and probably is the α_{1A}-fraction of Polonovski et al. (1958). Two other α_1-globulins can be detected which remain yet to be identified (see also Hirschfeld, 1960b; Polonovski et al., 1959; Scheiffarth and Götz, 1960).

In the α_2-globulin area have been found at least 6 fractions; 12 have been listed in one recent paper describing the use of discontinuous buffer immunoelectrophoresis in the analysis of human serum (Hirschfeld, 1959a, 1960b,c). The slowest of those fractions detected by conventional immunoelectrophoresis often is α_2-lipoprotein. However, its peculiar behavior toward agar and its "self-slowing" effect as it is analyzed immunoelectrophoretically in progressively greater quantities make this globulin difficult to place exactly; its apparent mobility is greater when it is used dilute than when it is concentrated (Uriel and Grabar, 1956b; Wieme, 1959a). Thus, it can appear in either the α_2 or α_1 area, depending upon experimental conditions. This fraction is the β-lipoprotein of paper electrophoresis, and it is found adjoining the γ-globulin in starch gel electrophoresis (Moretti et al., 1959). In it is 55–66% of the total serum conjugated lipid (Uriel and Grabar, 1956b). One or two haptoglobins

(α_{2HI} and α_{2HII}), or their combinations (Fine and Battistini, 1960), are located in the anodic span of the α_2-globulins if unhemolyzed serum is analyzed (Burtin *et al.*, 1954; Grabar and Burtin, 1959; Moretti *et al.*, 1959; Scheidegger, 1957); which one appears, seems to depend upon the genetic constitution of the serum donor (Moretti *et al.*, 1959). About midway in this α_2-globulin area is the copper-binding globulin, ceruloplasmin (Grabar and Burtin, 1959; Moretti *et al.*, 1959; Scheidegger, 1957; Uriel *et al.*, 1957), which also is in approximately the same area by starch gel electrophoresis (Moretti *et al.*, 1959). Behind this and in the cathodic region of α_2-globulins is an α_2-macroglobulin which has been isolated and studied by ultracentrifugation (Filitti-Wurmser *et al.*, 1958). Among the 12 α_2-globulins detected by Hirschfeld using a discontinuous buffer system (1959a, 1960b,c) are two group-specific components whose possible presence in an individual's serum depend upon genetic background. In Hirschfeld's scheme, component I is found between an α_1-globulin and the α_2-lipoprotein; component II is situated between the two haptoglobins.

At least four β_1-globulins are demonstrable (Bergrahm, 1960; Grabar and Burtin, 1955a, 1959; Müller-Eberhard and Nilsson, 1960; Müller-Eberhard *et al.*, 1960; Scheidegger, 1957; Scheiffarth and Götz, 1960). The two fastest have nearly equal mobility (Grabar and Burtin, 1959); they are β_{1C}- and β_{1B}-globulins (Müller-Eberhard *et al.*, 1960). Usually following these two is the fraction whose function is best understood: siderophilin (Grabar, 1955a) or, as it is more popularly known in the United States, transferrin (Müller-Eberhard *et al.*, 1960). However, this serum component also has been located both as the slowest (Grabar and Burtin, 1955a) of four β_1-globulins, and as the fastest (Scheiffarth and Götz, 1960), illustrating the hazards of trying to determine definitely the absolute mobility of any fraction by its position in a given immunoelectrophoretic experiment. A lipoprotein, β_{1L}, is likely to be found in mid-β_1-globulin range (Scheiffarth and Götz, 1960). Transferrin is an iron-transporting globulin with a molecular weight of about 90,000; β_{1B}-globulin probably is the same as the β_{1P}-fraction recently shown to be properdin (Scheiffarth *et al.*, 1958b). Two papers published recently by Müller-Eberhard *et al.* (1960) suggest that β_{1C} may be serum complement which on standing becomes a closely related but different immunoelectrophoretic fraction, β_{1A}, which has no complementary activity. β_{1A}-Globulin has a sedimentation constant of 6.9 S, while that of β_{1C} is 9.5 S. Both are euglobulins and glycoproteins. They are antigenically closely related, β_{1C} being antigenically somewhat more complex according to double diffusion plate tests than β_{1A}. β_{1A} will complex with hemoglobin, myoglobin, and cytochrome c. It is perchloric acid-soluble (Biserte *et al.*, 1960).

The β_2- and γ-globulins can be called, collectively, "immunoglobulins," because most appear to be some form of antibody (Heremans, 1959). These antigens tend to cross-react, particularly if they are analyzed with rabbit rather than horse antibodies in immunoelectrophoresis. There are two trace β_2-fractions, β_{2X} and β_{2B}, and two more obvious fractions, β_{2M} and β_{2A} (Heremans, 1959; Moretti et al., 1959; Scheidegger, 1957). The mobilities of three are nearly equal and somewhat less than that of β_{2X}. The nature and functions of the two trace globulins is unknown. β_{2A} is a euglobulin with the same molecular weight as γ-globulin and is antigenically related to it (Havez and Biserte, 1959b); it seems to be an antibody (Heremans, 1959). Interestingly, it is a pre-albumin (I) in starch gel electrophoresis (Moretti et al., 1959). β_{2M} is a macroglobulin with a sedimentation constant of 19 S (Filetti-Wurmser et al., 1958) and is known to constitute antibody activity in a human serum against red blood cells (e.g., isoagglutinins) (Faure et al., 1955; Heremans, 1959). β_{2M}-Globulins account for the H-type antibodies formed in horses upon prolonged immunization against protein antigens (see section on Horse Antiserum, below).

According to Rybak (1959), plasmin exists immunoelectrophoretically as two zones in the beta region. Its electrophoretic locality could be demonstrated after it had been isolated from human plasma by precipitation with magnesium ions.

Most reports suggest that human serum γ-globulin produces only one precipitin band (Grabar and Burtin, 1959; Moretti et al., 1959; Scheidegger, 1957; Scheiffarth and Götz, 1960). This band is uniquely long and skewed, apparently because the molecules defined as γ-globulin by serologic identity which constitute it belong by electrophoretic mobility to a smoothly changing series of electrophoretically different molecular species. Thus, when electrophoresed γ-globulin is eluted from succeeding sections of agar and re-electrophoresed, each section from which a portion was eluted is found to have yielded γ-globulin molecules with electrophoretic mobility evenly distributed about a center corresponding with that in the original section area (Grabar, 1955c). The principal γ-globulin precipitin arc can extend all the way into the α_2 area (Grabar, 1955c). In addition to this γ-globulin (γ_A), Heremans (1959) recently has reported finding a trace component, γ_B, which nestles closely within the γ_A arc and stops where it begins to cross the β_{2A} precipitin band. Hence, it seems to be related to this β-globulin but electrophoretically is slower and antigenically less complex. Augustin and Hayward have reported recently (1960) that γ-globulin in serum which is stored can split to secondary components. This might account for the trace constituents described by Heremans.

Immunoelectrophoresis clearly has proved its great value as an analytic tool in analyses of human serum (and plasma) by permitting demonstration of more than two dozen of its antigenic fractions and helping to define and/or isolate many of these. Nine such fractions have been studied individually in Schultze's laboratory (Schultze and Schwick, 1959). Pre-albumin has been shown immunologically distinct from albumin by the short-trough method (Schultze et al., 1956). Alimentary induction of hyperlipemia has been discovered to increase the quantity of "self-slowing" lipoprotein (α_2-lipoprotein) but not of either ρ- or α_1-lipoproteins (Uriel and Grabar, 1956b). Chylomicrons analyzed by immunoelectrophoresis and double diffusion experiments have been observed to contain a small quantity of protein, not a contaminant, identifiable as a mixture of the two serum α-lipoproteins (Scanu and Page, 1959). Immunoelectrophoresis has been used to follow a progressive fractionation of human serum with Zephiran (Polonovski et al., 1959) and with antibiotics of the tetracycline group (Lacko et al., 1959), and to identify serum antigens which remain soluble after its treatment with trichloracetic or perchloric acids (Robert et al., 1959).

Although, because of its tremendous versatility and ability to resolve and define simultaneously individual components in complex antigenic mixtures, immunoelectrophoresis has provided more general information on the constitution of human serum than other immunodiffusion methods, these have been applied profitably for particular purposes. Thus, human serum albumin has been fractionated by treatment with various enzymes into as many as three subconstituents with different antigenic determinants detectable by double diffusion tests (Kaminski and Tanner, 1959; Lapresle et al., 1959a,b). Untreated human serum albumin has been shown, by employing paper curtain electrophoresis in connection with double diffusion tests, to be more heterogeneous electrophoretically than commonly has been suspected (Karjala and Nakayama, 1959; Larson and Feinberg, 1954). Photometric studies of single diffusion tests in which human serum was allowed to diffuse into its rabbit antiserum have been used to detect appearance in experimental subjects of serum antigens connected with conditions of stress (Glenn, 1958b, 1959b; Glenn et al., 1958a). Exhaustive single diffusion test analyses of precipitates obtained by treating human serum with progressively greater quantities of ammonium sulfate have disclosed at least 25 distinct antigens, according to a recent paper published by Oudin (1960b). A special gradient double diffusion technique has been utilized for determining simply and accurately the molecular weights of human serum albumin, transferrin, γ-globulin, and α_2-lipoprotein (the β-lipoprotein of paper electrophoresis) (Allison and Humphrey, 1959). Korngold (1956b) has used double diffusion plate tests to study the antigenic relationships between γ-globulins, cryoglobulins, and macro-cryoglobulins.

Since the above data amply illustrate the analytic usefulness of immunodiffusion techniques in defining complex mixtures of antigens, the following information is intended primarily as a compendium of biologic data which have been obtained by these techniques in analyses of various materials not discussed specifically in later sections of this book.

Human Embryo Serum Antigens

The successive appearance and development of human embryo serum antigens have been studied immunoelectrophoretically. Serum of the 8-week-old embryo was found to contain only five fractions: ρ, albumin, α_1, α_2, and β_1-globulins. Other fractions including γ-globulin appeared by the twelfth week of embryonic life. Qualitatively, this pattern remained unchanged until delivery, so that at birth at least three known serum antigens were found wanting. These were the immunoglobulins β_{2A}- and β_{2M}- and α_2-globulin, probably a haptoglobin (Scheidegger, 1956, 1957; Scheidegger et al., 1956). The two lacking immunoglobulins did not become detectable in these studies until after the fourth week of extra-uterine life (Scheidegger, 1957). Evidence has been presented suggesting that the appearance of γ-globulin and perhaps several other serum constituents in the human fetus may result from their passive transfer from maternal serum (von Muralt and Gugler, 1959).

Rabbit antisera to human hemoglobin used in the double diffusion test against adult and fetal hemoglobins show that the latter contain two antigenic constituents and the former only one (Naylor and Adair, 1959). Human placental albumin has been found identical with adult serum albumin, but placental γ-globulins appear to be antigenically more complex than serum γ-globulin, perhaps because those studied may have been tissue rather than humoral antigens (Subrahmanyam and Maurer, 1959). Human serum β_{2A}-globulin has been demonstrated to be identical immunoelectrophoretically with that in plasmocytes, suggesting that these cells manufacture it (Havez and Biserte, 1959b).

Human Body Fluids

Since blood serves every part of the body, the question of whether other body fluids such as cerebrospinal fluid or synovial fluid are derived without qualitative change from blood serum is an interesting and important one; it has been examined successfully in several instances by immunoelectrophoresis (see Table IV-2). Human cerebrospinal fluid differs in enough respects from human serum to indicate that it is not merely a serum "filtrate." It contains most serum antigens, but several of these occur in distinctly different proportions from those found normally in serum (Burtin, 1959a; Crouch, 1958; Gavrilesco et al., 1955; Scheidegger, 1956). Individual constituents such as albumin, γ-globulin, and transferrin in cerebrospinal fluid immunologically are identical with those in serum (Burtin and Pocidalo, 1954a; Frick and Scheid-Seidel, 1957).

TABLE IV-2

ANTIGENIC CONSTITUENTS OF SOME NORMAL HUMAN FLUIDS AS
DETERMINED BY IMMUNOELECTROPHORESIS

Fluid	Constituents
Synovial	Same as in serum, but in much lower quantity; more ρ-antigen by proportion to other constituents.
Exudate and transudate	Same as in serum, but in much lower quantity.
Cerebrospinal	Most serum antigens, but in different proportions and in much lower quantity. Lacks α_{2M}, α_{2H}, α_{2C}.
Eye, anterior chamber	Same as those in serum, but in lower quantity; lacks β_{2M}.
Sperm plasma	At least 10 human serum antigens; lacks immunoglobulins.
Milk	At least 8 serum antigens, including γ- and β_{2A}-globulins. Five more antigens peculiar to itself.
Colostrum	Most serum antigens and greater quantities of immunoglobulins than milk, including β_{2M}-globulin.
Urine	Most serum antigens in exceedingly low concentrations; α_{1L}-, α_{2L}-, α_{1M}-, and β_{2M}-globulins normally absent. At least 12 antigens peculiar to it, the principal one being a mucoprotein.

Such fractions as α_2-macroglobulin, ceruloplasmin, and haptoglobin appear to be absent (Burtin, 1959a). The antigens of human synovial fluid are the same as those of human serum (Cleve, 1958; Scheidegger, 1957; Schmid and Macnair, 1956), but this fluid may contain, proportionally to other constituents, considerably more pre-albumin than serum (Schmid and Macnair, 1956). Exudates and transudates are not different from serum except in having much lower total quantities of antigenic solutes (Scheidegger, 1956, 1957). Eye anterior chamber fluid may lack β_{2M}-globulin, but otherwise it seems to be merely a dilute derivative of serum (Scheidegger, 1957).

Preliminary studies of human sperm plasma analyzed with horse antiserum to human serum indicate that it contains 8 immunoelectrophoretic fractions when fresh and 10 after it has stood for 32–48 hr. (Hermann, 1959). Human milk contains several antigens serologically identical with or related to serum proteins including albumin, one α_1-

and one β_1-globulin, β_{2A}-globulin, γ-globulin, and two α_2-globulins, and probably ρ (Hanson and Johansson, 1959b). However, at least 5 milk fractions are different from any in serum. Human colostrum and pre-colostrum differ somewhat from milk both quantitatively and qualitatively. The following colostrum proteins antigenically appear to be identical with those in serum: albumin, an α_1-, two α_2-, two β_1-, β_{2A}-, β_{2M}-, and γ-globulins (Hanson and Johansson, 1959b). Human milk casein consists of α-, β-, and γ-globulin fractions; it contains at least 9 antigens. There are 5 or more immunologically distinct fractions in human lactal-bumin, one of which is identical with human serum albumin (Hanson and Johansson, 1959a).

Most human plasma antigens can be demonstrated in concentrated human urine (Grant, 1959), but it contains some 12 nonplasma proteins apparently originating from the urinary and genital tracts. Principal among these is a mucoprotein (Grant, 1959). Normal urine colloids include albumin, seromucoid, an α_1-, two α_2-, a β_1-, and γ-globulins. Urine does not normally contain the α_1- and α_2-lipoglobulins and α_1- and β_2-macroglobulins of immunoelectrophoresis (Keutel *et al.*, 1959), nor hapto-globin or ceruloplasmin (Heremans *et al.*, 1959a).

Hormones

Recent demonstration of the production of antibodies in rabbits to human growth hormone useful for immunodiffusion analyses (Grumbach *et al.*, 1960) suggests that the biochemistry of hormones could be studied with immunodiffusion techniques.

Human Tissue Antigens

Definitive studies on tissue antigens comparable with those on serum have only begun. As pointed out in one of these (Grabar *et al.*, 1954), a formidable difficulty is to be certain that antigens being studied are being derived from the tissue cells of interest and not as contaminants from body fluids or other cells. Careful experiments on human blood leukocytes sonicly disrupted and examined by Ouchterlony's double diffusion technique with rabbit antiserum showed that these contain some 3 or 4 antigens, none common to those of serum. One of these antigens could not be found in leukemia leukocytes (Grabar *et al.*, 1954; Seligmann *et al.*, 1955). Antibodies to leukocytes precipitate antigens in lysates of normal leukocytes, leukemia leukocytes from chronic lymph-oiditis, leukemic granulocytes, and leucoblasts of acute leukemia, but not any in lysates of thrombocytes (Seligmann, 1957b). Double diffusion analysis indicates that fibrinogen is intimately attached to blood plate-lets (Seligmann, 1957a). Red blood cell lysates appear to contain 4 major components immunoelectrophoretically, one of which splits during analysis; lysates of cells taken from cord blood of the new-born infant contain 5. These antigens are of both hemoglobinic and nonhemoglobinic origin (Boivin *et al.*, 1959a). Immunoelectrophoresis demonstrates a small percentage of protein in chylomicrons apparently consisting of a mixture of the two α-serum lipoproteins (Scanu and Page, 1959).

Sera from Lower Animals

Immunoelectrophoretic patterns for sera from the lower animals are similar to those of human serum, but there are differences great enough not to permit generalizations beyond categorizing antigens in these sera

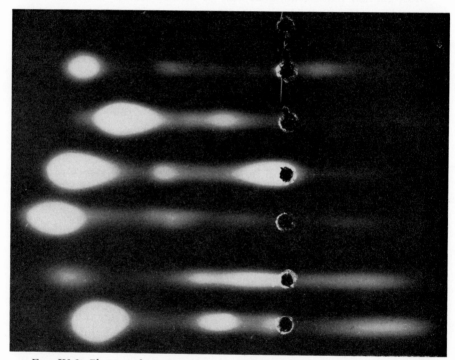

Fig. IV-3. Photographic print showing differences in electrophoretic mobilities of proteins in chicken, guinea pig, horse, rabbit, mouse, and human sera (top to bottom). All sera were electrophoresed simultaneously on one glass plate in agar and barbital buffer at pH 8.2, ionicity 0.1, and their fractions then stained with thiazine red R.

into the usual major groupings of globulins, albumin, and ρ; the mobilities and quantities of individual fractions may differ considerably (see Fig. IV-3). A schematic summary of current knowledge on this subject is presented in Table IV-3, the data for which were obtained as follows: guinea pig serum (Kaminski, 1957c; Pernot, 1956), bovine serum (Brown and Graves, 1959; Hanson and Johansson, 1959c; Kaminski, 1957c; Pernot and Szumowski, 1958), horse serum (Grabar and Courcon, 1958; Kaminski, 1957c), rabbit serum (Grabar and Courcon, 1958; Kaminski, 1957c), goat serum (Kaminski, 1957c), chimpanzee and ape serum

TABLE IV-3

IMMUNOELECTROPHORETICALLY KNOWN ANTIGENS IN THE SERA
OF SEVERAL SPECIES OF MAMMALS[a]

Species	Number of studies	γ	β_3	β_2	β_1	α_2	α_1	A	ρ_2	ρ_1
Human[b]	Many	2	–	3	5	9	6	1	1	1
Chimpanzee	2	2	–	2	5	3	4	1	–	1
Baboon	2	2	–	–	2	2	6	1	–	1
Macacus cynomolgus[b]	1	1	–	1	3	1	6	1	–	–
Cebus capucinus[b]	1	1	–	1	2	1	3	1	–	–
Horse[b]	2	2	1	3	3	4	4	1	–	–
Bovine[b]	2	1	–	1	3	2	3	1	–	–
Goat[b]	1	2	–	1	1	2	3	1	–	–
Pig[b]	1	1	–	1	2	2	2	1	–	–
Sheep[b]	1	2	–	1	2	1	2	1	–	–
Dog	1	1	–	1	2	2	2	1	–	–
Rabbit[b]	2	1	–	3	3	6	3	1	–	–
Guinea pig[b]	2	1	–	1	2	2	1	1	–	–
Rat	2	2	–	2	2	2	2	1	–	–
Mouse[b]	2	1	3	4	1	6	4	1	–	1

[a] Each number of antigens in this table represents a minimum; sera from some species apparently lacking many of the antigens found in those of other species simply have not yet been studied with sufficiently potent antisera.

[b] Species of animals whose sera have been analyzed with homologous antiserum.

(Kaminski, 1957c; Paluska and Kořínek, 1960), sera of Old World monkeys, New World monkeys, and lemurs (Paluska and Kořínek, 1960), sheep and dog serum (Kaminski, 1957c), rat serum (Grabar and Courcon, 1958; Kaminski, 1957c), and mouse serum (Clausen and Heremans, 1960; Grabar and Courcon, 1958).

Chicken Eggs, Embryos, and Serum

Kaminski and her co-workers have published several papers on immunodiffusion analyses of chicken eggs and chicken embryos as well as on serum constituents of adult chickens relative to these (Durieux and Kaminski, 1956; Kaminski, 1954d, 1957a,b; Kaminski and Durieux, 1954, 1956). Egg white contains the following constituents in order of decreasing electrophoretic mobility in agar: ovalbumin, α_1-globulin, two α_2-globulins (which proved to be immobile, apparently being unable to diffuse through agar), two β_1-globulins, two β_2-globulins, conalbumin with a mobility between β_2 and γ areas, and, finally, γ-globulin. Some egg white antigens usually are present only in embryo serum (ovalbumin and ovomucoid), but conalbumin immunologically identical with that in egg white can be demonstrated in the sera of chickens in all stages of development. Similar investigations by Croisille (1959) have demonstrated 14 immunoelectrophoretic constituents in extracts of chicken liver.

Reproductive Organ Antigens

Animal semen and seminal plasma have attracted some analysis. Bull seminal plasma contains at least 11 antigens, only 2 of which appear to be antigenically identical with bovine serum constituents (albumin and β-globulin). The principal antigen is found in the α-globulin area (Pernot and Szumowski, 1958). There also are at least 11 antigens in guinea pig seminal plasma among which albumin, one α_2-globulin and γ-globulin are the same as found in guinea pig serum. Of 7 antigens demonstrable in guinea pig spermatozoa tail extracts, 6 are antigens also found in the seminal plasma. Constituents of seminal plasma not occurring in the serum include ρ_1-, ρ_2-, Pα_1-globulin, and Pα_2-globulin; no ρ-fraction appears to be detectable in guinea pig serum (Pernot, 1956). Double diffusion tests have shown that guinea pigs produce 3 specific testes and spermatozoa antigens while no tissue-specific antigen is demonstrable in guinea pig ovary, in which there are at least 5 antigens also found in guinea pig testes, kidney, lung, uterus, spleen, and adrenal gland (Isojima and Stepus, 1959). Rabbit seminal plasma contains at least one isoantigenic component while rabbit spermatozoa contain none (Weil and Finkler, 1959).

Eye Antigens

Seven protein antigens have been disclosed in one study (Rao et al., 1955) in bovine vitreous humor, of which 5 occur in bovine serum and 2 in bovine eye lens. In the lens are large quantities of 3 proteins not found in bovine serum. Bovine aqueous humor contains at least 6 antigens, 3 in common with serum constituents and the other 3 identical with those in the lens. Another study shows beef vitreous humor to have at least 8 antigens which can be separated immunoelectrophoretically into three major groups, the slowest with a mobility of γ-globulin and the fastest with one of α-globulin (Wieme and Kaminski, 1955).

Miscellaneous Data

In studies on horse antibodies, β- and γ-euglobulins precipitated from horse antiserum at pH 8 by a lowering of solvent ionicity have been found immunologically identical but only partially related to normal horse serum euglobulins (Sandor and Sandor, 1960). The discrepancy between agar electrophoresis and paper or classic electrophoresis regarding location of lipoproteins and consequently their naming is emphasized by Uriel and Grabar (1956b), who, in reporting results from agar electrophoretic analyses of sera from numerous animal species, never found any lipoproteins in γ or β areas. In most other forms of electrophoresis, the principal serum lipoprotein would be expected to migrate as a β-globulin. Their data show serum from the snake *Vipera aspis* to be particularly rich in ρ-lipoprotein. Experiments on the mechanisms of blood coagulation using immunodiffusion techniques have been encouraged by demonstration that highly specific antibodies to cattle prothrombin and thrombin can be produced in horses which exert physiologic effects on the process of blood coagulation (Schwick and Schultze, 1959). Silkworm blood has been analyzed by single diffusion tests in connection with studies on insect metamorphosis and shown to contain at least 9 different constituents (Telfer and Williams, 1953). Double diffusion tests have been used to demonstrate that upon hyperimmunization with appropriate antigens, rabbits can produce antibodies against liver microsomes and ribonucleoproteins (Zalta and Khouvine, 1956). Rat liver lipoprotein synthesis has been followed using specific goat antiserum (Marsh and Whereat, 1959). Double diffusion plate tests utilizing highly specific mouse anti-rat and rat anti-mouse sera have shown that lethally irradiated mice saved from death by passive transfer of rat bone marrow do not produce rat serum proteins, contrary to what has been suspected by previous workers using less specific antisera (Gengozian, 1959). The molecular weights of mouse urinary proteins, hen ovalbumin, sheep thyroglobulin, and hemocyanin from species of *Caminella* and *Janus* have been determined with a gradient double diffusion test (Allison and Humphrey, 1959).

Pathology

Principal reasons for the popularity of immunodiffusion analyses of human serum are that knowledge so gained can improve understanding of pathological processes in the human being, and could aid diagnosis of diseases and simplify their therapy. Despite much work toward these goals, immunodiffusion still is in its infancy as a practical aid to the physician. The following résumé of contemporary knowledge, resulting mostly from immunoelectrophoretic analyses of pathologic human serum specimens, is offered both as a record of research which has been done and as an illustration of the great potential advantage that immuno-diffusion analyses have over conventional analytic methods (e.g., paper electrophoresis) for detecting specific minor fractions, the presence or absence of which may be of considerable clinical significance and, by the conventional techniques, cannot be ascertained. They also permit reliable estimation of the antigenic relationship that newly appearing abnormal fractions may have to normal fractions. The use of immunoelectro-phoresis in analyses of pathological human serum recently has been re-viewed by Scheiffarth and Götz (1960).

Gamma Globulins

As in any kind of electrophoretic study, the most obvious and readily identified pathologic change in the pattern of human serum antigens is that in which γ-globulin is lacking—agammaglobulinemia. Immunoelectrophoretic experimentation with this disease has been re-viewed recently by Burtin (1958). Aside from γ-globulin, the other immunoglobulins (β_{2A} and β_{2M}) also tend to be affected, singly or to-gether, but the quantities and distribution of other serum proteins tend to remain undisturbed (Barandun et al., 1959; Bridges and Good, 1959; Burtin, 1958; Gitlin et al., 1956; Grabar and Burtin, 1959; Grabar et al., 1958; Heremans, 1959; Hitzig et al., 1959; Scheidegger, 1956; Scheiffarth and Götz, 1960). Both β-globulins may be lacking, while a small amount of abnormally slowly migrating γ-globulin or normal but nonantibody γ-globulin persists (Hitzig et al., 1959). Either or both of the β-globulins can occur in abnormally low concentration along with scarcely detectable γ-globulin (Bridges and Good, 1959; Gitlin et al., 1956; Grabar and Burtin, 1959; Grabar et al., 1958; Heremans, 1959). On the other hand, in a β-myeloma, β_2-globulin may seem to replace the absent γ-globulin (Scheiffarth and Götz, 1960). An important piece of information con-tributed by immunoelectrophoretic analyses has been that true agamma-globulinemia (complete absence of γ-globulin) is very uncommon, per-haps nonexistent.

Increases as well as decreases in the three immunoglobulins are detected readily by immunoelectrophoresis in some pathologic sera such as, for example, that obtained from patients with cirrhosis (Heremans, 1959) or polyarthritis (Cleve and Hartmann, 1957a). New forms of γ-globulin can appear as they tend to in neoplastic and inflammatory diseases (Heremans, 1959), in which this and the other immunoglobulins are produced in varying states of abnormality to become known as para-proteins, mentioned more fully below.

Higher-than-normal quantities of γ-globulin in serum are signaled by strengthening and broadening of the usually thin γ-globulin precipitin band of an immunoelectrophoretic pattern which, if developed with R-type antiserum, shows the characteristics of precipitating under conditions of antigen excess. There also may be a split accompanying band intensification, the usual single γ-globulin band doubling. Scheiffarth and Götz (1960) classify these possible changes as (1) a simple intensification of the single γ-globulin band which sometimes also is considerably shortened, (2) a splitting of the band into a weak and a strong arc both arising from globulins of equal electrophoretic mobility, and (3) formation of two γ-globulin bands, one of normal intensity, shape, and position, and the other very heavy, acutely curved, and arising from a fraction electrophoretically either more or less mobile. The new bands show characteristics of partial but not complete antigenic identity with normal γ-globulin (see Fig. IV-4).

Hypergammaglobulinemia immunoelectrophoretically is most strikingly demonstrable, as in other types of electrophoresis, in multiple myeloma (Grabar et al., 1955b). The γ-globulin zone is unusually heavy and is acutely curved. This signifies that there is an increase in concentration of proteins with true γ mobility and a repression of other immunologically similar globulins with greater mobilities which form the usual long γ-globulin precipitin band (Grabar and Burtin, 1959). Multiple myeloma γ-globulin is related to normal γ-globulin, but it is not the same (Korngold and Lipari, 1956a,b; Slater et al., 1955; Scheiffarth and Götz, 1960; Scheiffarth et al., 1958). The abnormal globulins of this disease have been detected in bone marrow plasmocytes, apparently where they are manufactured (Serre and Jaffiol, 1958).

Acute leukoses cause little change in the immunoelectrophoretic serum pattern; but lymphoidal leukemias induce anomalies among the γ-globulins (Grabar and Burtin, 1959). Lipoidal nephrosis causes a considerable decrease in γ-globulin (Grabar and Burtin, 1959; Scheidegger, 1956). Hepatic disease, particularly infectious jaundice and alcoholic cirrhosis, provoke augmentation of all electrophoretic species of γ-globulin, rather than of one type as seen in multiple myeloma (Scheidegger, 1956). The quantity of serum γ-globulin may rise in lupus erythematosis, but it remains immunochemically normal (Seligmann and Hanau, 1958). The γ-globulin precipitin arc tends to be weaker than normal in macroglobulinemia in which there is a tremendous increase in β_{2M}-globulin (Grabar and Burtin, 1959), and abnormal γ-globulins may be detected (Burtin et al., 1957).

In any condition, whether artificially induced or the result of an infection, in which there has been a strong stimulation of a body's antibody-making system, moderate to marked hypergammaglobulinemia may result (Scheiffarth and Götz, 1960). This increase can be limited to γ-globulins in a narrow range of electrophoretic mobility. Presumably, if formation of antibodies is unduly suppressed, as it would be by isolating

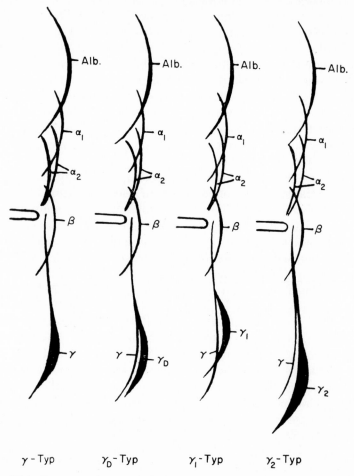

FIG. IV-4. Diagram of agar immunoelectrophoretic patterns of human sera obtained from patients with various forms of γ-myeloma, and in which hypergammaglobulinemia is manifested as over-production of different types of γ-globulin. (Courtesy Scheiffarth and Götz, 1960.)

an animal from the time it is born from bacteria and other agents which normally would induce it to form antibodies, a lower than "normal" quantity of γ-globulin should be detected by immunoelectrophoretic analysis.

Beta-2 Globulins

Production of the principal β-globulins, β_{2A} and β_{2M}, tends to be altered whenever that of γ-globulins is affected, as mentioned above, because all three are immunoglobulins, have similar functions, and probably are manufactured by closely related or identical body cells.

Immunoelectrophoretically, the β-myelomas (see Fig. IV-5) are particularly striking. In these, there is a striking increase in quantity of one or more of the β-globulins which results in their forming heavy precipitin bands. Serum from a patient with Waldenström's macroglobulinemia

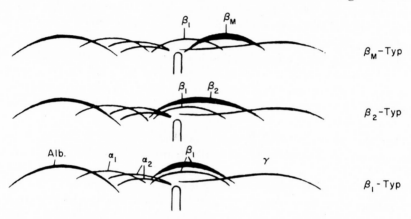

Fig. IV-5. Human serum agar immunoelectrophoretic patterns in three forms of β-myeloma, showing in particular the span of affected β-globulin precipitin arcs. (Courtesy Scheiffarth and Götz, 1960.)

also shows such an increase in the β_{2M}-globulin; the ordinarily scarcely visible β_{2M}-globulin precipitin arc, which in normal sera is readily demonstrated only if these sera are concentrated before they are electrophoresed, is very prominent (Burtin *et al.*, 1957; Grabar and Burtin, 1959; Scheidegger, 1957; Scheidegger *et al.*, 1958; Scheiffarth and Götz, 1960; Wunderly, 1958b). It can be distinguished from β_2-myelomas because sera from patients with the latter produce their heavy β-precipitin bands nearer the antibody source than most of the other precipitin bands in the immunoelectrophoretic pattern, while increases in β_{2M}-globulin detected in sera from patients with Waldenström's disease cause the formation of a heavy precipitin band quite near to the source of antigen diffusion and extending from the origin and even from the α_2-globulin region down among the γ-globulins (Scheiffarth and Götz, 1960). Presumably, this is due to the heavy molecular weight of β_{2M}-globulin as contrasted with that of β_{2A}-globulin; regardless of its con-

centration, the former diffuses much more slowly than the R-type antiserum (with which this type of pattern differentiation is seen) used to
precipitate it and consequently precipitates near its source of diffusion.
Symptomatic macroglobulinemias can develop from chronic liver disease,
cirrhosis, nephrosis, rheumatoid arthritis, eosinophilic granulomatosis,
and hyperglobulinemic purpura, but the β_{2M}-globulin whose concentration increases apparently remains antigenically the same as the normal
fraction. This globulin in Waldenström's disease by contrast apparently
develops some subtle changes. Its precipitin band generally is heavier,
shorter, and ends in sharply curved tips (Scheiffarth and Götz, 1960); it
may develop as a double arc (Wunderly, 1958b). Antigenically, it is not
identical with normal β_{2M}-globulin nor with that of which there are increases in the symptomatic macroglobulinemias which, itself, seems to
be normal (Burtin et al., 1957; Grabar and Burtin, 1959; Scheidegger,
1957). For example, absorption of normal serum with antiserum to γ- and
β_2-globulins will remove γ-, β_{2A}-, and β_{2M}-globulins, but absorption of
Waldenström serum will not remove all of its β_{2M}-globulin (Scheiffarth
and Götz, 1960).

As has been mentioned before, β_{2M}-globulins tend to be antibodies,
and, consequently, stimuli which affect the manufacture of the antibodies that they represent, such as cryoglobulins, (Grabar and Burtin,
1959) may cause an increase in their quantity.

Multiply, myeloma not only causes an increase in γ-globulin; it also
tends to provoke a decrease in serum quantities of β_{2A}-globulin. Sometimes, however, it may cause an increase in this fraction (Grabar and
Burtin, 1959). Serum from patients with lipoidal nephrosis contains
very little of this fraction (Grabar and Burtin, 1959; Scheidegger, 1957).
It is likely to be absent all together in macroglobulinemias. Changes in
the quantities of both β-globulins in pathologic sera quite often tend
to parallel those in γ-globulin (Seligmann and Hanau, 1958). Such
changes occur in lymphoid leukemias. Secondary bone cancers induce
increases in both β-globulins (Scheidegger, 1957).

Beta-1 Globulins

Changes in the quantities of these globulins have been observed to
occur in the sera of patients with a number of afflictions. However, so
little is understood of the nature and functions of these antigens that
the meaning of these changes is obscure. β_1-Globulin myelomas, of
course, are readily recognized by the position of the antigen being produced in abnormally large quantities in the immunoelectrophoretic pattern (Scheiffarth and Götz, 1960). The fraction which usually is affected
is transferrin. However, the cause of such an increase also may be an

acute form of rheumatoid disease. The quantity of transferrin tends to drop below normal during acute or chronic hepatitis or in nephrotic syndrome. Biliary cirrhosis induces increases among the β_1-globulins (Scheiffarth and Götz, 1960). Patients with hyperparathyroidism develop β_1-globulin anomalies which disappear after they have been treated surgically (Komárková and Kořínek, 1959). In view of recent suggestions that β_{1A}-globulin may represent part or all of serum complement, it is interesting that the concentration of this globulin consistently drops in the serum of patients with lupus erythematosis who are undergoing an acute attack and rises again during remissions; the acute attack seems to be accompanied by gross cellular destruction within the patient, an effect probably requiring complement (Grabar and Burtin, 1959; Seligmann and Hanau, 1958).

Alpha-2 Globulins

A marked increase in globulins of this kind in serum from patients with nephrotic calcification is accounted for largely by the α_2 high molecular weight glycoprotein (Scheiffarth and Götz, 1960), although the quantities of other α_2-fractions also rise significantly. Abnormally high quantities of this antigen also are consistently produced by patients with sclerosis (Moretti et al., 1959). Tumor-induced hyperglobulinemia in this area of the immunoelectrophoretic pattern can be attributed primarily to increases in quantities of macroglobulin and of ceruloplasmin (Scheiffarth and Götz, 1960). Acute rheumatoid arthritis induces rises in fractions which probably are the haptoglobins. Acute hepatitis causes α_2-globulin changes which are transitory, and two fractions which are not seen in normal serum have been demonstrated among the α_2-globulins in sera from patients with biliary cirrhosis (Scheiffarth and Götz, 1960). Acute lupus erythematosis is accompanied by increases in α_2-globulins (Seligmann and Hanau, 1958). While quantities of most other serum fractions decrease in cases of lipoidal nephrosis, those of the nonlipoidal α_2-globulins rise (Grabar and Burtin, 1959; Scheidegger, 1956). The quantity of copper-binding globulin, ceruloplasmin, is specifically and strikingly below normal in sera from victims of the congenital Wilson's disease, and the position of this globulin in the immunoelectrophoretic pattern seems to be abnormal (Williams, 1960).

Alpha-1 Globulins

Serum from someone with rheumatoid arthritis on immunoelectrophoresis may show either an increase in the number of precipitin bands or an increase in the intensity of a normal number of these in the α_1 area; α_1-seromucoid seems particularly likely to be involved. A striking decrease in α_1-glycoprotein has been observed to occur in the serum of tuberculosis patients (Scheiffarth and Götz, 1960).

Albumin

The syndrome of analbuminemia exists comparable to that of agammaglobulinemia. This congenital disease is rare, but it has been studied immunoelectrophoretically (Lohss and Kallee, 1959). Hypoalbuminemia of varying degrees has been demonstrated immunoelectrophoretically in lipoidal nephrosis and in acute lupus erythematosis (Grabar and Burtin, 1959; Seligmann and Hanau, 1958). Certain liver diseases occasionally cause hyperalbuminemia (Scheiffarth and Götz, 1960). Immunoelectrophoretic and immunodiffusion studies indicate that in such instances increases in albumin can be accounted for by a protein antigenically the same as normal serum albumin (Burtin, 1954a; Burtin et al., 1955b).

Pre-albumins

Antigens with electrophoretic mobility greater than that of albumin as they occur in pathologic sera have received almost no immunoelectrophoretic study, probably because they often are difficult to detect. In place of the usual two demonstrable in normal serum with adequate techniques, four have been detected in the sera of patients with Waldenström's macroglobulinemia (Scheiffarth and Götz, 1960).

C-Reactive Protein

This protein, CRP, tends to appear in the serum of people suffering from any of a number of apparently unrelated inflammatory conditions or physiologic stress. Immunoelectrophoresis places it in the β_1 area according to some workers (Burtin, 1957; Scheidegger, 1957; W. Muller et al., 1958), in the β_2 region according to others (Augustin and Hayward, 1955; Cleve and Hartmann, 1957b), and among the γ-globulins according to still others (Bustamante, 1957; Zach and Zimmermann, 1959). Although CRP is a substance of two and probably three distinct antigenic constituents (Fishel, 1960; see Fig. IV-6; Libretti et al., 1955), it is generally detected with specific antiserum in immunoelectrophoresis as a single band. Its antigenic heterogeneity might account partially for disagreement on its mobility in agar. Perhaps an even more likely reason for disagreement is that, like the immunoelectrophoretic α_2-lipoprotein, this fraction adheres to the agar gel or in other ways does not move freely through agar during electrophoresis. Thus, Fishel (1960) observed that its position in immunoelectrophoretic patterns produced at different pH values ranging from 6.9 to 8.6 did not change relative to the origin,

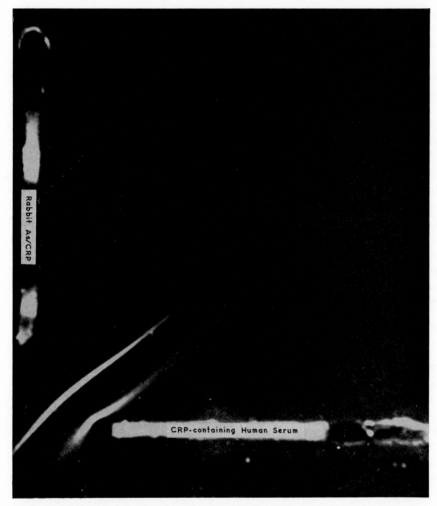

Fɪɢ. IV-6. Photograph of a micro double diffusion gradient test in which rabbit antiserum to C-reactive protein was reacted with human serum containing this protein. At least two and possibly three precipitin bands are visible. (Courtesy C. W. Fishel.)

while the positions of other serum constituents in the same runs, except the major lipoprotein, changed predictably.

CRP has been detected specifically by immunodiffusion techniques in sera of patients with polyarthritis, rheumatoid arthritis, and other similar inflammatory diseases (Burtin, 1957; Cleve and Hartmann, 1957b; Grabar and Burtin, 1959; Scheiffarth and Götz, 1960), as well as in animal sera (Gotschlich and Stetson, 1960). The protein is likely to be produced under the influence of diseases such as viral hepatitis, alcoholic cirrhosis, reticulosis, and sclerosis, all of which appear to affect the reticulo-endothelial system, regardless of the site of primary inflammation, and tend also to augment production of immunoglobulins (Cleve and Hartmann, 1957b; Grabar and Burtin, 1959; Francq *et al.*, 1959) as well as of new fractions in the α_2 and β regions (Francq *et al.*, 1959).

Human serum antigens possibly related to CRP, actually or functionally, have been detected in single diffusion tube tests. Especially developed electrophotometric devices used in these experiments to measure the densities and shapes of precipitin bands, produced by serum antigens diffusing into their rabbit antiserum, detected subtle changes in quantities of these antigens which could be correlated to some extent with the clinical states of the patient donors of serum (Glenn, 1958b; Glenn *et al.*, 1958a, 1959). According to these studies, a normally faint or absent serum antigen (apparently a mucoprotein) tended to become readily detectable in sera obtained from patients with nephrosis, suspected malignancy, or with severe thermal or traumatic injuries, and changes in the distribution and densities of other serum components in the precipitin pattern could be observed.

Perchloric Acid-Soluble Serum Antigens

Immunoelectrophoresis shows that some normal human serum antigens (β_{2M}-globulin, acid seromucoid, a β_1-mucoprotein, and an α_1-globulin) are soluble in perchloric acid; others normally are not. By contrast, in sera from patients with such disorders as pulmonary cancer, leukemia, purpura, and renal tuberculosis, in addition to these, β_{2A}- and a β_1-globulin, additional α_1- and α_2-globulins, some γ-globulin, and albumin, have proved to be significantly soluble in this acid, although to variable degrees (Vaux Saint-Cyr, 1959). Experiments performed by Biserte and co-workers (1960) suggest that β_{1A}-globulin is a perchloric acid-soluble fraction.

Urine

Examination of urine for its content of antigens can be diagnostically useful, particularly in connection with diseases of the kidney. Normal human urine contains many serum antigens in minute quantities; the serum macroglobulins, however, are conspicuously absent. Kidney injury is suggested if the quantities of normally present antigens begin to increase, or if some of the larger serum proteins appear (Gell, 1955a; Scheidegger, 1957). Interestingly, changes in blood proteins also may be reflected by similar changes among analogous antigens in urine.

Of the urine antigens, Bence-Jones proteins have received the most study by immunodiffusion. These low molecular weight proteins, which by original definition precipitate at 50°–60°C. in acid medium and redissolve on being boiled, can be divided into three different groups by double diffusion tests (Burtin et al., 1955a, 1956; Korngold and Lipari, 1956b), all closely related to normal serum γ-globulins and apparently fragmentary forms of these, perhaps resulting from their imperfect synthesis (Burtin et al., 1956; Korngold and Lipari, 1956b; Scheidegger, 1957). Because of their low sensitivities, neither the classic test of heating urine nor that of paper electrophoresis detect Bence-Jones proteins in normal urine, but double diffusion tests performed upon sufficiently concentrated normal urines show that they commonly contain these proteins (Burtin et al., 1955a).

Studies on the origin of urinary calculi have revealed that urines associated with them essentially are normal. However, some serum proteins not normally present in urine are detectable in oxalate calculi themselves (Keutel, 1959).

Cerebrospinal Fluid

Immunodiffusion tests apparently have only begun to be applied to examination of pathologic cerebrospinal fluid. In one study, the constituents of this fluid obtained from patients with mental illness were compared with those of normal fluid; minor variable differences were detected (Burtin, 1959a). Among various samples, one showed a very strong β_1-globulin, in another the quantity of α_2-globulins was abnormally high, and in a third β_2-globulin, not ordinarily found in normal fluid, could be detected. In another study, the double diffusion plate test was used to verify the specificity of antibodies used for quantitation of γ-globulin in the cerebrospinal fluid (Mollaret et al., 1956).

Synovial Fluid

Synovial fluid from patients with rheumatoid or traumatic arthritis or with neural arthropathy has been comparable qualitatively and in relative but not absolute quantities with plasma obtained from the same patients. Any changes from normal which had occurred among their plasma antigens due to these disorders were paralleled by similar changes in their synovial fluid (Schmid and Macnair, 1956).

Eye Anterior Chamber Fluid

This fluid in cases of iritis contains considerably more protein than fluid in the healthy individual, but by immunoelectrophoretic analysis qualitatively it is not abnormal (Scheidegger, 1957).

Sputum

Bukantz and Berns (1959) have used double diffusion plate tests to analyze sputum from asthma patients. They found samples of sputum to contain blood group antigens corresponding to those antigens found in the erythrocytes of the patients. Rabbit antiserum to sputum failed to react with either human serum or with antigens from bacteria commonly found in the bronchial tree.

Autoantibodies

Immunodiffusion analyses seem to be outstandingly useful for detecting and especially for identifying antibodies produced by an animal which react with its own tissues. Organ and species-specific antibodies to thyroglobulin have been demonstrated in the serum of patients with Hashimoto's thyroiditis by such analyses (Belyavin and Trotter, 1959; Doniach and Roitt, 1957; Goudie *et al.*, 1959; Roitt and Doniach, 1958a). Immunoelectrophoresis suggests that these are γ-globulins (Doniach and Roitt, 1957). Nonprecipitating and co-precipitating autoantibodies to thyroglobulin can be detected with double diffusion techniques and appropriate auxilliary techniques (Goudie *et al.*, 1959). Autoantibodies to leukocytes and to cellular deoxyribonucleic acid (DNA) have been found and identified in sera from patients with disseminated lupus erythematosis (Deicher *et al.*, 1959; Seligmann, 1957b, 1958b), especially during its acute phases (Deicher *et al.*, 1959). The anti-DNA antibodies discovered differed from leukoprecipitins also identified in some of these experiments (Seligmann, 1957b), the latter being directed against non-DNA leukocyte constituents (Seligmann, 1958b). These anti-DNA antibodies have been postulated to be responsible for the LE phenomenon in lupus, since they have been shown to induce it in normal leukocytes. Antibody damage to white cells in acute myeloid leukemia might be inferred from the observation that leukocyte antigens detectable only in minute quantities in normal human serum occur in much larger quantities during acute phases of this disease (Seligmann, 1956). Acute leukoses, by contrast, present no evidence of such releases of leukocyte antigens into the serum.

Species-specific precipitating antibodies against kidney, liver, and lung tissues have been detected in children with renal disease (Liu and McCrory, 1958). Sera from children with ulcerative colitis contain precipitins which react with normal human tissues, particularly those of the colon (Broberger and Perlmann, 1959). Greater than normal quantities of a hemoglobin-precipitating factor (probably haptoglobin) are found in sera from patients with acquired hemolytic anemia. Although this precipitating factor is not an antibody, its effect is demonstrable more readily by double diffusion tests in agar than by mixing it with hemoglobin in aqueous medium (Peetoom *et al.*, 1960).

Immunoelectrophoretic patterns for human red blood cell lysates from patients with thalassamy have been found the same as those obtained with normal human fetal cord red blood cell lysates and, consequently, different from those of normal adult blood cells (Boivin *et al.*, 1959a).

Lower Animals

Immunodiffusion experiments on pathologic serum and tissues from lower animals are few. Double diffusion tests have indicated that pathologic changes in the lungs of rats injected with rabbit antibody against rat kidney and vice versa are due to the cross-reactivities of antibodies to tissues of one organ with those of the other (De Oliveira, 1958). Guinea pigs have been shown to produce antibodies to rabbit connective tissue which cross-reacts in the double diffusion plate test with the cytoplasmic constituents of rabbit leukocytes (Heller *et al.*, 1959). Preliminary immunodiffusion experiments have failed to discriminate between normal rat blood plasma and that from animals bearing tumors (Darcy, 1957).

Practical to the veterinarian, immunodiffusion tests can be used to detect albumin in bull seminal plasma, the presence of which in quantity suggests disturbed spermiogenesis and that impairment of reproductive faculties occurs (Pernot and Szumowski, 1958).

Diagnosis

Among the most practical dividends that immunodiffusion studies in pathology should yield is that of easier, surer diagnosis. Of course, the ultimate scope of immunodiffusion techniques for such a purpose remains to be seen, but data already on hand preview it.

Diphtheria

Some of the earliest immunodiffusion experiments were attempts to ascertain diphtheria bacillus toxigenicity, that is, the potential ability of a strain of these bacilli to cause disease. Practical methods for accomplishing this have been developed by Ouchterlony (1948b, 1949a,b) and by Elek (1948, 1949b). They consist of growing streaks of these bacilli upon nutrient agar across a source of diffusion of horse antitoxin. This source of antitoxin is a strip of paper soaked with antiserum and laid upon the agar, or a mixture of antitoxin and melted agar poured into a trough and allowed to gel. A strain capable of producing toxin exudes it, so that a precipitin band forms between the bacterial streak producing toxin and the source of antitoxin. Nontoxigenic bacilli also can form precipitin bands, in this primitive form of double diffusion gradient test,

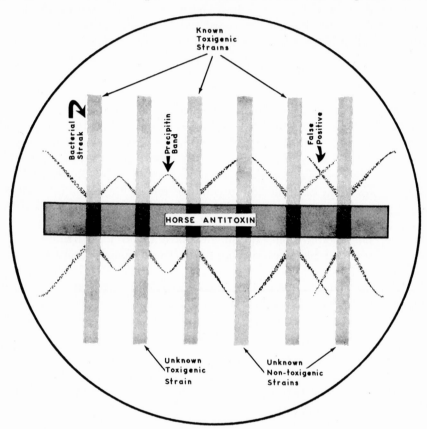

Petri Dish of Nutrient Agar

Fig. IV-7. Diagram showing how the diphtheria bacillus toxigenicity test is set up. Unknown toxigenic strain produces toxin which forms precipitin band with horse antitoxin fusing with similar band produced by known toxigenic reference strain. Nontoxigenic strain may produce precipitin band by exuding some other antigen, but this band crosses true toxin band produced by known reference strain.

as their nontoxin antigens diffuse into the agar, and toxigenic strains also can produce more than one precipitin band, since toxin is merely one of many antigens diphtheria bacilli manufacture. Hence, successful application of this test rests upon the specificity of the antitoxin used and upon recognition of which band among those it produces is due to the toxin-antitoxin reaction (see Fig. IV-7). Several publications attest to the usefulness of the test applied with adequate precautions against false-positive reactions (Carter and Wilson, 1949; Elek, 1948; Freeman, 1950; Gendon, 1958; Hussels, 1955, 1958; King *et al.*, 1949; Maegraith, 1933; Marcuse, 1955; Oakley and Fulthorpe, 1953; Ouchterlony, 1948a, 1949a,b). Since diphtheria can be diagnosed easily by other methods, clinical and laboratory, the double diffusion gradient test is more of an epidemiologic than a diagnostic tool. However, the toxigenicity test forcefully illustrates how immunodiffusion could be used diagnostically.

Tuberculosis and Leprosy

Numerous unsuccessful attempts have been made to adapt various types of serologic tests to the diagnosis of tuberculosis. Preliminary single diffusion tests with tuberculopolysaccharide antigen have suggested that these might be useful (Yamaguchi, 1955). Extensive trials of a similar double diffusion tube test in which culture medium concentrate serves as antigen have shown that tuberculous individuals are likely to have specific antibodies (Lester and Colton, 1959; Parlett and Youmans, 1959), but the detectable incidence of these has not yet been sufficiently high for this double diffusion test to replace other methods for diagnosing tuberculosis. A technique for increasing this test's sensitivity has been developed recently (Parlett and Reher, 1959) which may increase its value.

Immunodiffusion tests have detected antibodies specific for lepromin in the sera of leprosy victims and in people exposed frequently to this disease (Burrell and Rheins, 1957). Sera from patients with tuberculosis apparently do not react with this antigen.

Staphylococcus and Streptococcus

Perhaps more interesting epidemiologically than diagnostically is the observation that sera from most human beings contain potent precipitins to staphylococcal antigens, particularly to strains likely to be pathogenic (Beiser *et al.*, 1958). Similarly, antibodies to *Streptococcus* readily are detected in healthy individuals by immunodiffusion tests (Halbert *et al.*, 1955a,b). In some experiments (Halbert *et al.*, 1955a), single diffusion tests have shown that antistreptolysin O activity in sera from people with or without history of recent infection is associated with a precipitating antibody, and this has been found true also in guinea pig antisera (Halbert *et al.*, 1955a). Antistreptolysin has been demonstrated in α_2-, β_1-, and β_2-globulins of patient sera (Scheiffarth and Götz, 1960).

Gram-Negative Bacteria

Reactions between antisera and Gram-negative bacteria have been detected with a novel method for observing agglutination on filter paper (Castañeda, 1950; Spalding and Metcalf, 1954; see Chapter V). Although the method gives results analogous to those of an agglutination test, it does not seem likely in its present form to replace the latter for diagnostic purposes.

Parasites, Fungi, Viruses

Precipitating antibodies to *Toxoplasma* antigen have been demonstrated in the aqueous humor of toxoplasmosis victims (O'Connor, 1957a) as well as in their sera (O'Connor, 1957b). Diagnosis of visceral larvamigrans can be aided with double diffusion tests, since patients infected with the causative agent produce precipitating antibodies to it

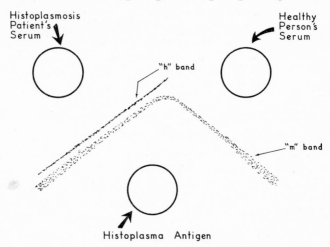

Fig. IV-8. Double diffusion diagnostic test for histoplasmosis is set up using *Histoplasma* antigen and appropriate sera. Serum from patient with disease produces two precipitin bands (*h* and *m*), while healthy person's serum may produce only one (*m*) band, if this person previously has been skin-tested with histoplasmin, or none. (Adapted from Heiner, 1958.)

while healthy individuals do not (Heiner, 1956). The degree of *Distomum hepaticum* infestation in a herd of cattle can be ascertained with the double diffusion test; the serum of any infected animal gives a positive test (Spuhler *et al.*, 1958).

Sera from persons proved infected with the dermatophyte *Trichophyton rubrum* contain precipitins which react with antigens from this fungus in the double diffusion test; precipitins for *Aspergillus* have been detected similarly in the sera of others presumably infected with it (Pepys *et al.*, 1959a). The same type of immunodiffusion test is reliable in diagnosing histoplasmosis (Fig. IV-8) and promises to be valuable for diagnosing blastomycosis (Heiner, 1958).

Immunodiffusion tests lend themselves readily to typing strains of infecting poliomyelitis viruses (Grasset *et al.*, 1958; Le Bouvier, 1957), and they may be equally useful for typing infectious agents in other viral diseases (see section on Virology, below).

Allergy

Although reagins as antibodies responsible for atopic hypersensitivity have not yet been detected by immunodiffusion techniques (Ebel, 1955; Wodehouse, 1954a), these techniques may aid diagnosis and treatment of various allergic disorders indirectly. Discovery of the common anti-staphylococcal antibody content of human serum, particularly to *aureus* strains, leads workers in one laboratory to conclude that these antibodies might be responsible for some allergies involving staphylococci (Beiser *et al.*, 1958). Schiott (1953) using double diffusion plates detected precipitins to an antigen of horse dander in sera from patients hypersensitive to this dander. Diabetes patients treated repeatedly with insulin may undergo allergic reactions apparently instigated by this drug or impurities in it. Immunoelectrophoretic analyses on some commercial insulins have shown them to be impure. At least one impurity is highly antigenic, although it may not necessarily be responsible for either the allergic or resistance reactions of treated patients (Lapresle and Grabar, 1957). Immunodiffusion tests potentially are useful for diagnosing endophthalmitis phacoanaphylactica, since autoprecipitins to eye lens proteins can be detected in the serum of affected individuals (Rao *et al.*, 1955).

In their studies attempting to identify in rabbit antiserum to chicken ovalbumin antibodies capable of sensitizing human skin to this antigen, Vaughan and Kabat (1953) employed single diffusion tube tests to help show that no correlation existed between the presence of precipitins to ovalbumin in such antisera and their abilities to passively sensitize human skin to solutions of ovalbumin.

Autoprecipitins already have been mentioned in connection with Pathology. Whenever autoantibodies can be detected by immunodiffusion, this technique can aid in diagnosis and studies on the etiology of an autoimmune disease. This is illustrated by research on Hashimoto's thyroiditis (Doniach and Roitt, 1957; Goudie *et al.*, 1959), disseminated lupus erythematosis (Seligmann, 1958b), renal disease (Liu and Mc-Crory, 1958), ulcerative colitis (Broberger and Perlmann, 1959), and

myeloid leukemia (Seligmann, 1956). Immunoelectrophoresis has been
employed to diagnose and identify types of thalassanemia by demonstrating characteristic blood hemoglobin changes. Thus, in thalassanemia
minor there is an increase in a hemoglobin which, in almost all forms
of thalassanemia major, is decreased (Boivin et al., 1959a). The physician studying cold agglutinins may be aided by noting increases or
absences of the agglutinins and β_2-globulins which often occur simultaneously (Heremans, 1959). A nonantibody serum constituent which
reacts with hemoglobin and possibly is involved in hemolytic anemia
can be detected and studied by immunodiffusion techniques. It occurs
in normal serum, but its quantity rises significantly in this disease (Peetoom et al., 1960).

Rose and Arbesman (1960) have reported that patients treated with
tetanus antitoxin and showing symptoms of serum sickness are likely to
have developed readily detectable precipitins to horse serum antigens.
Both the precipitins and the antigens with which they react can be
identified by immunoelectrophoresis.

Organic Diseases

Changes in the quality or quantity of blood serum antigens in certain diseases often are strikingly demonstrable by immunoelectrophoresis
(Grabar and Burtin, 1955b, 1959; Heremans, 1959; Scheidegger, 1956;
Scheidegger and Roulet, 1955; Scheiffarth and Götz, 1960; Schultze and
Schwick, 1959) and, to a minor extent, by other immunodiffusion methods (Gell, 1955a, 1957; Glenn, 1958b; Peetoom et al., 1960). These already have been mentioned briefly above. Unfortunately, such changes,
as have been observed so far, rarely seem to be so specific as to be
pathognomonic, because different diseases equally may affect organs responsible for metabolic maintenance of any given antigen or for the
production of unusual ones. Nevertheless, the very high resolution and
sensitivity of immunoelectrophoresis enables the researcher to perform
hitherto impossible analytic feats, which when fully applied will tell a
great deal about the basic effects of a disease and may lead to information in the future permitting ready specific diagnosis for many more
diseases than can be diagnosed with this method at present. The following summary of work along these lines clearly shows that it still is
superficial, although intensely earnest.

As in paper electrophoresis, multiple myeloma serum is readily
identified by immunoelectrophoresis by changes among the immunoglobulins (Grabar and Burtin, 1959; Grabar et al., 1954, 1956a; Scheidegger, 1957; Scheiffarth and Götz, 1960). The characteristic and almost
pathognomonic precipitin arc pattern for this disease is one in which

Bence-Jones proteins can be detected and are associated with a tremendous increase of γ-globulin with a narrow electrophoretic mobility range and the disappearance of β_2-globulins (Grabar *et al.*, 1956a). The localized increase of γ-globulin is distinct from increases of γ-globulin in all its electrophoretic varieties, which is seen in certain infectious diseases and cirrhosis of the liver (Grabar *et al.*, 1956a). However, final diagnosis is complicated by the practical difficulty of generally not having antiserum sufficiently reactive to detect all the abnormal serum components (Grabar and Burtin, 1959). Ganglionary sarcomas, diffuse decalcification, and renal disease are other disorders which may give rise to similar immunoelectrophoretic patterns (Grabar and Burtin, 1959).

Waldenström's macroglobulinemia is very strongly suggested when a serum shows extraordinarily large quantities of β_{2M}-globulin (see Fig. IV-5), for patients with the symptoms of macroglobulinemia or dysproteinemia who do not actually have this disease do not show such increases (Cleve and Schwick, 1957). Waldenström's disease is likely to cause some increase in other β_2-globulins as well (Burtin *et al.*, 1957). However, despite its outstanding characteristics, this disease cannot be diagnosed by immunoelectrophoresis alone, since other diseases apparently can cause similar selected protein increases (Grabar and Burtin, 1959; Scheidegger, 1957; Scheiffarth and Götz, 1960). Quantities of serum β_2- and γ-globulins can rise above normal in liver diseases (Bargob *et al.*, 1958; Hartmann *et al.*, 1956). For example, chronic hepatitis may be accompanied by an increase in β_{2M}-globulin; primary biliary cirrhosis can boost the quantity of both β_2-globulins, two β_1-globulins, and a slow-moving α_2-globulin (Bargob *et al.*, 1958). Disseminated lupus erythematosis augments the quantity of β_2-globulins to match that of γ-globulin and, in the acute phase, a consistent falling of the β_{1A}-titer (Seligmann and Hanau, 1958). Rheumatic joint diseases, polyarthritis, and similar disorders tend to induce increases in β_2-globulins (Cleve, 1958; Cleve and Hartmann, 1957a,b). The distinguishing characteristics of various types of β-globulin increases in immunoelectrophoretic patterns as discussed by Scheiffarth and Götz (1960) have already been mentioned in the section on Pathology.

Immunoelectrophoretic serum patterns in such diseases as reticuloses, scleroses, virus hepatitis, or cirrhosis are distinct enough to suggest appropriate diagnoses (Cleve, 1958; Cleve and Hartmann, 1957a; Grabar and Burtin, 1959), but in its present state of knowledge immunoelectrophoresis can do no more. Certain consistent increases in α_1-, α_2-, and β_2-globulins suggest rheumatoid arthritis (Cleve and Hartmann, 1957b), and α_2-macroglobulin consistently has been found augmented in sera from sclerosis patients (Moretti *et al.*, 1959). Detection of C-reactive protein with specific antiserum in immunoelectrophoresis or other immunodiffusion tests might be of some diagnostic value (Glenn, 1958b; Grabar and Burtin, 1959; Libretti *et al.*, 1955).

Decreases of specific serum antigens are readily detected by immunodiffusion techniques either for diagnosis or for following the effectiveness of therapy (Gell, 1955a, 1957; Gitlin *et al.*, 1956; Grabar and Burtin, 1959; Lohss and Kallee, 1959; Uriel *et al.*, 1957). Congenital hepatolenticular degeneration (Wilson's disease) is marked by a deficiency and abnormalities in ceruloplasmin (Gell, 1957; Uriel *et al.*, 1957). Immunodiffusion studies on hypogammaglobulinemia have shown that it may have several causes and that true agammaglobulinemia probably does not exist (Grabar and Burtin, 1959). Techniques have been developed for simple, rapid, accurate quantitation of γ-globulin in patients being treated by passive transfer of this protein (Gell, 1957). Lipoidal nephrosis causes sufficient lowering of γ-globulin levels to suggest classic hypogammaglobulinemia, but it can be distinguished from the latter because its immunoelectrophoretic pattern also shows considerable loss of albumin and increases in α_2-globulins which do not occur in classic hypogammaglobulinemia (Grabar and Burtin, 1959). Hyperparathyroidism provokes changes in the normal distribution of β_1-globulins which are reversed by surgical treatment (Komárková and Kořínek, 1959).

Recent observations that several human serum proteins normally insoluble in perchloric acid become at least partially soluble when obtained from patients with various diseases (Vaux Saint-Cyr, 1959) suggest that perhaps study of these changes might be useful diagnostically. They are easily detected and identified by immunoelectrophoresis.

Whenever the presence of Bence-Jones proteins in the urine becomes important diagnostically, double diffusion precipitin tests offer more sensitivity and information than any other tests available for their detection (Burtin *et al.*, 1955a, 1956). Immunodiffusion tests also are eminently satisfactory for detecting lipoglobulins or macroglobulins in urine, whose presence indicates severe kidney damage (Keutel *et al.*, 1959). A rise in the quantities of other proteins in urine above normal indicates, in proportion to their size and quantity, varying degrees of renal injury or disease.

Accurate serological quantitation of any given antigen in the cerebrospinal fluid, which may be helpful diagnostically or prognostically, is abetted if immunodiffusion techniques are used to ascertain the specificity of reagent antibodies (Burtin and Pocidalo, 1954b).

With the aid of immunoelectrophoresis, pure serum antigens have been isolated and identified, and specific antibodies to them have been prepared. These, in turn, can be used for qualitative and quantitative analyses of human serum components helpful in diagnosis of several diseases, particularly dys- and para-proteinemias (Schultze and Schwick, 1959). Such methods show the promise and potentialities of immuno-diffusion techniques for future experimentation. All together, when the full potentialities of immunodiffusion tests become applied in medicine, it seems probable that in some instances they may become the most reliable criteria for establishing diagnoses, and that certainly they will contribute greatly to information on disease etiology and epidemiology.

Taxonomy

Taxonomy is no better than the criteria on which it is based. In many instances it has reached an impasse for lack of sufficiently definitive differentiating tests applicable to members of a given genus or species. Immunodiffusion techniques with their extraordinary abilities to dis-tinguish between molecules appear to offer ready access to finer defini-tion than hitherto has been possible of any living being to which they are applied. The potentialities of these techniques in taxonomy are il-lustrated well by work in those laboratories where they have begun to be applied.

Bacteriology

Perhaps because most bacteriologists have some training in serologic techniques, they as a group so far have made the most use of immuno-diffusion as a taxonomic tool. Several of the earliest immunodiffusion experiments, reported more than a decade before Ouchterlony, Oudin, and Elek made their well known studies, proved that bacteria could be categorized according to species and type by using very simple single diffusion techniques. Thus, meningococci, gonococci, pneumococci, and Gram-negative bacteria were identified by this novel serologic test, and the toxins of different species of *Clostridium* were distinguished (see Chapter I). Now that immunodiffusion techniques have been more re-fined and more is known about the significance of their results, their use in bacterial taxonomy rests firmly established.

The utility of double diffusion gradient tests for distinguishing cul-tures of virulent diphtheria bacilli from those which are avirulent, by their potential abilities to produce diphtheria toxin, has been docu-mented above in the section on Diagnosis. Because this satisfied the practical medical question of which strains are toxigenic and which are not, little interest in other taxonomic problems among members of the genus *Corynebacterium* has been aroused. However, a comparison of different strains of mitis-type diphtheria bacilli with 15 strains of *Corynebacterium belfanti* has been described recently. It showed that although the two types of bacillus share several antigens, intragroup relationships appear to be closer than those between groups (Gundersen, 1959).

Double diffusion tube tests employing rabbit antiserum against different heat-killed strains of Group A streptococci have been utilized to compare antigens obtained from three different strains of streptococci: Bailey, S 23, and S 94. M protein proved to be a specific antigen for the Bailey strain, but it was identical in the other two (Pierce, 1959). Toxins from different species and even types of clostridia can be differentiated readily with double diffusion tests (Björklund and Berengo, 1954). Immunodiffusion tests also are useful for rapidly identifying gas gangrene clostridia (Gendon, 1958).

Attempting to categorize various strains of tubercle bacilli and related mycobacteria, particularly from the evolutionary point of view, has been complicated and confusing. Consequently, numerous essays have been made into this field with immunodiffusion techniques (Affronti, 1959; Gendon, 1958; Lind, 1959; Mankiewicz, 1958; Parlett and Youmans, 1956, 1958; Pepys *et al.*, 1959b). Results from these seem to agree in their basic aspects that (1) mycobacteria can be differentiated from other acid-fast bacilli such as members of the genus *Nocardia* (Affronti, 1959; Parlett and Youmans, 1958), (2) parasitic and saprophytic mycobacteria can be distinguished from each other serologically (Lind, 1959; Mankiewicz, 1958; Parlett and Youmans, 1956; Pepys *et al.*, 1959b), (3) so-called chromogenic mycobacteria closely resembling tubercle bacilli, the tubercle bacilli which cause tuberculosis in fowl, and those which tend to cause skin tuberculosis usually can be distinguished from bovine and human strains of tubercle bacilli and often from each other (Lind, 1959; Mankiewicz, 1958; Parlett and Youmans, 1956, 1958; Pepys *et al.*, 1959b), and (4) that future experimentation may show sufficient resolution among strains of one type of tubercle bacillus to distinguish among these (Lind, 1959).

Among the Gram-negative bacteria, taxonomic studies have been reported on the genera *Pasteurella, Proteus, Salmonella,* and *Hemophilus.* In an attempt to define more satisfactorily the polysaccharide somatic complex moiety of *Salmonella* species which is partially responsible for their specific agglutination, acid hydrolysis polysaccharide extracts were prepared from *Salmonella typhimurium, S. paratyphi B,* and *S. typhi,* group D, and analyzed by both single diffusion and double diffusion techniques. Two different antigens could be demonstrated in the *S. typhi* extract, and three in each of the other two species. Antigenically,

S. typhimurium and *S. paratyphi B,* by comparison of these antigens, were closely related, but both differed distinctly from *S. typhi.* Moreover, some precipitin reactions could be demonstrated with species-specificity, while others were merely genus-specific (Staub and Pon, 1956).

Comparison of the antigenic structures of *Proteus* forms 3 BL and stabilized 3 AL using various tests including immunodiffusion showed the 3 BL complex of somatic antigens to be more complete than the 3 AL complex (Loriewicz *et al.*, 1957). Double diffusion plate tests have demonstrated that avirulent strains of *Pasteurella pestis* lack antigens found in virulent strains, and that in at least one instance this lack can be correlated with a simultaneous lack in the deficient strain of both toxigenicity and immunogenicity (Crumpton and Davies, 1956).

Strains as well as types of *Hemophilus* are differentiated with ease by immunodiffusion tests (Jensen and Francis, 1953; Olitzki and Sulitzeanu, 1959; Tunevall, 1953). Capsular polysaccharide on encapsulated types of the influenza bacillus has been shown with monovalent rabbit antiserum to be type-specific (Tunevall, 1953). The two closely related *Hemophilus* species, *influenzae* and *aegyptius,* contain many common antigens, but they can be differentiated; strains of *aegyptius* isolated from widely different sources, in the United States and Israel, consistently proved to be very similar (Olitzki and Sulitzeanu, 1959).

Appropriate rabbit antisera prepared against cell wall antigens or endotoxin polysaccharides and used in the double diffusion test, served specifically to identify various species and types of *Salmonella, Shigella, Escherichia, Listeria,* and *Enterococcus* (Seeliger, 1955). They proved their utility most strikingly in definitively identifying cultures of bacteria wrongly named according to less certain criteria.

Fungi

Double diffusion tests carried out in connection with development of a diagnostic technique for histoplasmosis showed culture filtrates of *Coccidioides immitis, Blastomyces dermatitidis,* and *Histoplasma capsulatum* to contain what appears to be one common antigen. However, another distinctive for *Histoplasma* was identified, and two more were described which seemed to be produced exclusively by *Blastomyces* (Heiner, 1958). Rabbit antibodies to *Candida albicans* have been used to study the taxonomic relationships between this fungus and *C. brumpti, C. zeylanoides, C. tropicalis,* and *C. stellatoidea.* Sonic extracts of these various microorganisms examined by double diffusion and immunoelectrophoretic tests in conjunction with absorption experiments showed clearly that specific differences could be detected among the various species (Biguet *et al.*, 1959). The short paper describing these experiments provides a crisp example of the potentialities of immuno-diffusion as a taxonomic tool and of how it can be used. The antigenic relationships between various other fungi and yeasts including strains of *Madurella, Monosporium, Sporotrichum, Cryptococcus, Histoplasma, Blastomyces, Candida, Saccharomyces,* and *Aspergillus,* have been examined purely with double diffusion tests in another laboratory (Seeliger, 1955). Generally, the results from these experiments tend to confirm the currently accepted taxonomic status of these genera. Occasionally, identity reactions were observed between certain antigens from two different genera.

Viruses

Application of immunodiffusion techniques to identifying viruses is both practical and informative. Influenza virus not only can be detected but also typed directly by immunodiffusion tests as it multiplies in human fibroblast tissue cultures (Gendon, 1958). Double diffusion tests comparing myxomatosis and fibromatosis viruses using their respective antisera showed that the two contain closely related but not identical antigens (Fayet *et al.*, 1957). Small pox and cow pox viruses can be differentiated by double diffusion tests, but vaccinia, neurovaccinia, rabbit pox, small pox, and alastrim viruses appear to be identical in reactivity with standard vaccinia antiserum (Gispen, 1955). Foot-and-mouth disease virus can be typed (Bodon, 1955). The three types of this foot-and-mouth disease virus (O, A, and C) give type-specific precipitin reactions in double diffusion tests with either guinea pig or bovine antiserum (Brown and Crick, 1957). Double diffusion tests indicate that the type-specific antigen, which also seems to be associated with the infectivity of this virus, is the larger of two which can be detected (Brown and Crick, 1958). Monkey, guinea pig, and human antisera can be used in either single or double diffusion tests to type poliomyelitis virus (Grasset *et al.*, 1958; Le Bouvier, 1957).

Animal Microorganisms

The antigenic constitution of some microscopic protozoa and metazoa has been studied by immunodiffusion. For example, specific antisera against antigens G and E of stock 28, variety 2 of *Paramecium aurelia* could distinguish between these two antigens, even though they cross-reacted to some extent. Practically, these antisera were used to follow type transformation of type G protozoa to type E as the quantity of the first antigen declined and that of the second increased (Balbinder and Preer, 1959). Comparison of several tissue antigens and a polysaccharide obtained from pig *Ascaris* with antigens from human, cat, and dog *Ascaris* (using rabbit antiserum in double diffusion tubes along with appropriate absorption procedures) showed that many antigens among these parasites were shared. These results explain why serological specificity is not obtained with classic precipitin tests in aqueous medium and why *Ascaris* parasites isolated from different sources are not ordinarily distinguishable by this type of test (Kagan, 1957). Kagan and his co-workers (1958) have extended this study of *Ascaris* to a detailed investigation of the nature of *Ascaris lumbricoides* polysaccharide antigens using double diffusion tubes. A preparation obtained from larvae of *Trichinella spiralis* by acid extraction has been shown, by double diffusion tube tests with antisera from rabbits infected with this microorganism, to contain at least three distinct antigens (Kagan and Bargai, 1956).

Sea Life

As animals become more complex, their distinguishing characteristics become more numerous and their identification simpler not only by conventional techniques, but also by immunodiffusion tests. Taxonomy shifts largely to evolutionary problems. The simplest living constituents of multicellular organisms are the cells themselves, especially the reproductive cells. Such cells (specifically eggs) of the sea urchin are easy to obtain and to study. Rabbit antiserum to unfertilized eggs from several species of sea urchin has been used in immunodiffusion tests not only to identify individual egg antigens important to studies on the cytology and mechanisms of egg fertilization and development, but also to differentiate eggs obtained from the various species (Perlmann, 1959). Eggs of closely related species have several antigens in common, but they each also contain antigens peculiar to themselves; the more distantly related eggs share the fewest antigens (Perlmann, 1953). Antibodies produced simultaneously in one rabbit against hemocyanins of the crabs *Limulus polyphemus* and *Callinectes sapidus* clearly were able to distinguish these two hemocyanins serologically in double diffusion plate tests; no cross-reaction was noted. Similar experiments showed that antisera against *Cancer magister* hemocyanin would cross-react to varying degrees with that of *C. pagurus*, *C. productus*, and *C. maenus* (Leone *et al.*, 1955).

Snakes

Established taxonomic relationships among various snakes were confirmed by immunodiffusion comparison of their venoms using their respective horse antivenins. Moreover, close enough antigenic correspondence was discovered between venoms of some of these snakes to suggest that emergency cross-protection could be obtained with selected heterologous antivenins if homologous ones happened to be unavailable (Grasset *et al.*, 1956).

Fowl

As the kinship of other fowl to the chicken becomes progressively more removed in studies on a series of these, cross reactions between constituents in their eggs with those of chickens tested with antiserum to the latter become succeedingly smaller. This, for example, has been

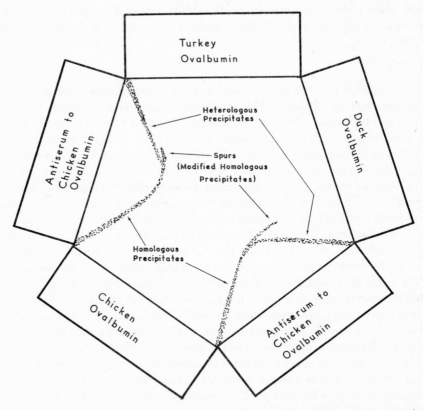

Fig. IV-9. Pentagonal double diffusion test simultaneously comparing reactions of two heterologous antigens (turkey and duck ovalbumins) with homologous antigen (chicken ovalbumin) using antiserum to the latter. Shortness of precipitin spurs formed by homologous antigen indicates taxonomic closeness of this antigen to the compared antigen. Composition of portions of various precipitin bands in particular regard to types of antibody forming them also is indicated. (Adapted from Jennings, 1959c.)

observed for egg white prepared from stork, marabou, Egyptian goose, duck, and turkey eggs (Kaminski, 1955b; Kaminski and Nouvel, 1952). The closeness of relationship between hen, duck, and turkey has been judged roughly by how short a precipitin spur the chicken ovalbumin forms beyond the band of the heterologous antigen (Fig. IV-9); by this test, turkey ovalbumin antigenically is more similar to hen ovalbumin than duck ovalbumin (Jennings, 1959c).

Mammals

In any comparative taxonomic immunodiffusion studies, the significance of a set of results depends entirely upon the type of antiserum which has been employed. This point is nicely illustrated in several comparisons which have been made of mammalian blood sera. For example, rabbits manufacture antibodies to rat serum which cross-react extensively with mouse serum antigens, and vice versa (Gengozian, 1959). This has led to some confusion regarding whether lethally X-irradiated mice, treated with rat bone marrow to permit them to recover, form rat serum proteins. The answer seemed to be affirmative when rabbit antiserum to rat serum absorbed with mouse serum was employed to answer this question. However, when naturally more highly specific mouse antirat serum antiserum was utilized, the answer was negative (Gengozian, 1959). This antiserum owed its outstanding specificity to the fact that mice will not form detectable antibodies cross-reacting with any constituents of their own sera. Ideally, then, if two species of animals as closely related as mice and rats are to be compared serologically, they themselves should be used to produce the analytic antisera. This idea will be re-emphasized below.

When horse or rabbit anti-human sera are used against sera from ox, calf, lamb, pig, rat, rabbit, chimpanzee, baboon, *Rhesus* monkey, horse, goat, dog, or guinea pig, they produce precipitin bands, the patterns for which show varying degrees of cross-reaction with human serum from nearly complete for the chimpanzee to only poor for dog serum (Kaminski, 1957c; M. Muller *et al.*, 1959; Scheiffarth *et al.*, 1958a). The same is true, to a varying degree dependent very likely on methods of vaccination, with other types of antiserum against serum of any of the various mammals listed. Aside from the caution that this suggests in interpreting the taxonomic significance of immunodiffusion results, it has practical importance as, for example, in medico-legal tests (M. Muller *et al.*, 1959). One way of obtaining highly species-specific antisera already has been mentioned. Another, useful in forensic medicine, is to employ antiserum from an animal which has had only a short, unintensive vaccination. Thus, rabbit antihuman serum prepared in this way produced no precipitin bands with sera from various other mammals while hyperimmune horse anti-human serum cross-reacted with all (M. Muller *et al.*, 1959).

The cross-reactions that antisera of limited specificity yield among antigens from several species of animals can be used in immunodiffusion tests, just as they have in the past in aqueous medium precipitin tests, to generally rather than specifically examine taxonomic relationships. Thus, photoelectric measurements of precipitate band intensity in single diffusion tubes developing various intensities of cross-reaction have been used to confirm previous findings made with classic quantitative precipitin tests on the taxonomic relationships between cattle, sheep, and goats (Glenn, 1958b). Certain serum components from various species of animal seem to be the most often involved in cross-reactions, that is, the least species specific. One in particular, identified by immunoelectrophoresis, is an α_2-globulin (Scheiffarth *et al.*, 1958a).

Such refined distinctions in which the frequency of cross-reactivity among antigens in a complex mixture of these, such as serum, is made rather than comparison of antigenic sites on a given species of just one antigen often offer useful data for taxonomy. This approach has been made toward relationships between sera obtained from various primates (Paluska and Kořínek, 1960). Rabbit anti-human and rabbit anti-*Macacus* sera were employed in comparative immunoelectrophoretic analyses of sera from Old and New World monkeys, from lemurs, and from man. Results suggested that the Old World monkeys are the most closely related antigenically to the human being, chimpanzee serum, for example, giving the same number of immunoelectrophoretic precipitin bands as human serum itself with anti-human serum. Lemurs are the least closely related. In double diffusion tests, chimpanzee albumin, α_1-, α_2-, and β-globulins gave "identity" reactions with analogous human serum with rabbit anti-human serum used as the analytic reagent; other serum proteins, however, could be differentiated. Reactions of identity among serum antigens of other species of Old World monkeys and human serum antigens were found only among the β-globulins. No such identity reactions were detected between New World monkeys and lemurs, and man. Despite occasionally very close relationships, all of the primates used in this study could be identified readily by their characteristic double diffusion precipitin patterns. Over-all results agreed with established taxonomic categorization.

Just as for the finest inter-species serologic discrimination one ideally should use the species being studied for antibody production, so, for intraspecies experiments, it is necessary to use one species as source of both antigen and antibody. Immunodiffusion tests promise to help not only the taxonomist but also the geneticist. They have made it possible for experimenters to demonstrate that some rabbits can form precipitins against some serum constituents of other rabbits (Dray and Young, 1958, 1959; Oudin, 1956a,b). Tests run on sera taken from 90 normal rabbits using 6 rabbit anti-rabbit antisera indicated that these 90 rabbits could be divided into 13 different groups on the basis of the presence or absence of precipitin bands formed by such isoprecipitins, and into 30 groups if the number of bands produced also was considered (Dray and Young, 1958). By immunoelectrophoresis, these isoprecipitins could be shown to react with α-, β-, and γ-globulins (Dray and Young, 1958). Use of the last of these three alone as a taxonomic instrument allowed division of 500 rabbits into one of three groups having one or the other or both of two antigenic types of γ-globulin (Dray and Young, 1959). Preliminary experiments of the same nature also have succeeded in guinea pigs (Oudin, 1957).

Plants

Probably, immunodiffusion tests could gain considerable use in plant taxonomy. Some studies reported on allergenic grass pollens illustrate this. Pollen extracts of four common hay fever plants of the Amaranthaceae tested against rabbit anti-carelessweed serum were shown to share very similar antigens in nearly the same proportions (Wodehouse, 1957). Five common Chenopodiaceae hay fever pollens compared similarly using Russian thistle antiserum showed much less similarity, although apparently common antigens were detected. One antigen was identified as a constituent of Timothy grass, June grass, and Red-top, Sweet, Vernal, and Orchard grass pollens, although few of the minor antigens detected in the same tests were the same. Bermuda grass was completely different antigenically from all of these grasses (Wodehouse, 1955b). Tall and short ragweed can be distinguished from each other with rabbit antiserum to either (Wodehouse, 1954c). Pollens from a variety of grasses occurring on the British Isles share many closely related antigens, but they can be differentiated grossly by observing the number of antigens any two share (Augustin, 1955, 1959a). So-called "identical" antigens common to pollen of two different plants very likely actually are not, only appearing so because they are closely enough related not to be distinguishable with antisera usually employed. Critical tests have borne out this notion (Feinberg and Grayson, 1959).

In some instances, immunodiffusion tests probably will be no more than supplementary tools in taxonomy, but in others their particular capabilities seem to warrant making them the primary investigational technique.

Genetics

Once again, it is the tremendous resolving power of immunodiffusion methods which makes them potentially so useful for another field of investigation—genetics. In this field, some particular trait in an organism controlled by a genetic characteristic receives primary attention, and the more distinctive this trait is, the finer a study can become.

Mammals

Some experiments on formation by rabbits of serum isoprecipitins already have been mentioned (Dray and Young, 1958, 1959; Hirschfeld, 1959c; Oudin, 1956a,b, 1960a; Scheiffarth et al., 1958). One publication lists a division of 500 rabbits into three groups on the basis of antigenic differences in their serum γ-globulins, 24 having one kind of γ-globulin, 379 having the other, and 97 having both (Dray and Young, 1959). Rabbits of the latter type cannot, of course, be used for production of antibodies to either of the two types of γ-globulin, since they themselves already have both antigens naturally. The rabbit serum antigens which have instigated these experiments seem to be genuinely serum antigens, since they are not found in red blood cells or lysed red blood cell preparations but only in the plasma and serum, except for very small concentrations in leukocytes, whole or lysed (Dray and Young, 1958).

Different rabbits tend to have among them several antigenically similar serum components, but other serum antigens are found only in certain individual animals. Careful immunoelectrophoretic analyses of sera from five different rabbits using a horse hyperimmune antiserum showed that among these sera, 11 components consistently were found in all, but from 3 to 8, mostly in the α_2-globulin region, were detected only in certain ones (Hirschfeld, 1959c).

Similar genetically controlled differences have been noted among sera from different human beings, particularly in the type of haptoglobin that they contain. These differences in haptoglobin have been detected readily by starch electrophoresis, but they are as readily observed by immunoelectrophoresis which also identifies what Hirschfeld has called "group-specific" components 1 and 2, the first situated between α_1- and α_2-serum constituents, and the second in the middle of the α_2 range, in his particular experiments using a discontinuous buffer system (Hirschfeld, 1959a,b, 1960b,c). These experiments surely augur the introduction of immunoelectrophoresis as a tool for studying human genetics analogous to, and perhaps rivaling in theoretical significance, that of red blood cell typing.

Invertebrates

Apparently, the only invertebrates which have been used in immuno-diffusion experiments oriented toward genetics are sea urchins. The be-ginning stages of sea urchin egg reproduction have been analyzed by Went and Mazia using antibody to egg mitotic apparatus (1959). Their double diffusion tests indicated that this apparatus is assembled from materials already present in the cells at the time of division.

Bacteria

Transformation experiments with *Hemophilus influenzae* have been followed by double diffusion plate tests. Thus, in rough bacilli there is a group-specific substance (M substance), but the type-specific sub-stance which occurs in the polysaccharide capsule is not present. Im-munodiffusion tests showed that there was no change of somatic antigens in the rough form newly transformed to the smooth, and that the only antigenic changes accompanying transformation occurred in acquisition of type-specific capsular polysaccharide (Tunevall, 1953).

Cytology

Since immunodiffusion tests can be used to identify individual species of molecules, their potential usefulness for mapping cellular and tissue constituents is considerable. They have been used in such analyses ex-tending from the subcellular through the multicellular.

Virus-Infected Cells

An antigen could be separated by immunoelectrophoresis from ad-enovirus-infected HeLa cells which presumably was produced by the virus but differed from virus particles themselves (Pereira *et al.*, 1959). Three distinct antigens were found in preparations of adenovirus, none cross-reacting with HeLa cell antigens. One of these after isolation and purification was shown to be responsible for the early cytotoxic effect of the virus.

Bacteria

Experiments with *Hemophilus influenzae* showed that strains within the species possess many common antigen components, but that type specificity is determined or indicated by capsular polysaccharide (Tune-vall, 1953). Protoplasts have been isolated from group A *Streptococcus*

L forms by enzymatic treatment, which by double diffusion plate tests have been proved free of cell wall carbohydrate and M protein (Freimer *et al.*, 1959). With rabbit antibodies to *Chromatium* chlorophyll-containing particles, Newton and Levine (1959) have demonstrated that the chromatophore particles of *Chromatium* are not distinct from its cell wall. Thus, these pigmented macromolecules contain not only some antigen of the colorless soluble cytoplasmic material, but also antigens related to those in the cellular surface.

Reproductive Cells

Rabbit antiserum to sea urchin eggs may activate their development. Immunodiffusion experiments show that the antibody responsible for this activation is not directed against an antigen of the jelly layer of the egg but rather against an egg antigen proper, although the latter sometimes may occur in the jelly layer (Perlmann, 1957); precipitating antibodies specific for the various jelly antigens cannot activate the egg. Distinct differences can be detected by double diffusion tests between the egg cytoplasm and the jelly layer as well as between extracts from eggs and those from sea urchin sperm (Perlmann, 1959). One might follow the development of maturing sea urchin embryos by analyzing their soluble antigens at different stages. In doing this, Perlmann and Kaltenbach (1957) found no particular changes in two selected antigens whose presence they followed with the single diffusion tube test, other than their quantitative diminution with increasing age of the embryos.

Extracts of guinea pig spermatozoa heads and tails contain a number of different antigens which have been compared immunoelectrophoretically with guinea pig seminal plasma and guinea pig serum (Pernot, 1956). Sperm tail extracts contain in common with seminal plasma one α_1-, three α_2-, one β_1-, and one β_2-globulins. They have also a very slow β-globulin, designated β_3, with a mobility almost the same as that of the serum γ-globulin. This fraction apparently also is present in sperm heads.

Tissues and Organs

The antigenic constitution of rabbit bone marrow has been compared with that of other rabbit tissues and plasma using horse antiserum and double diffusion tests (Björklund, 1952b, 1953b,c). Four marrow antigens could not be detected in rabbit plasma but were found in various combinations in other tissues, although none of these tissues contained the complete set of four. The spleen contained three, interesting, perhaps because of its hemopoietic role.

At least 9 antigens can be identified immunoelectrophoretically in mouse liver extracts (Nachkov and Nachkova, 1959). Some of these (albumin, and certain β- and γ-globulins) are the same antigenically as mouse serum fractions, but others belong distinctly to the liver. These include one fraction of slower mobility than serum γ-globulin and at least 5 others detected by specific absorption of rabbit anti-mouse antiserum. Rat liver homogenates have been analyzed with double diffusion tests (Perlmann and D'Amelio, 1958; Perlmann et al., 1959). These tests have proved capable of distinguishing between antigens characterizing different structural elements isolated from liver homogenate by means of centrifugation. Cellular antigens of these liver homogenates were different both chemically and antigenically from rat serum proteins. Antigens peculiar to mitochondria, microsomes, "cell sap," cell membrane, and nucleoprotein were identified in some of these studies (Perlmann et al., 1959). Antibodies specific for the antigens of human leukocytes and not directed against any human plasma constituents have been prepared and tested by immunodiffusion techniques (Grabar et al., 1955a; Seligmann et al., 1955).

Malignant Tissue

Hyperimmune horse serum to human malignant tissue employed in the double diffusion precipitin test against normal human plasma, 16 normal human tissues, and tumor tissue enabled the Björklunds (1956, 1957; Björklund, 1953a) to identify four different strictly cellular antigens none of which, however, was specific for the tumor tissue. One was found in the liver, spleen, lung, kidney, and brain, but not in any of 11 other normal tissues; 2 other antigens were generally distributed. Experiments in another laboratory (Korngold, 1957) suggest that certain types of tumor cells can be differentiated from each other. Thus, carcinomas and sarcomas very frequently can be distinguished quantitatively. Antigens from carcinoma of one organ may not be found in that of another. Such comparative studies always are complicated by the fact that the tissues upon which the tumor grows are, of course, antigenically complex making difficult distinction between normal and tumor antigens. However, this very disadvantage has helped to show that human tumor cells which have been cultivated through many generations on foreign tissues (rat, egg, hamster) retain their normal spectrum of human-specific antigens and neither incorporate antigens from the tissues upon which they are cultured nor produce any with their antigenic specificity (Korngold and Lipari, 1955b). The globulin found in myeloma patients' bone marrow plasmocytes seems by immunodiffusion tests, to be identical with the abnormal globulin present in their sera (Havez and Biserte, 1959b).

Virology

Some papers on the use of immunodiffusion in virology already have been referred to in connection with Taxonomy (Brown and Crick, 1958; Fayet *et al.*, 1957; Gispen, 1955; Grasset *et al.*, 1958; Jensen and Francis, 1953; Le Bouvier, 1957; van Slogteren and van Slogteren, 1957), and Cytology (Pereira *et al.*, 1959). Several others which do not fall into these or other preceding categories can be mentioned here.

Serum taken from cattle 7 days after their infection with foot-and-mouth virus, type Vallée O, sub-type Channel Island, reacted in immunoelectrophoresis with this same sub-type as well as with sub-type M 11, but 14- and 21-day convalescent sera precipitated only the homologous sub-type (Brown and Graves, 1959), and apparently rare example of increasing antiserum specificity with increasing vaccination time. Interestingly, the less specific antibody was located in the immunoelectrophoretic β-globulin region, while the specific antibody was a γ-globulin. Foot-and-mouth virus solutions obtained from vesicles on infected guinea pigs and analyzed with double diffusion tests using guinea pig antiserum showed these solutions to contain two species of antigens (Fig. IV-10), one 20 mμ and the other 7 mμ in diameter (Brown and Crick, 1959). The former apparently is responsible for viral immunogenicity in this disease.

Several proteins have been prepared from purified tobacco mosaic virus and detected in double diffusion tests with rabbit antisera (Jeener *et al.*, 1954; Kleczkowski, 1957). They differ antigenically; none possess all the antigenic determinant groups of the intact virus. Three low molecular weight proteins which are not infectious and contain no ribonucleic acid but react with antiserum to tobacco mosaic virus have been obtained from leaves of systemically but not locally infected tobacco plants (Chahbasi, 1957; Commoner and Rodenberg, 1955). Results from immunodiffusion experiments suggest that they are small protein units constituting portions of the virus nucleoprotein.

With a specially designed double diffusion tube technique, van Regenmortel (1959) has succeeded in determining the diffusion coefficient of turnip yellow mosaic virus particles and has estimated their diameter to average 27.4 mμ. The same technique has been used by its originator, Polson (1958), to quantitate poliomyelitis virus in vaccine preparations. Poliomyelitis virus can be typed with any of various immunodiffusion techniques; both single and double diffusion have been used for this purpose (Le Bouvier, 1957). Canine virus hepatitis, lymphocytic choriomeningitis, and swine fever have been studied with such techniques (Gendon, 1958).

The relative antigenic simplicity of viruses by comparison with bacteria and the larger microorganisms should make them particularly apt subjects for immunodiffusion experiments, especially now that micro techniques have been devised which are extremely sensitive and require only very small quantities of antigen.

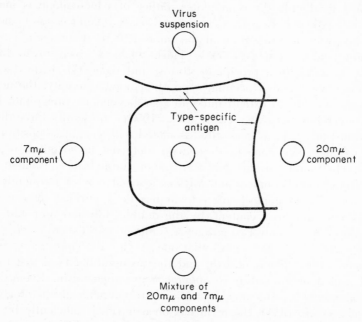

Fig. IV-10. Diagram of double diffusion test identifying type-specific 20 mμ antigen of foot-and-mouth disease virus, obtained from guinea pig vesicular fluid, and showing how this and the lighter 7 mμ component are differentiated and identified not only antigenically but also by the respective curvatures of their precipitin bands. The center well was charged with guinea pig antiserum. (Courtesy Brown and Crick, 1958.)

Bacteriology

Sections devoted to mycology and parasitology have not been composed because very little immunodiffusion work has been reported in these fields. That which has is mentioned elsewhere, particularly under Taxonomy, above. Bacteria, on the other hand, rival human serum as popular subjects for immunodiffusion analyses.

Staphylococcus

Staphylococcus antigens often exhibit physiologic activities by which they can be identified. Plate and tube double diffusion tests have proved *Staphylococcus* toxins and their protein subfractions to be antigenically complex (Kovaleva, 1958). In these experiments, however, while *Staphylococcus* toxins and proteins produced several precipitin bands, polysaccharide components did not. Ammonium sulfate precipitates of *Staphylococcus* culture filtrates contain leukocidin. This material can be fractionated by column chromatography into at least two components, identified in double diffusion plates, either of which alone is inactive (Woodin, 1959). Different effects of various *Staphylococcus* hemolysin make possible their detection in the same agar used for their immunodiffusion analysis (Elek, 1950a). Thus, when a given toxin diffuses against its antitoxin a precipitate forms, and when this toxin's activity is observed by its own peculiar type of hemolytic activity, the activity will be found not to extend into the agar beyond its precipitate band. This convenient fact was used by Elek (1950a) to identify three distinct hemolysins (α, β, δ) as generally associated with coagulase-positive bacterial strains, since none of these were detected in coagulase-negative strains. He found β-lysin characteristic of staphylococci isolated most often from animals, and α- and δ-lysins associated most frequently with human strains. *Staphylococcus* α-toxin has been purified to a stage of high activity and to a content, by the double diffusion tube test using horse antitoxin, of only two antigenic components (Turpin *et al.*, 1954). Indeed, Oeding (1959) reports that one precipitate band among several produced by the toxin-antitoxin and the toxin-antibacterial systems can be identified as caused by *Staphylococcus* α-hemolysin. Even though *Staphylococcus* enterotoxin preparations are antigenically heterogeneous (Surgalla *et al.*, 1954), the toxin has been purified sufficiently by Bergdoll *et al.* (1959) so that by any of various immunodiffusion techniques it produces only a single precipitin line, suggesting that antigenically it has been prepared pure. With this purified antigen, production of a monovalent antiserum whose specificity can be proved has become simple.

   Staphylococcus antigens appear to cross-react with those of *Listeria* (Seeliger and Sulzbacher, 1956).

Streptococcus

   A notable seldom realized fact is that sera from clinically normal human beings often contains *Streptococcus* precipitins. Hanson (1959) showed that these are readily demonstrated with double diffusion plate tests using β-hemolytic *Streptococcus* culture filtrate as antigen. In fact, in Hanson's studies the number of precipitin lines produced with antisera from animals vaccinated with these streptococci usually was lower than that produced by such "normal" human sera. There seems to be little quantitative difference in reactions of these sera and others with high streptolysin O titers. Hanson could not identify any of the many precipitin bands he observed as due to streptolysin O antigen.

Streptococcus M protein consists of some 10 different antigens, all apparently proteins, since increasingly intense trypsinization progressively suppresses their precipitation by antiserum. These M antigens are not strain-specific (Pierce, 1959). Detection of M protein in human sera may be of clinical interest. In a study of possible ways which could be used for this purpose, Schmidt (1957) employed the double diffusion tube test to test serologic reaction specificity and to help assess its significance. Jennings (1953) has succeeded in identifying a precipitin band in single diffusion tests as due to *Streptococcus* erythrogenic toxin antigen.

A factor produced by streptococci apparently bound to M protein which precipitates fibrinogen in the plasma of various animal species has been studied by immunodiffusion techniques, although the type of precipitation is not due to an antigen-antibody reaction (Kantor and Cole, 1959).

Pneumococcus

Perhaps because several other older serologic tests offer practical methods for identifying pneumococci, immunodiffusion tests have seldom been applied to these cocci. Pneumococcus type-specific capsular polysaccharide has been for many years a favorite subject for classic serologic experimentation. It was used by Oudin (1948b) for preliminary experiments with immunodiffusion.

Corynebacterium

The bacterial exotoxin probably most often responsible for fatal human disease, diphtheria toxin, has been subjected to frequent and persistent investigation and, particularly, to attempted purification. The last task was raised out of an impasse reached some years ago when immunodiffusion techniques became available for demonstrating impurities in preparations of the toxin and for effectively following various steps in its purification (Ouchterlony *et al.*, 1950; Pope *et al.*, 1951; Poulik, 1952). Ouchterlony *et al.* (1950) discovered that what had been presumed to be pure toxin in reality consisted of at least three distinct antigens, since it yielded three precipitin bands with antitoxin. Pope and coworkers (1951) detected at least 24 antigens in crude diphtheria culture filtrates from which the toxin is prepared. Poulik (1952) observed that among four zones separated on paper electrophoretically from purified diphtheria toxoid, one produced a specific precipitate with antitoxin. Since these earlier investigations, diphtheria toxin has been obtained ever more refined (Raynaud and Relyveld, 1959; Relyveld and Efraim, 1959). Crude toxin fractionation by paper and starch electrophoresis has been followed by immunodiffusion analyses (Branham *et al.*, 1959; Poulik, 1953, 1956). Preparations with the physiologic activity of toxin have been obtained which produce only a single precipitin line with specific antitoxin (Pope and Stevens, 1958a,b; Relyveld *et al.*, 1956).

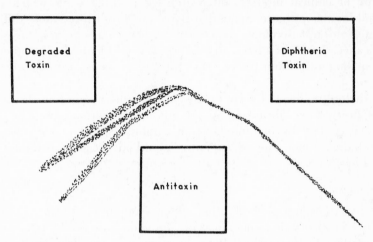

Fig. IV-11. Schematic representation of double diffusion test showing how highly purified diphtheria toxin which produces only one precipitin band with antitoxin can be degraded chemically to reveal two and perhaps three different antigenic determinants, each now attached to separate fragments of the original toxin molecules (Adapted from Pope and Stevens, 1958b.)

Indeed, this single antigen itself has been subfractionated. On progressive degeneration, it is revealed to have several antigenic determinants (Pope and Stevens, 1958a,b; see Fig. IV-11). At present, experimenters are trying to equate toxic activity of the whole antigen with one or more of these determinants. Relyveld and colleagues (1956) find the toxin to have an immunoelectrophoretic mobility similiar to that of a human serum α_1-globulin.

Clostridium

Clostridial exotoxins have invited the same kind of investigation applied to diphtheria toxin. Thus, efforts are being made to purify and define tetanus toxin (Turpin and Raynaud, 1959). Immunodiffusion analysis shows that before purification the crude toxin consists of a complex mixture of antigens liberated along with it into the culture medium from which it is prepared. Its antigenic complexity has been shown to increase as the culture medium from which it is obtained is allowed to age (Rafyi *et al.*, 1954). Consequently, any attempted purification of the toxic mixture's toxic principle should be aided by use of filtrates from young cultures. Crude toxins from *Clostridium welchii* and related bacilli are complex. They contain group factors some of which are species-specific and others type-specific (Björklund and Berengo, 1954; Oakley and Fulthorpe, 1953). The antigenic constitution of botulinus and tetanus toxins, and the toxins of the bacilli causing gas gangrene have been studied by immunodiffusion (Oakley and Fulthorpe, 1953). *Clostridium perfringens* ε toxin has the interesting property, unlike most other exotoxins, of losing its ability to precipitate with specific antibody after formalin treatment meant to transform it to a toxoid (Schuchardt *et al.*, 1958). As early as 1951 Lamanna and Lowenthal reported their single diffusion tube experiments on crystalline type A botulinal toxin, from which they concluded that the hemagglutinating and toxic activities of this toxin are due to two different antigenic moieties.

Mycobacterium

Filtrates from tubercle bacillus broth cultures have been used in one form or another for many years as skin-test antigens. Antigenically, these filtrates are proving to be complex. They have been studied in immunodiffusion experiments with guinea pig (Crowle, 1954, 1958b; Efford, 1952; Fuks, 1956, 1958; Smith, 1956), rabbit (Burtin, 1959b; Burtin and Kourilsky, 1959; Crowle, 1956, 1958b,c, 1960b; Fuks, 1956, 1958; Seibert and Soto-Figueroa, 1957), and human (Crouch, 1958; Efford, 1952) antisera. Double diffusion tests have detected 11 antigen-antibody systems for a single filtrate preparation (Crowle, 1958c; Efford, 1952); commonly these crude preparations have been found to contain two polysaccharide and several protein antigens (Burtin and Kourilsky, 1959; Pepys *et al.*, 1959b; Seibert and Soto-Figueroa, 1957). Immuno-electrophoresis of culture filtrates in one series of experiments indicates that they may contain at least 10 distinct fractions (Crowle, 1960b), although these seem to be divided antigenically into only four groups (Crowle, 1956, 1960b). In another immunoelectrophoretic study of four filtrate components, not necessarily the same as those just mentioned, three appeared to be predominantly proteins and the fourth poly-saccharide (Smith, 1956). The French workers Burtin and Kourilsky (1959) report finding 6 different antigens in culture filtrates, two of which are polysaccharides and four proteins. Burtin (1959b) has isolated and studied two tuberculopolysaccharides by immunoelectrophoresis. He finds that although they have different electrophoretic mobilities, they seem to share a common antigenic determinant. One tuberculopolysaccharide isolated with formamide from tubercle bacilli has been studied by the single diffusion method (Fuks, 1956, 1958).

Trypsin digestion of avirulent tubercle bacilli releases from them a water-soluble antigen which immunizes mice against tuberculosis as effectively as entire tubercle bacilli (Crowle, unpublished). Double diffusion analyses with specific guinea pig antisera disclose that this substance consists of at least 7 individual antigens, three of very low molecular weight and four of about the same molecular weight as guinea pig antibody. One of the three low molecular weight antigens contains considerable lipid which can, however, be removed from the crude extract without impairing its immunogenicity.

Pseudomonas

Diastase obtained from cultures of *Pseudomonas aeruginosa* provoked antibody formation in rabbits. The resulting antiserum used in double diffusion plates to analyze this enzyme indicated that it was complex antigenically (Richou *et al.*, 1959).

Enterobacteria

Several species of these bacteria have been analyzed by immunodiffusion. Flagella obtained from *Proteus vulgaris* X 19 have been shown to contain three antigens (Gard *et al.*, 1955). While one appeared to be H antigen, another apparently was O antigen present in small quantities as a contaminant. The third remained unidentified. The Vi antigen of *Paracolobactrum ballerup* in its natural form may provoke formation of two species of antibodies, one directed against its fully acetylated form and the other against it partially de-acetylated from (Whiteside and Baker, 1960). Oudin used *Salmonella typhi* antigens in some of his early single diffusion experiments (1948b). Cluff (1954) employed immunodiffusion techniques to confirm the current notion that *Shigella flexneri* endotoxin is a conjugate of polysaccharide, protein, and phospholipid. He succeeded in showing that the purified toxin is antigenically heterogeneous and that only its polysaccharide and protein components possessed serologic activity.

Brucella and Related Bacteria

Double diffusion plates in which sonic extract antigens of *Brucella suis* were being analyzed with rabbit antisera developed as many as 7 precipitin bands, in the experiments of Sulitzeanu (1958). Absorption experiments and agglutination tests indicated that there was no correlation between the plate precipitin patterns and bacterial agglutination titers, suggesting that antigens concerned with agglutination are insoluble and remain attached to sonically disrupted cells. Since agglutinogens are responsible for immunizing mice against *Br. suis* infection, the lack of correlation between vaccine content of precipitinogens and immunogenicity for these animals which was observed in these experiments was expected.

Extracts of disrupted *Hemophilus pertussis* contain at least three antigens detectable by double diffusion plate tests, one of which is the agglutinogen (Munoz, 1959). Comparison of acetone-dried saline extracts of *H. pertussis* with extracts from disintegrated cells shows that both preparations contain at least two antigens in common. Three to four more antigens were present in extracts of these bacteria in their smooth phase than in rough phase extracts (Munoz, 1954).

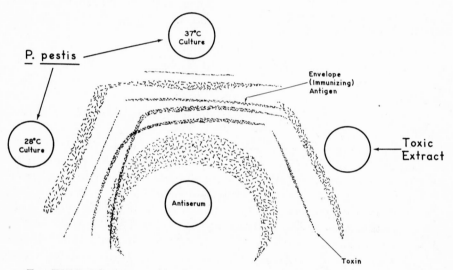

FIG. IV-12. Schematic representation of double diffusion test comparing antigens in *Pasteurella pestis* grown at 28°C. and at 37°C., and a toxic extract of this bacterium. Two precipitin bands are equated with specific activities of the whole bacteria: toxicity and immunogenicity. The culture grown at 28°C. does not produce antigen responsible for either of these activities. (Adapted from Crumpton and Davies, 1956.)

Chen and Meyer (1955) found *Pasteurella pestis* to produce four precipitin bands in double diffusion plates. Two of these fused with two formed by somatic antigens of *P. pseudotuberculosis* analyzed simultaneously in the same plates, but the other two were specific for *P. pestis*. One of the latter two zones was formed by precipitation of a toxin. Bent *et al.* (1957) have purified the murine toxin of *P. pestis* from a form producing two precipitin bands in the single diffusion tube test to one producing only a single band. Crumpton and Davies (1956) have reported some interesting analyses of *P. pestis* antigens by which they succeeded in identifying some constituting precipitin bands with various activities or properties of the entire bacteria (see Fig. IV-12). Thus, among 10 bands produced by the Pjiwideg strain, which they used, one was due to the envelope antigen immunogenic for mice, another corresponded to plague toxin, and the specificity of the third was determined by a polysaccharide component. These three antigens were not produced when the strain was grown at 20°C. instead of 37°C.

The immunogenic principle of *Pasteurella tularense* appears to be released from aqueous suspensions of these bacteria if they are treated with ether. By immunodiffusion analyses, the released material has been shown to contain 4 to 6 antigens, all apparently derived from the bacterial cell wall (Ormsbee and Larson, 1955).

Virulence and Pathogenicity

Some instances in which immunodiffusion tests can be helpful in studying virulence and pathogenicity of infectious agents have been given indirectly in preceding sections. For example, double diffusion methods for ascertaining the pathogenicity (toxigenicity) of diphtheria bacilli were mentioned in the section on Taxonomy and their usefulness documented with a large number of references (see Fig. IV-7). To reiterate, differentiating toxigenic from nontoxigenic diphtheria bacilli depends (in the double diffusion gradient test, one form or another of which has been the most frequently employed for this purpose) upon demonstrating the presence of toxin in the strain being examined. This is accomplished by comparing the unknown strain with a strain known to be toxigenic, using antitoxin as the analytic reagent. Each strain may produce one or more precipitin bands with the antitoxin, one of which for the known toxigenic strain is formed by the toxin itself. If the unknown strain also produces this toxin, its toxin will form a precipitin band which coalesces with the toxin band of the known toxigenic strain. On the other hand, if it does not produce this toxin, no band corresponding to and coalescing with the toxin band of the toxigenic strain will be formed by the unknown, and this is demonstrated, then, to be nonpathogenic (cf. Ouchterlony, 1958; see Fig. IV-7).

The toxigenicity of gas gangrene bacilli has been determined by the same methods (Petrie, 1943).

The ability of certain coagulase-positive strains of staphylococci to produce a greater variety of diffusible antigens than others might be correlated with staphylococcal virulence, since although each precipitating antigen is not necessarily a toxin, every diffusible toxin will yield a precipitate. Hence, the number of bands produced has been suggested as a measure of toxigenicity (Pope *et al.*, 1951). For the study from which this idea was derived, 359 strains of staphylococci were examined for precipitin reactions with a single antitoxin produced against the Wood 46 TH strain. All coagulase-positive strains produced specifically reacting antigens, while no coagulase-negative strain did.

Individual staphylococcal hemolysins can be studied by immunodiffusion, as has been mentioned above (Elek, 1950a). Although Bergdoll *et al.* (1959) have been able to identify staphylococcal enterotoxin from a particular strain of cocci and to prepare specific monovalent antiserum against it, they note that enterotoxin from various strains may differ sufficiently that cross-reactions are not likely to be total and may not be seen at all for enterotoxins of these other strains tested with the monovalent antiserum.

Whenever bacterial virulence depends upon the presence of an antigenically specific capsule (e.g., pneumococci), then the single diffusion plate test can be used to differentiate virulent from avirulent strains. Thus, it is easy to demonstrate whether or not given strains of pneumococci or meningococci produce capsular antigen by growing them on nutrient medium in which type-specific antiserum has been incorporated (Maegraith, 1933; Petrie, 1932). Meningococcus polysaccharide, the antigen which immunizes mice against infection with this coccus, has been detected and studied with this kind of test (Pittman *et al.*, 1938).

Pasteurella pestis toxins have been identified by double diffusion tests as have also the conditions for their production (Crumpton and Davies, 1956). These same tests can distinguish virulent from avirulent strains.

Pereira *et al.* (1959) have used immunoelectrophoresis to detect three antigens obtained from adenovirus-infected HeLa cells, and to show that one of these is responsible for the early cytotoxic effect of this virus.

Biology

Ways in which immunodiffusion serves biology have been touched upon above in such sections as Taxonomy, Cytology, and Bacteriology. Embryology is another branch of biology which has benefited from applications to it of immunodiffusion techniques. For example, immunoelectrophoretic analyses have suggested the order in which human serum antigens first appear during development of the human embryo (Bodman, 1959; Scheidegger *et al.*, 1956). Since these analyses have been detailed above in connection with immunoelectrophoretic studies on human serum constituents, they will not be repeated here.

Single diffusion tube tests have been utilized to identify antigens in frog eggs, early embryos, and adult serum (Cooper, 1950). Thus, adult frog serum contains, according to these experiments, 6 to 7 antigens. Saline extracts of eggs, neural plate, and early neural fold stages contain 6 to 8 antigens. The antigens found in early developmental stages of the frog and its eggs are immunologically related to adult serum antigens but are not identical with them.

Similar experiments have been reported on chicken egg albumin (Vaughan and Kabat, 1954a,b), and they have been carried out in considerable detail on chickens, their eggs, and their embryos by Kaminski (1954, 1957a,b) and Kaminski and Durieux (1954, 1956). Using double diffusion and immunoelectrophoresis tests, these workers compared the antigenic constitution of fresh egg white, allantoic liquid, allantoic liquid mixed with yolk, amniotic liquid, and the blood of the embryo, as well as sera from the newly hatched chick, the adult hen, and the adult rooster. They found significant quantities of egg white constituents in all liquids of the incubated egg as well as in embryo blood. In the first stages of chicken embryo development, these antigens constitute most of the proteins that the liquids of fertilized eggs contain. They tend to remain detectable in chick embryo serum until the last day of incubation. After the chick has hatched, however, usually only conalbumin among these embryonic antigens is found in its serum. Rarely, ovalbumin can be discerned in the serum of egg-bearing pullets.

The adult chicken liver contains at least 14 distinct antigens, according to Croissile (1959), with the same immunoelectrophoretic mobility range as chicken serum constituents but clearly different from them serologically, since antiserum absorbed with chicken serum could be used to detect them. Three of these antigens were absent from 5-day-old chick liver. Two more were missing in 17- to 18-day embryo liver, and progressively less were demonstrable in progressively more primitive samples of liver that were examined. Six of the 14 could be demonstrated in 6-day embryo, but only one was present in 5-day embryo liver.

The following two reports illustrate how immunodiffusion techniques can be employed in enzymology. One of these reports was concerned with determining whether cytochrome C, obtained from beef heart, is antigenic, since opinions on this point conflicted. Becker and Munoz (1949a) vaccinated rabbits with this enzyme and were able to detect in antiserum that they obtained from these animals antibodies to three different antigens in cytochrome C preparations, when this enzyme was reacted with the antisera in single diffusion tube tests. The other report was made in connection with mechanisms by which the activity of Old

Yellow Enzyme can be inhibited specifically by its antibody. In double diffusion tests, this antigen, of crystalline purity, formed only one precipitin band with its antibody (Kistner, 1959). Moreover, the entire enzyme and the apoenzyme behaved identically with rabbit antiserum, both producing only one band of precipitate.

Chemistry

Whenever a problem in chemistry involves a substance which can take part in antigen-antibody precipitation, immunodiffusion becomes a usable analytic tool. Thus, it has proved excellent for identifying subunits of protein molecules obtained by mildly degrading these molecules by chemical or enzymatic digestion.

Human Serum Albumin

Two substances of different electrophoretic mobilities but identical serologically and able to cross-react in double diffusion tests with whole human serum albumin (HSA) are obtained from this antigen treated with trypsin (Lapresle *et al.*, 1959a). HSA degraded with an extract of human spleen until no native albumin remained nevertheless yielded a product antigenic for rabbits which produced two different types of antibody against it (Lapresle and Durieux, 1958). One was produced in response to specific groups of the native albumin, while the other was specific for new antigenic groups unmasked by the degradation. Antiserum obtained from rabbits vaccinated with HSA and having antibodies to three different specificities for degraded albumin have been used by Lapresle and Durieux (1957b) to follow the course of enzymatic HSA degradation and to identify each antigenic determinant as it was exposed. From these various studies and others, it seems clear that HSA has at least three different specific serologic determinants (Lapresle, 1955; Lapresle and Durieux, 1957a). However, the interrelationships of these antigenic determinants may appear to differ according to which enzymes and experimental procedures are used for HSA degradation (Lapresle *et al.*, 1957b). Thus, trypsin does not split the albumin into different precipitating components; chymotrypsin splits it into two; pepsin and rabbit spleen extract split it into three. Chymotrypsin at pH 4.5 splits the molecule also into three components, but these are different from subunits obtained by pepsin digestion.

Other Albuminoids

Bovine serum albumin (BSA) treated with chymotrypsin yields a dialyzable fragment which is precipitated faintly by antiserum to BSA and cross-reacts with the complete antigen. It inhibits specific precipitation of native BSA in absorption experiments (Porter, 1957). Chicken ovalbumin treated in the same way did not yield a dialyzable subunit. This ovalbumin so far has been split by enzymatic digestion into two antigenically distinct constituents which react with antiserum from animals vaccinated with the whole antigen (Kaminski, 1960). During digestion with chymotrypsin and trypsin, one of these is destroyed, but the second remains intact even after the enzymatic reaction ceases.

Immunoelectrophoretically homogeneous ovomucoid has been obtained by Jutisz and co-workers (1957) using column electrophoresis at a pH near this antigen's isoelectric point.

Antisera to sea urchin eggs have a parthenogenetic action which is directed against a certain egg antigen. Enzyme degradation studies coupled with immunodiffusion experiments have been used in attempts to identify this antigen (Perlmann and Perlmann, 1957).

Tubercle bacillus culture filtrates which contain large quantities of albuminoid tuberculoproteins, have been submitted to the effects of heat, enzymes, alcohol, and trichloracetic acid and then analyzed by immunodiffusion. Culture filtrate proteins are very little damaged by trypsin or chymotrypsin, under certain conditions, or by trichloracetic acid precipitation, but all are thermolabile (Burtin and Kourilsky, 1959). Under other conditions, however, tuberculoprotein apparently can be degraded sufficiently so that it no longer is able to react with anti-tuberculoprotein antibodies. Thus, double diffusion precipitin tests utilizing the analytic virtues of specific stains for precipitin bands appearing in the agar when specific antisera were reacted with trypsin digests of proteins from human and bovine tubercle bacilli and from *Mycobacterium johnei* suggest that cross-reacting antigens among these various bacilli are contaminating polysaccharides, since the proteins apparently were destroyed by trypsin digestion, but the cross-reacting precipitinogens survived this digestion (Pepys *et al.*, 1959b).

Allergens

Immunodiffusion tests early showed the antigenic complexity of ragweed pollens (Becker and Munoz, 1949b). As an aid to setting up standards of ragweed pollen extracts, the antigens of these extracts have been aged artificially with heat, and their progressive loss of precipitability with specific antiserum was followed by double diffusion plate tests (Wodehouse, 1953, 1954b). The same has been attempted with extracts of the parasite *Trichinella* (Wodehouse, 1956b). More extensive experiments which included submitting pollens to pH changes, organic solvent treatments, and digestions with pepsin, trypsin, or protease have indicated that most, if not all, allergens in grass pollens are proteins, since none of the carbohydrates demonstrable by double diffusion tests and immunoelectrophoresis could elicit skin reactions in hypersensitive individuals that could be elicited by the native allergens (Augustin, 1959b). Goldfarb and his co-workers (1956, 1959) have applied double diffusion plate tests to identifying the antigenic components of giant ragweed pollens and have isolated, thereby, one fraction which they believe to be responsible for allergic reactions caused by such pollens in human beings. Schiott (1953) compared horse dander and horse serum in double diffusion plate tests utilizing rabbit antiserum and found, with the aid of auxiliary electrophoretic fractionation of the serum, that a common antigen detected in both was horse albumin. Stanworth (1957b) using similar techniques obtained essentially the same results, showing that albumin is the common antigen of both dander and serum from horses.

Fibrinolysis

Seligmann and Grabar (1958), in investigating the potential utility of immunochemical techniques for studying the process of fibrinolysis, found that they could identify degradation products of fibrinogen and fibrinolysin immunoelectrophoretically and by double diffusion plate tests. They also were able to detect breakdown derivatives of fibrinogen treated with plasmin. Caspary in 1956 reported some preliminary investigations with human fibrinogen. Salmon (1959) used rabbit antisera in immunoelectrophoresis experiments to analyze fibrinogen, and concluded that this substance has three specific sites for combination with antibody, one of them possibly the fibrinopeptide liberated by thrombin. He found the products of fibrinolysis and of fibrinogenolysis to be precipitated by anti-fibrinogen serum.

Blood Coagulation

Antibodies specific for substances essential to the process of blood clotting can interfere with this process. Halick and Seegers, concerning themselves with this idea, have used single diffusion tube tests to analyze bovine prothrombin and rabbit antibodies produced against it (1956).

Antigens

An approach to protein chemistry amenable to immunodiffusion experiments which is the reverse of that described above is to create rather than degrade antigens. Preliminary double diffusion plate experiments have been reported in which antigen consisted simply of two molecules of arsanilic acid diazotized to one of resorcinol (Feinberg and

Grant, 1957). In more extensive but similar work, Stahmann *et al.* (1955, 1959a,b), for example, synthesized polypeptides and polypeptidyl proteins and then studied the abilities of their products to induce antibody formation and to react in immunodiffusion tests with sera from rabbits injected with them. Such experiments showed that when glutamic acid, lysine, leucine, or phenylalanine polypeptides are conjugated to bovine serum albumin or to rabbit serum albumin and these conjugates are used to stimulate antibody formation, the vaccinated animals form three types of antibodies. There are those which are specific for the peptide attached to the carrier protein, those specific for the carrier protein itself, and more rarely a third type which react only with the entire conjugate (see also Buchanan-Davidson *et al.*, 1959a, and Fujio *et al.*, 1959).

Antigens which must be treated chemically in some way as part of an experiment may be altered structurally in an undesirable fashion. These structural changes are readily detected by immunodiffusion techniques if they affect the antigenic constitution of a molecule; conversely, the absence of important structural changes can be verified similarly. Wilson and Pringle (1956) purposely produced changes in the antigenic structure of bovine serum albumin by treating it with iodine solutions to obtain variants of this antigen for studying spurring and the nature of cross reactions in double diffusion plates. On the other hand, Martin du Pan and co-workers (1959) verified by immunodiffusion tests that the antigenic specificity of γ-globulin tagged with radioactive iodine was not sufficiently changed by the procedure that they used to interfere with its use in experiments which they wished to perform on the transfer of maternal γ-globulin to the fetus in human beings.

Double diffusion plate tests enabled Briner and co-workers (1959) to show that human serum low density lipoproteins can withstand being frozen and thawed, stored at $-20°C$., and heated to $56°C$. for 45 minutes without notable immunological change. Bacterial decomposition of lipoprotein could be detected with the aid of these tests.

Enzymes

As antigens which can evoke formation in injected animals of antibodies not only able to precipitate them but also able specifically to neutralize their chemical activities, enzymes always have been held in considerable interest by the immunochemist. McIvor and Moon (1959) have reported double diffusion plate experiments showing that rabbits injected with adjuvant-elastase mixtures produce precipitins specific for electrophoretically purified elastase.

Immunodiffusion tests in chemistry, useful enough in themselves, can be rendered even more so by use of appropriate indicator reactions upon specific precipitates to detect polysaccharides, lipids, glycoproteins, acetylphosphatides, metal-containing proteins, and so forth (Uriel and Grabar, 1956a).

Physical Chemistry

The usefulness of immunodiffusion tests in physical chemistry depends upon the characteristics of diffusion or electrophoretic migration of macro-molecules through semisolid media, and it is in their resolution and definition of chemically and physically indistinguishable antigen and antibody molecules that these techniques excel. For example, the molecular weight of a given antigen in a mixture of antigens can be determined without ever having to purify it and, indeed, the molecular weights of other constituents of the mixture can be estimated at the same time. Electrophoretic mobilities can be measured for one or more antigens or species of antibodies in complex mixtures of either by immunoelectrophoresis, even though two may have such similar mobilities as to be unresolvable by other electrophoretic techniques. Unfortunately, immunodiffusion techniques can be used with too much confidence in the results which they yield both on diffusion coefficients and electrophoretic mobilities, since the complexity of factors affecting determination of these values not only often is not realized but also is not yet fully understood.

The diffusion coefficient and molecular size of an antigen in solution sometimes can be determined accurately by single diffusion tube tests. As is explained in detail elsewhere, in principle the front of antigen diffusing through antibody-charged agar corresponds to the front of its visible precipitin band, and hence, measurement of the rate of apparent migration for this band indicates rate of diffusion for the antigen. Providing that the suppressing effect of antibody on antigen diffusion rate is negligible, the agar gel is thin enough to permit free antigen diffusion and it has no propensity for combining with the antigen, effects of interfering additives (e.g., nonspecific substances) are accounted for, and the initial concentration of antigen is known, the laws of gas diffusion can be used to calculate the antigen's diffusion coefficient and, if it is spherical, its molecular size and probable weight (cf. Becker et al., 1951; Munoz, 1954). Because of difficulties associated with its practical application, the single diffusion test has been used for such purposes with commonly available already purified antigens, such as serum albumins and ovalbumin, principally for theoretical studies (Augustin et al., 1958; Becker et al., 1951; Munoz, 1954; Neff and Becker, 1957b; Oudin, 1948a, 1954; Rubinstein, 1954). It is not yet reliable enough to serve as a primary method for determining antigen diffusion co-efficients.

Rough ideas of antigen or antibody size are, of course, readily obtained with single diffusion tube tests. An alternate method, which often simply is an incidental product of double diffusion plate tests, is to note the curvature of precipitin bands forming between opposing reactants in this test, as has been described in Chapter III. This technique has been used to identify large and small foot-and-mouth virus antigens (Brown and Crick, 1958) and to differentiate heavy (19S) from light (7S) human immunoglobulins (Fahey and Horbett, 1959; Korngold and van Leeuwen, 1959a; Korngold et al., 1959). For example, autoprecipitins against thyroglobulin in sera from four patients with Hashimoto's disease were shown to be of the 7S type in three and of the 19S type in the fourth (Korngold et al., 1959).

A refinement of this double diffusion method is one in which the time required for a specific precipitate to appear between antigen and antibody depots under standardized conditions as well as for this precipitate to grow to a certain length are used as indirect indicators of antigen diffusion coefficient, antigen concentration, antibody diffusion coefficient, and similar data (Aladjem et al., 1959). Thus, the rate of an antigen's radial diffusion from its source is assumed to govern the curvature of any precipitate band it forms. It also should be proportional to time passing before it combines with sufficient antibody to make a visible precipitate and to the rate of the visible precipitin band's lateral growth. This rate of radial diffusion, in turn, is proportional to the concentration and molecular size of the antigen. Still too new to have been proved useful practically, this technique like all double diffusion tests eliminates the interference of one reactant on the diffusion of the other (by antigen-antibody interaction), a major complication inherent in single diffusion tubes. With it, its originators have arrived at diffusion coefficients for bovine and human serum albumins, ovalbumin, and rabbit antibodies which agree reasonably well with values for these substances determined by other methods.

Ways in which the double diffusion gradient test can be used for determining antigen and antibody diffusion coefficients have been explained in Chapter III. This method has been used successfully to estimate diffusion coefficients for chicken ovalbumin, human serum albumin, human γ-globulin, rat liver catalase, sheep thyroglobulin, and human serum β-lipoprotein (Allison and Humphrey, 1959).

Diffusion of molecules and larger particles through semisolid gels requires that the "mesh" of the gel be loose enough not to entrap and immobilize individual particles. Diffusion of molecules of a given size ceases when the mesh is condensed so that the diameter of the average molecule is greater than individual "spaces" in the mesh. This fact has been used to determine the sizes of a number of different antigen molecules. Wunderly (1959) thickens agar gels for this purpose with carboxymethylcellulose. Allison and Humphrey (1959) have used increasing concentrations of gelatin and of agar gels (see Fig. IV-13). For example, while nearly all known negatively-charged antigens will diffuse readily through 1% agar or 2% gelatin gels, higher agar concentrations up to 7% provide increasingly thick gels, the most concentrated of which can prevent diffusion of antigens with molecular weights as low as 450,000. Gelatin gels can be prepared considerably more concentrated; a 32% gel curtails diffusion of hen ovalbumin which has a molecular weight of only 44,000.

Antigen and antibody diffusion coefficients have been determined in double diffusion tubes on the theory that if antigen and antibody initially are equivalent in their respective depots, when they meet they will form a non-moving precipitate band at a position in the agar between their respective depots determined by the ratio of their diffusion coefficients to each other (Preer, 1956). This method has been used to estimate diffusion coefficients for hemocyanins, poliomyelitis virus, and diphtheria antitoxin (Polson, 1958), as well as the size of the turnip yellow mosaic virus (van Regenmortel, 1959).

The potential value of immunoelectrophoresis as a technique for determining electrophoretic characteristics of individual antigens in complex mixtures of them, which otherwise could not be studied without extensive if not prohibitive attempts to purify them, should be clear from immunoelectrophoretic experiments described elsewhere in this book. So far, this has not been done very commonly because certain peculiarities of agar electrophoresis, particularly electroosmosis and solubility effects, do not permit direct measurements of antigen electrophoretic mobility in this kind of gel. At present, the mobility of an antigen, or an antibody, is usually related to that of some known substance such as serum albumin electrophoresed at the same time and expressed in ratio to this. However, progress on this problem suggests that before long immunoelectrophoresis in agar, or very likely in other media such as Cyanogum 41 or gelatin, will begin to supply electrophoretic mobility values for the innumerable antigens and antibodies which can be studied with it. Relative mobilities were reported for various human serum constituents in one of the first publications on immunoelectrophoresis (Williams and Grabar, 1955a). They have been

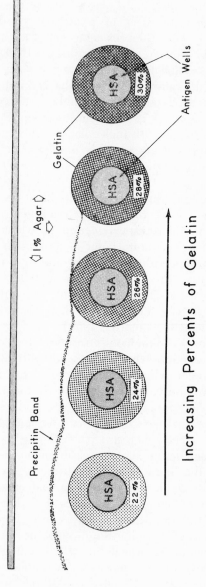

Fig. IV-13. Diagram of a double diffusion test used for determining reactant molecular sizes. Increasing percentages of gelatin surrounding sources of human serum albumin antigen diffusion (HSA) increasingly restrict diffusion of this antigen into surrounding agar, where it can precipitate with antiserum. A gelatin concentration of 28% completely restricts it, indicating that its molecules are too large to diffuse through this thick a gel and thus revealing their size. (Adapted from Allison and Humphrey, 1959.)

determined for various types of horse antibodies (Raynaud, 1958; Raynaud *et al.*, 1959a,b). Recently, even the mobility of hemagglutinins has been measured by immunoelectrophoresis (Hanson *et al.*, 1960).

Quantitation

Immunodiffusion methods which can be used to determine diffusion coefficients of antigens also can be employed to quantitate them. Some additional methods are suitable for quantitation alone. Early experiences with such techniques led to the opinion that only a relative quantitation could be achieved, but more recent experiments with improved methods show that absolute quantities of either antigen or antibody can be obtained by immunodiffusion tests.

Single Diffusion Tests

Single diffusion tube tests have been used to quantitate human serum γ-globulin in hypogammaglobulinemias (Hitzig *et al.*, 1959), to show a correlation between the anti-streptolysin O titers of human, rabbit, and guinea pig sera and their content of specific precipitins (Halbert *et al.*, 1955a), to quantitate several different serum constituents in connection with basic analyses of human serum (Oudin, 1958b), and to observe changes in quantities of two antigens in sea urchin eggs during their differentiation into embryos (Perlmann and Kaltenbach, 1957). In these tests, quantitation is based on the idea that under appropriate conditions the diffusion rate of antigen through antibody-charged agar is directly proportional to the initial quantity of antigen layered upon antibody.

Another type of single diffusion quantitative test is one in which one reactant or the other is used in serial dilutions in a series of tests each with a constant quantity of the indicator reactant. If this is done in a series of tubes, for example, in one of this series the reactants will be equivalent and form a precipitin band at their interface which moves into neither antigen nor antibody layer. As explained in Chapter III, this tube represents an equilibrium ratio between the two reactants which is not, however, necessarily the same as equivalence determined by classic precipitin tests or double diffusion tests. This kind of test has been used with ovalbumin (Becker and Neff, 1959), bovine serum albumin (Wilson, 1958), bovine γ-globulin (Crowle, 1960b), and with pollen antigens (Hayward and Augustin, 1957), using rabbit and guinea pig antisera.

Double Diffusion Tests

Double diffusion quantitative tests can be of several types. There are the tube tests in which the position of a band between two sources of reactants indicates their quantitative ratios, or those in which the quantity of one reactant is adjusted in serial dilutions to equilibrate in some measurable way with the other. In plate tests of diverse well patterns, the same object is achieved, but by somewhat different design (see Chapters III and V).

Quantities of pollen antigens as well as potencies of antibodies to them have been measured by the tube double diffusion gradient test of Augustin and Hayward (Augustin, 1955; Hayward and Augustin, 1957). Augustin (1957) used this technique to assay fractions of a microgram of ovalbumin and very small quantities of diphtheria toxoid at levels of sensitivity beyond those usable in single diffusion tubes. Feinberg (1959) has used double diffusion plates to assay quantities of grass pollen allergen mixture constituents within ranges of +6.7 and −9%.

Equivalence ratios determined in double diffusion tubes by formation of sharp, nonmoving precipitate bands have been used in quantitative tests with the antigen excelsin, a protein extracted from Brazil nuts, and with diphtheria toxin (Boerma, 1956), with viruses in poliomyelitis vaccine (Polson, 1958), and with serum proteins (Gell, 1955a). Pollen antigens (Hayward and Augustin, 1957), bovine serum albumin (Jennings and Malone, 1955), human serum proteins (Gell, 1957), and ovalbumin and bovine γ-globulin (Crowle, 1960b) have been measured quantitatively with moderate accuracy using double diffusion plate tests in which the visual characteristics of precipitin bands of known and unknown quantities of antigen are compared.

Double diffusion plate tests are very convenient as aids to classic precipitin tests in analyzing supernatant fluids from each of a series of tubes, or simply different mixtures of antigen and antibody, for free antigen or antibody (Wright, 1959). They have been used for this purpose, for example, with human serum transferrin (Wright, 1959).

Immunodiffusion has been used quantitatively to date only rather infrequently, largely because of technical difficulties. Now that most of these have been removed, quantitation with single and double diffusion tests probably will become frequent and widely accepted.

Preparation and Purification

The analytic definitiveness of immunodiffusion techniques qualify them as ideal for following the preparation and purification of antigens and antibodies. Indeed, they often take an active part in preparatory experiments. This is exemplified classically by work done with diphtheria toxin, which occurs in culture filtrates with as many as 23 other antigens (Pope *et al.*, 1951), but which by persistent attempts by several investigators has been purified to give only one precipitate with its specific antitoxin (Pope and Stevens, 1959). The most direct method for its preparation, its dissociation from an antigen-antibody complex (Uyeu and Pavageau, 1956), illustrates one way of using immunodiffusion itself as a preparatory technique. A respectable list of publications documents the application of single and double diffusion and immunoelectrophoresis to isolating and characterizing diphtheria toxin and antitoxin (Bowen, 1952; Poulik, 1953, 1959; Poulik and Poulik, 1958; Relyveld and Raynaud, 1958; Relyveld et al., 1954, 1956, 1957). Tetanus toxin has been prepared highly purified using similar methods (Rafyi et al., 1954; Turpin and Raynaud, 1959).

Special immunodiffusion methods developed to follow purification of *Staphylococcus* enterotoxin (Surgalla et al., 1952) also were employed to aid in preparing a monovalent antiserum to it (Bergdoll et al., 1959). Halbert (1958) used continuous flow electrophoresis in connection with double diffusion tests to prepare 12 distinct *Streptococcus* antigens and to identify streptolysin O, diphosphopyridinenucleotidase, and proteinase precursor among these. Pereira and co-workers (1959) isolated by immunoelectrophoresis a cytotoxic substance produced by adenovirus in infected HeLa cells, and they showed it to differ from the virus particles themselves.

The excellence of immunoelectrophoresis for identifying, preparing, and characterizing serum antigens is demonstrated by the discussion of this subject in the first section of this chapter. Below, its utility for rapid and definitive studies on antibodies also is documented. A superlative technique for preparing individual antigens from a complex mixture of them is to combine elution chromatography with immunodiffusion. For example, Fahey and Horbett (1959) have been able to obtain from human serum γ-globulin 5 fractions among which they could identify the high and low molecular weight antigens.

In connection with their successful attempts to prepare leukocytes free from serum proteins, Grabar and his colleagues (1955a) identified leukocyte antigens and serum antigens and used double diffusion tests to show that adequate washing removed all of the latter from these cells. Nachkov and Nachkova (1959) employed immunoelectrophoresis to identify various mouse liver antigens with specific enzymatic activities. Stanworth (1957a) succeeded in identifying the single horse dandruff fraction among 7, producing specific precipitates in double diffusion plate tests with rabbit antiserum, which was responsible for skin test reactions in asthmatic patients. Using double diffusion tests, he showed that this fraction is carbohydrate-rich but also contains 64% of the total protein of the whole dandruff extract.

The advantage of immunodiffusion tests in preparatory procedures over most others, just as in qualitative analyses, is that if the constituent being isolated is an antigen, then a highly specific reagent (antibody) can be manufactured to order to detect it; for other techniques, identification of complex molecules often depends upon use of relatively non-specific reagents. Moreover, this reagent can be used directly for preparing the constituent.

Characterizing Antibodies

Until the advent of immunoelectrophoresis, characterizing antibodies electrophoretically was an uncertain, difficult, time-consuming, and expensive enterprise. Now, it remains occasionally uncertain, because antibodies may be attached to substances which move so strongly of their own accord during electrophoresis that the true mobility of the antibodies is masked, but it hardly can be called difficult or time-consuming, and it certainly has become relatively inexpensive, the apparatus required for such endeavors being very simple.

Horse Antiserum

By immunoelectrophoresis, horse diphtheria antitoxins formed during the first stages of immunization have been identified as γ-globulins with the same physical and specific precipitating characteristics as rabbit precipitins; that is, their complexes with toxin are relatively insoluble in antibody excess. As the time after immunization lengthens, horses begin to produce β_2-globulin antibodies of high molecular weight (members of the classic electrophoresis "T" component) which form complexes in precipitin tests with toxin antigen readily soluble in antibody excess and which are typical flocculating or H-type antibodies (Raynaud, 1958; Raynaud *et al.*, 1959a; Relyveld and Raynaud, 1957, 1958; Relyveld *et al.*, 1957; Williams and Grabar, 1955b). Horses which for any of several reasons have previously been immunized with diphtheria toxin and are used later for manufacturing antitoxin produce β_2-globulin antibodies of the flocculating type from the beginning of this second exposure to diphtheria toxin. From these data, Relyveld and his colleagues (1957) conclude that upon primary immunization horses begin making γ-globulin precipitating antibodies, and that secondary immunization causes them to form β_2-globulin flocculating antibodies.

Flocculating β_2-globulin antibodies are produced by horses vaccinated with tetanus toxoid (Raynaud *et al.*, 1959b), with streptococcal antigen (Hanson, 1959), or with human serum antigens (Scheidegger, 1957). One instance has been recorded in which after immunization with tetanus toxoid of high purity a horse developed γ-, β_2-, and α-globulin precipitins at different stages of its vaccination period (Raynaud et al., 1959b). Production of α-globulin antibody was only temporary.

Rabbit Antiserum

Rabbit antibodies so far studied immunoelectrophoretically have proved to be γ-globulins. For one example, this was demonstrated in some elegant experiments performed by Adler (1956b; see also 1956a) using guinea pig antiserum to rabbit serum to analyze rabbit antiserum to bovine serum albumin. The rabbit antiserum was electrophoresed in agar, and then its many separated antigen components were detected with guinea pig antiserum. However, another analytic step was added to this otherwise usual form of immunoelectrophoresis. The agar with its various precipitin bands was flooded with fluorescein-labeled bovine serum albumin. This antigen reacted with its rabbit antibody which already had been precipitated as the γ-globulin arc, thereby clearly indicating that all precipitins to the albumin antigen in this rabbit antiserum were immunoelectrophoretically γ-globulins. More conventional immunoelectrophoretic techniques have shown rabbit antibodies to Old Tuberculin constituents (Burrell et al., 1956) and tubercle bacillus culture filtrates (Lind, 1959) to be located in the γ-globulin area. However, in this area some heterogeneity has been detected. Thus, rabbit γ-globulin antibodies were reported in early immunoelectrophoretic studies to have slightly different mobilities (Williams and Grabar, 1955b). Hyperimmune rabbit antiserum to antigens extracted from tubercle bacilli have shown three distinct mercuric chloride precipitate zones taking up protein stain in the γ-globulin area after simple agar electrophoresis and the presence of several species of antibodies in this area with distinctly and comparably different mobilities upon immunoelectrophoresis (Crowle, unpublished).

Nonprecipitating antibodies to human serum albumin which block precipitation by more complete antibodies have been detected in some rabbit antisera by immunoelectrophoresis (Gillert, 1958).

Human Antiserum

With the rather generalized exception of antibodies directed against red blood cell antigens, most human antibodies are γ-globulins. Pooled "normal" human γ-globulin is a good source of antibodies to *Streptococcus* antigens for immunodiffusion tests (Halbert et al., 1955b); patients with streptococcal disease also produce γ-globulin antibodies (Hanson, 1959). Antibodies to human thyroglobulin in sera from patients with Hashimoto's disease have been shown to be of either precipitating or flocculating varieties, but in the paper reporting this (Roitt et al., 1958) both were said to be γ-globulins immunoelectrophoretically. However, antibody location was apparently estimated by identification of fractions by staining rather than by the much finer technique of specific anti-human antiserum reactions. Since β_{2M}-globulins are heavy molecules with electrophoretic migration rates very similar to those of γ-globulins, and since double diffusion plate analyses show Hashimoto sera to contain antibodies with either the molecular weight of γ-globulin (7S) or of "T" component (β_{2M}-globulin) with a sedimentation constant of 19S (Korngold et al., 1959; Pressman et al., 1957), more definitive experiments probably will show that these flocculating-type human autoprecipitins are β_{2M}-globulins. That other β_{2M}-anti-protein antibodies will be detected in human sera in future experiments therefore seems very likely. Application of a new immunoelectrophoretic technique to human sera has shown that their erythrocyte agglutinins are β-globulins, even of the β_1-type (Hanson et al., 1960).

Antibodies to horse serum causing serum sickness in patients treated with horse antitoxin appear to be γ-globulins (Rose and Arbesman, 1960). Human serum tuberculopolysaccharide precipitins also are γ-globulins (Burrell et al., 1956). Although some human antibodies to typhoid bacilli may be α_1-globulins, most are γ-globulins (Bustamante, 1957). As has already been suggested, human isohemagglutinins most often occur in the β-globulin area (Faure et al., 1955).

Human pre-colostrum and colostrum contain antibodies to streptococcal antigens (Hanson and Johansson, 1959b). Hashimoto sera can contain in addition to precipitating and flocculating antibodies, others of coprecipitating and precipitation-inhibiting characteristics, also demonstrable in double diffusion plate tests (Goudie et al., 1959).

Antiserum from Other Animals

Immunoelectrophoretic characterization of antibodies produced by animal species other than man, rabbits, and the horse has been sparse. Donkey precipitins which so far have been studied are γ-globulins (Williams and Grabar, 1955b). Sheep diphtheria antitoxin has an immunoelectrophoretic mobility intermediate between β_2- and γ-globulins, and its precipitating characteristics are intermediate between flocculating and precipitating antibodies (Relyveld et al., 1959). The precipitates it forms with diphtheria toxin are moderately soluble in antibody excess.

Chicken antisera differ from mammalian antisera by specifically precipitating antigens best in liquid media at salt concentrations ten times greater than required for optimal precipitation by the latter antisera. According to Makinodan and co-workers (1959), this could be due to a coprecipitation effect of nonantibody chicken serum protein.

They suggest that a heavy (20 S) β-globulin, which they found in chicken antiserum specific precipitates, might have such a function. Crowle and Lueker have found recently (unpublished) that chicken antisera which precipitate antigens of various types (both heavy and low molecular weight) optimally in liquid media at high salt concentrations precipitate these same antigens in semisolid media much better at physiologic electrolyte concentrations. This has held true whether the semisolid medium was agar (purified or standard), gelatin, or cellulose acetate, and whether phosphate or barbital served as buffer.

Antibody Characterization

As has been suggested in Chapter III, double diffusion and, especially, single diffusion tube tests readily indicate whether an antibody is of H- or R-type and suggest in what range of proportions a given antigen-antibody system will precipitate (Becker, 1953). The nature of a precipitin band in single diffusion tests also is a sensitive indicator of variations among R-type antibodies in their apparent avidity for antigen (Jennings, 1959a). Antibody purity can be ascertained. For example, immunoelectrophoresis, double diffusion, and single diffusion tests have been applied to defining the purity of horse antitoxin dissociated from diphtheria toxin (Uyeu and Pavageau, 1956).

Determinant group characteristics of a single species of antibody generally are very difficult to ascertain by classic precipitin tests in liquid medium. The ability of double diffusion plate methods to test simultaneously reactions of an antiserum with individual antigens in a mixture of different antigens and at the same time to indicate individually how antibodies in the antiserum react with each antigen in relation to any other antigen have made this problem simpler. The utility of these methods in gross differentiation already should be evident from the section above on Taxonomy. There are some other examples of similar nature. Rabbit antiserum to bovine serum albumin has been shown to cross-react to varying degrees with serum albumins from 10 other species of animal, and the albumin from each species showed some degree of identity with any other (Weigle, 1960). Most important, regarding antibody characterization, this study illustrates how the range of antibody heterogeneity can be estimated, since the degree of cross-reactivity with antigen from each different species must depend upon the variety of antibodies present. For example, an antiserum containing antibodies only of high specificity might have cross-reacted only with antigen from an animal species very closely related to the cow, while an antiserum containing various species of antibodies of widely varying specificity could precipitate heterologous antigen nearly as well as homologous antigen. The degree of cross-reactivity between various precipitin systems has served Jennings (1959a,b,c,d) well in elucidating some mechanisms of immunodiffusion reactions and contributing cogent information on their fullest interpretation.

Wilson and Pringle (1956) produced halogenated bovine serum albumin and used antibodies to it and to the native antigen in double diffusion plate tests to study the small but distinct differences that such treatment induced in the albumin. Augustin (1959a) employed similar immunodiffusion techniques to demonstrate antibody heterogeneity in an antiserum probably containing bi-specific antibodies. This antiserum was formed in response to immunization with an antigen having two determinant groups of particular interest. When this antiserum was used to compare a second and a third antigen, neither having antigenic characteristics common to the other but each having one of the two determinants of the original antigen, they formed precipitin bands in a pattern of partial identity. Thus, this antiserum contained antibodies reacting not only with the entire homologous antigen, but also antibodies able to react with any antigen having one or the other of the two determinant groups in question.

According to evidence from immunodiffusion tests presented by Finger and co-workers (1960), an antiserum may contain antibodies with different sizes of combining sites. Fujio and colleagues (1958) report that horse antitoxin molecules have two or more serologically active but different groups. Several immunodiffusion studies on antibody heterogeneity have been discussed in a recent review (Lapresle, 1959). Among these are the experiments of the reviewer himself who, for example, has demonstrated that antiserum formed against whole human serum albumin contains different antibodies directed against three individual antigenic determinant sites on the albumin molecule. These can be detected by using such an antiserum against successive products of systematically degraded antigen. Korngold and Lipari (1956b) showed the heterogeneity of antibody to human serum γ-globulin by using whole normal human serum γ-globulin, γ-globulin from myeloma patients, and subunits of γ-globulin obtained in the form of Bence-Jones proteins as test antigens in comparative double diffusion tests.

Just as antibodies have been studied by progressive chemical degradation, they can be analyzed by analogous physical treatment. Application of high hydrostatic pressure to horse pseudoglobulin antibody causes its molecular weight to increase (Chahbase, 1957). Prolonged treatment at very high pressures decreases and finally abolishes the antibody's precipitating activity.

Antigen-Antibody Reactions

In addition to their remarkable resolution, immunodiffusion techniques have the unique ability to "fix" precipitin reactions *in situ* and in various stages of progress, and they prevent mixing of the two reactants by anything more than diffusion, two advantages over precipitin tests in aqueous media which should make them valuable in experimentation on the mechanisms of antigen-antibody precipitation, particularly its aggregation stage (Crowle, 1960c). Some aspects of information which can be gained regarding type of antibody and influence of antigen in specific precipitation by noting the characteristics (e.g., breadth, sharpness of leading and trailing edges) of precipitin zones in single diffusion tests have been discussed. Thus, H-type antibodies produce sharply-defined precipitin bands, while the trailing edge of a band produced by R-type antibody is ragged (cf. Fig. III-2). Polysaccharides generally form fuzzier bands than protein antigens, but the fuzziness of precipitin bands produced by any particular protein may differ considerably from that produced by another and can approach that seen with polysaccharide antigens.

At its simplest as a technique for studying antigen-antibody precipitation, immunodiffusion has been used to supplement classic precipitin tests in liquid medium. The supernatant fluids in a series of tubes in the classic test are tested in a corresponding series of wells in agar for content of antigen or antibody or both. In this manner, Burtin (1955) and Burtin and Grabar (1954) were able to show that the supernatant fluid above precipitates of equine antibody and human serum albumin formed at equivalence contains soluble antigen-antibody complexes.

pH and Electrolytes

The best physical conditions for antigen-antibody precipitation in agar gels ordinarily are the same as in ungelled medium. For example, the optimal pH for horse antibodies to precipitate most human serum antigens in agar lies between 7.2 and 8.0, and 0.7–0.9% sodium chloride constitutes the proper electrolyte concentration for this system (Peetoom *et al.*, 1960). However, optimal conditions for all antigen-antibody systems, whether in agar gels or simply in aqueous media, by no means are the same; there are little understood accessory factors which must be submitted to experimentation for the best results to be obtained for each particular system. Currently interesting to many workers because of their potential use as a supplement to rabbit antisera are chicken antisera. In liquid media, they appear to require 8–10% sodium chloride for optimal or sometimes merely visible precipitation (Goodman, 1952;

Goodman *et al.*, 1951, 1957, 1958a,b; Munoz and Becker, 1952). Consequently, they have been used in agar media usually made up to contain 8–12% sodium chloride (Goodman *et al.*, 1957, 1958a,b; Munoz and Becker, 1952) despite the fact that no evidence has been published indicating that high salt concentrations need to be or even should be used in agar diffusion precipitin tests. One possible reason for employing these high electrolyte concentrations, to prevent dissociation of antigen-antibody complexes (Goodman, 1952), may not exist in agar gels which by their semisolid nature tend to prevent complex dissociation (Crowle, 1960c). Some evidence is available indicating that chicken antisera precipitate antigens efficiently at physiologic salt concentrations in agar gels. Staphylococcal enterotoxin apparently is precipitated by rooster antiserum in the single diffusion test under such physiologic conditions as well as it is by rabbit or monkey antisera (Surgalla *et al.*, 1952). As has already been mentioned in the discussion above of chicken antiserum itself, work in the author's laboratory (Crowle and Lueker, unpublished) shows that chicken antisera function better in semisolid media at physiologic salt concentration than at the high concentrations needed in liquid media.

High electrolyte concentrations suppress specific toxin-antitoxin precipitation obtained with horse antiserum (Raynaud, 1958). Even normally optimal physiologic concentrations may be inhibitory for some systems, as was discovered by Buchanan-Davidson *et al.* (1959c) in some of their immunodiffusion work. In single diffusion tests which they were performing, serum protein-polyamino conjugates as their antigens formed little or no precipitate with their rabbit antisera in agar made up in a physiologic concentration of salt, while precipitation could be detected readily when one third that concentration of salt was used.

Specific Ions

Recent discovery that certain cations specifically enhance antigen-antibody aggregation in double diffusion tests (Crowle, 1958a, 1960a) appears to offer a way of using semisolid media to study the mechanisms of antigen-antibody complex aggregation, that is, the second stage of specific precipitation (Crowle, 1960c). That originally subvisible antigen-antibody aggregates in a double diffusion plate which has received adequate incubation can be detected in the agar gel by soaking the gel in very weak solutions of such cations as cadmium, nickel, and lanthanum, indicates that these antigen-antibody complexes form within the gel in sufficient size to be "trapped" at their site of formation but are not large enough to be visible (see Fig. IV-14). Apparently, the precipitin

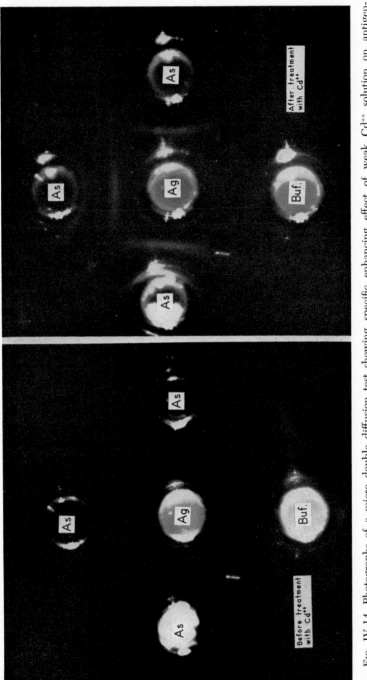

Fig. IV-14. Photographs of a micro double diffusion test showing specific enhancing effect of weak Cd⁺⁺ solution on antigen-antibody precipitation. The microscope slide at left was photographed before being soaked in 0.0125% cadmium acetate in physiologic barbital buffer but after incubation allowing antigen to diffuse from its depot and react (invisibly) with guinea pig antiserum. This same slide was photographed again (right) after a 10-minute soaking in the enhancing solution. No nonspecific precipitation of guinea pig serum is evident, but two precipitin bands now are evident between each antiserum depot and the antigen depot which before were absent. The bottom depot (Buf.) was charged originally only with buffer.

reaction involving these complexes, in contrast to those which eventually form visible precipitin bands without supplementary treatment with specifically acting cations, is arrested before visible aggregation can occur, and the process leading to visible aggregation is resumed only under the influence of these cations. The "fixing" effect of agar gel seems to favor demonstration of this enhancing effect, as might be postulated from what has just been suggested, since to demonstrate it in fluid medium has proved difficult. Only the three cations mentioned above, among many tested, enhance antigen-antibody aggregation, and they seem to act principally on the antiserum, possibly on some lipoidal constituent (Crowle, 1960a). Individual and species differences exist in antiserum sensitivity to this cation enhancing effect. However, it has been found to occur in double diffusion tests with antisera from the rabbit, guinea pig, rat, mouse, chicken, hamster, and horse, as well as man, these antisera being directed against any of various albuminoid antigens (ovalbumin, bovine serum albumin, human serum albumin, tuberculoprotein) (Crowle and Lueker, unpublished). Interestingly, and not unexpectedly, the process of antigen-antibody aggregation which has been brought to visible completion in agar with the aid of an active cation can be reversed, so that the specific aggregate (precipitin band) "dissolves" if the agar is soaked in a strong chelating agent with an affinity for the enhancing cations.

Certain anions also enhance specific precipitation in agar; barbital is outstanding in this respect. Preliminary experimentation suggests that the mechanism of this enhancement may differ from that of specific enhancement by cations (Crowle and Lueker, unpublished).

Reactant Proportions

The nature of the reactants and how they are used affect the characteristics and interpretations of immunodiffusion tests; something can be learned about the mechanisms of specific precipitation by studying these aspects of antigen-antibody combination. In the double diffusion plate, precipitates formed under conditions of initial optimal antigen-antibody ratios prove to be very resistant against the altering influences of sudden changes in reactant ratios purposely induced by replacement of reactant solutions originally used (Kaminski, 1954a). Precipitates formed by H-type antibody are more readily changed by such alteration of reactant ratios than R-type antibody. Antigens of low diffusion coefficient form precipitin zones less sensitive to change than those formed by rapidly diffusing low molecular weight antigens. To generalize this type of information obtained from double diffusion experiments, specific precipitates formed under optimal conditions favor the most complete antigen-antibody combination and the sturdiest aggregation and constitute the most stable precipitin bands; precipitin bands become progressively less susceptible to alteration with passage of time for their development, which presumably allows arrangement and rearrangement of antigen-antibody complexes into their most stable state; complexes formed by different kinds of antibodies, even from one species of animal, vary in the reversibility with which they combine with antigen, partly depending upon the nature of this antigen.

The effects of antigen upon the characteristics of antigen-antibody precipitation and the implications that they hold for explanations of how antigen and antibody precipitate are nicely demonstrated in single diffusion tube tests, as Glenn and Garner (1957) have illustrated using their specially devised photoelectric scanner for characterizing such precipitates. Their experiments show that human serum albumin forms a precipitate with rabbit antiserum which is moderately soluble in antigen excess, as indicated by the rapidly thinning trailing zone it leaves behind it as its front progresses down the tube, and that this antigen precipitates with its antiserum within only a short range of antigen:antibody ratios, suggested by the fact that its precipitin band front is quite sharp. Human serum γ-globulin, on the other hand, because its trailing edge maintains more of its original density and its zone's leading edge is considerably less sharp than that of the albumin, can be deduced to react more heterogeneously with its antibody than albumin; it precipitates over a greater range of antigen:antibody ratios. Experiments of the same nature performed in Glenn's laboratory also have shown that although precipitate zone density depends mostly upon the amount of antibody available to form it, it is influenced by the concentration of antigen employed. It also depends significantly upon the presence of nonantibody antiserum proteins; if these are removed and pure γ-globulin antibody is used instead of whole antiserum, resulting precipitin bands are less dense (Glenn, 1959a).

Cross-Reactions

Single diffusion studies using cross-reacting antigens have clearly demonstrated the heterogeneity of antibodies that an animal usually forms to a single antigen, and they have suggested that soluble antigen-antibody complexes can act as modified antibody molecules and that the serologic homogeneity of a purified antigen may be less than often has been taken for granted. The recent experiments of Buchanan-Davidson and Oudin (1958) are illustrative. These experimenters examined the mutual influences of hen egg albumin (HEA) and duck egg albumin (DEA) upon each others' specific precipitation with rabbit antiserum to

HEA. In most proportions, these two antigens were found to form two precipitin bands migrating down the antibody column of agar, but their migration rates rarely were the same as those of bands produced by one of the antigens used alone. The rate of penetration by the HEA band increased slightly in the presence of DEA, and penetration of the DEA zone increased greatly when HEA was present. These results indicate, for one thing, that the anti-HEA rabbit serum contained both moderately specific antibodies capable of reacting with either DEA or HEA and antibodies specific enough to react only with HEA. This idea was supported by the observation that when two zones were observed, that zone closer to the interface was formed by the homologous (HEA) antigen; that is, the heterologous antigen could precede the homologous antigen reacting with low specificity antibodies but leaving high specificity antibodies behind and free to react with the homologous antigen. When antigen concentrations were arranged so that the heterologous zone could not form ahead of the homologous zone, only the latter appeared, because precipitins, both specific and moderately specific, were removed by this homologous reaction leaving none uncombined to complex with the heterologous antigen. Although as a general rule, only one band forms under these conditions, Wilson (1958) reports that he obtained two bands in such experiments, even when the concentration of homologous antigen equaled or exceeded that of the cross-reacting one. He employed rabbit antiserum, and, respectively, as cross-reacting and homologous antigen, bovine serum albumin and this albumin iodinated. Tentatively, he explains his observation as indicating that the combining ratios for the two antigens with antibody may have differed, that is, that the ratio for the homologous antigen probably was sufficiently higher than for the cross-reacting antigen so that, within the limits of his experiment, sufficient concentration of homologous antigen was not attained, even when it was used in some excess of the cross-reacting antigen, for it to form a precipitin band below the diffusion front of the cross-reacting antigen.

Reasons why cross-reacting antigens influence each others' precipitin band migration rates are not known. Non-cross-reacting physically very similar antigens have no such effect. Somehow, the cross-reacting antigens must affect each others' effective antibody-combining concentrations. For example, the considerable accelerating effect of HEA upon DEA may indicate that the DEA front consists not only of DEA but also of (1) HEA molecules of a variety unable to combine with highly specific anti-HEA antibodies along with DEA combining with those of low specificity, or (2) HEA polymers or soluble complexes with specific antibody either of which can react only with the low specificity antibodies precipitating DEA. Regardless of the actual definition, single diffusion tests have shown that when HEA is used alone against its antiserum, there is in addition to the visible precipitin band front another front of antigen-antibody complexes not visible and located ahead of this front which can be coprecipitated to be made visible by soaking treatment with cross-reacting DEA (Jennings, 1959b,c,d).

Informative experiments on cross-reactivity and related problems such as the relative avidities of homologous and heterologous antigens for antibody are readily set up using double diffusion techniques (Wilson and Pringle, 1956). Experiments related to those in single diffusion tubes just discussed have been performed with the triangular double diffusion plate technique, so that ways in which HEA and DEA react with antiserum to HEA can be investigated under conditions in which precipitation of both antigens occurs only partly in the same area, and hence difficult to assess effects due to precipitation in the same space can be curtailed (Jennings, 1959a). Three types of precipitate were distinguished in these experiments: (1) strictly homologous formed by HEA and highly specific antibodies as a spur at the apex of the triangular zone of precipitate, (2) entirely heterologous precipitate formed between the cross-reacting antigen and moderately specific antibody, and (3) precipitate formed by the homologous antigen with antibodies of both high and low specificities and comprising the precipitate in the region between HEA and antibody (see Fig. IV-9). These experiments showed, furthermore, that heterologous precipitate is the more readily soluble in antigen excess, particularly homologous antigen. The ease of dissolution of these three types of precipitate varied, however, with antisera from different rabbits. These experiments tell something about the heterogeneity of antibodies in antiserum, about the extent of cross-reactivity they will give with closely or distantly related antigens, about the relative quantity of highly specific antibody present in the antiserum, and about the avidity of the various types of antibody for different antigens. Wilson and Pringle (1956) used double diffusion plates with native and iodinated bovine serum albumin to demonstrate that the minimum antigen concentration required for precipitate formation is inversely proportional to the immunologic affinity between antigen and antibody.

How double diffusion plate tests can detect the apparent bispecificity of antibody in an antiserum against, for example, antigen Cab which can react with a or b groups on normally unrelated antigens Aa and Bb already has been mentioned (Augustin, 1959a). Obviously, immunodiffusion tests could be very useful in following the changes in specificity of antibodies during immunization from apparently highly specific antibodies at the beginning to antibodies of more general reactivity later, and in discovering whether truly they are more generally reactive (less specific with regard to individual determinants) or whether they simply react to more determinants, thus having greater chance to find among heterologous antigens satisfactorily fitting antigenic sites to which to attach (Augustin, 1959a). An interesting approach to this type of problem has been to use albumin antigens with which polyamino acids have been conjugated, that is, altered antigens more closely approaching natural variations in antigen determinant groups than those whose structures have been changed by treatment with chemicals not normally forming portions of protein molecules. Stahmann and colleagues (1959b) used as antigens bovine serum albumin (BSA) and rabbit serum albumin (RSA) in their native forms and modified by addition of various polyamino acids, and immunoelectrophoresis as their analytic technique. They found that rabbit antiserum to modified BSA precipitated similarly modified RSA weakly and native and modified BSA, of course, strongly. When this antiserum was absorbed with unmodified BSA, it remained able to precipitate only the modified BSA and RSA antigens; that is, it retained only antibodies for the polyamino acid addition to the two serum albumins. Such experiments indicate, as have others before and after them, that antiserum against a single antigen may have antibodies of several specificities, in this case three types: (1) against the protein carrier, (2) specific for the introduced groups, and (3) reacting only with the molecules consisting of both the carrier and the conjugated group or with any section of entire molecules including this combination.

Fixation of Antigen-Antibody Complexes

Perhaps one of the most promising yet least explored aspects of studying antigen-antibody reactions by precipitin tests in semisolid media is the fact that these media can "fix" antigen-antibody complexes at their site of formation as soon as these reach a size exceeding the diameter of "spaces" in these media. Just as agar and gelatin can, at appropriate concentrations, prevent diffusion of individual antigen molecules (see above), so can gels at concentrations ordinarily used in immunodiffusion tests be expected to prevent diffusion of antigen-antibody complexes shortly after they have begun to form (Crowle, 1960c). Some of these complexes never grow to visible size without outside aid, as has been explained above in connection with discussion of cation specific enhancing effects. This is also illustrated by the experiments on antisera from patients with Hashimoto's disease published recently by Goudie et al. (1959). These workers found some of these antisera able to complex with thyroglobulin in double diffusion plates without forming a visible precipitate. The area of agar enclosing these complexes, probably because it contains more protein than agar around it, had a more transparent aspect, and a definite specific precipitate could be made visible in this area by treating the agar with the fumes of an appropriate protein denaturant (e.g., hydrochloric acid). Interestingly, these complexes also could be made to grow into visible aggregates of precipitate by treatment with co-precipitating antibodies from other antisera. Crowle and Lueker (unpublished) have observed horse antisera to form visible precipitin bands in agar with human serum albumin which lose their particulate appearance and come to exhibit the enhanced transparency noted above if the agar is soaked in distilled water. These clear areas take up protein stains just as do conventional precipitin bands. Easty and Ambrose (1957) observed antigen-antibody aggregation and subsequently dissolution, upon treatment with alkali or sodium dodecyl sulfate, microscopically in agar with the aid of interferometric techniques. Thus, it may be possible by appropriate measures in the future to arrest antigen-antibody complexing at various stages, or to reverse specific precipitation selectively. Knowledge obtained from such experiments almost certainly will enrich presently meager knowledge on the mechanisms of antigen-antibody aggregation and precipitation.

Criminology

It is difficult to estimate how many people engaged in law enforcement work are aware of the relatively new immunodiffusion techniques, for forensic information exchange media fall outside the ken of the medical immunologist who reviews the literature on immunodiffusion. At least three papers have been published on the use of these techniques for legal purposes, all from the same laboratory in France (M. Muller et al., 1958a,b; 1959). The first describes how either macro or micro double diffusion tests can be applied to identification of biologic fluids. It points out that these tests permit permanent preservation of original tests with their precipitin lines readily demonstrable, for example, by projection onto a courtroom screen. Antigen-antibody reactions are more easily seen than in conventional precipitin tests, quite readily differentiated from artifacts, and immunodiffusion tests do not require prior clarification of turbid reactants. In the experiments reported, the micro double diffusion technique proved more specific than precipitin tests in liquid medium. These double diffusion tests also were found more reliable than single diffusion tube tests. The only disadvantage mentioned is that results are not available within minutes but take about a day to develop. The second paper reports results of experiments showing that spots of such materials as sperm, urine, saliva, milk, cerebrospinal fluid, blood, and gastric liquid could be identified with regard to its animal or human source, and confirmed that turbid samples are not a detriment to the sensitivity of the test. The third paper emphasizes the importance of selecting proper antisera. Thus, hyperimmune horse antiserum to human serum could not be used because it cross-reacted readily with serum constituents of several other animal species. However, highly specific antiserum could be produced by carefully limited vaccination of rabbits.

Industry

Without any doubt many industries now are employing immuno-diffusion techniques. In instances where the methods are used for work on subjects of wide interest in medicine, biology, or biochemistry, reports and results have been published, but probably much experimentation connected with the private interests of an industry remains uncommunicated. Aside from the various purposes for which immunodiffusion techniques are useful that have been mentioned above, perhaps their application to various phases of quality control would be particularly useful in industry. An example illustrative of this was published recently in Europe as a report given in 1957 at the European Brewery Convention (Grabar, 1957b). This work, supported by the General Union of Brewery Syndicates in France, was aimed at determining the extent of change in the constituents of beer during the process of brewing. Immunoelectrophoresis and double diffusion plate analyses were performed on extracts of barley, malt, wort (both unfermented and mixed with hops), fresh beer concentrates, and a lyophilized beer dialysate. These experiments showed that the principal antigenic constituent of beer (a protein) underwent no appreciable modifications during the beer-making processes between the malt extraction phase and the bottling of the beer. However, it could be found at best only in traces in the barley extract. Beer also contains small quantities of other antigens, One of these disappears when beer concentrate is kept at refrigerator temperature. Essentially, these experiments are most valuable for showing the relationship between raw materials and beer constituents. Discussions following presentation of this paper suggest that immunodiffusion techniques would be useful in brewing for such purposes as distinguishing varieties of barley, establishing a beer "geneology," closely controlling beer quality in its manufacture, and coping with beer deterioration which occurs during its refrigeration by determining whether this is due to beer constituents or to the yeast. Immunodiffusion can be used for analyses of miscellaneous materials used in beer manufacture, particularly the yeast.

In the few years since its popularization, immunodiffusion has been applied to many problems and types of analysis. It has proved itself repeatedly to be worthy of a place among the most powerful analytic tools in biology and biochemistry. It combines into a single simple method the virtues of such outstanding and well accepted techniques as electrophoresis, chromatography, and serology, each in its own right a powerful tool. The only important limitation of immunodiffusion is that it can be used solely with substances which react specifically with antibodies and only when antibodies to substances being analyzed can be obtained. However, this limitation also is a virtue, for it is the antigen-antibody reaction which makes immunodiffusion so highly specific a tool for analyzing substances of exceeding complexity.

CHAPTER V

Immunodiffusion Techniques

Although a somewhat confusing variety of immunodiffusion techniques exists, all are basically similar. They differ only in refinements which fit them to particular purposes or which make them technically superior to their predecessors. Many of these techniques and accessory procedures will be described in this chapter as a guide for the user of immunodiffusion in choosing that method which should be best for solving his specific research problem. To accomplish this purpose of guidance, it will be necessary to consider subjects such as antiserum, gels and gel solvents, reactant arrangements, methods for reading and recording results, and auxiliary and staining techniques.

Reagents

Primary reagents for immunodiffusion are antigen, antiserum, gel solvents, and gels. Secondary reagents, such as stains which are applied after immunodiffusion reactions have taken place, are discussed in a different section.

Antigen

If antiserum is the subject of study, then its antigen must be the analytic reagent. Such a study can be one of two general types. In the first, an antiserum to some particular antigen has been obtained and is to be characterized. In the second, a hypothetical type of antibody is to be studied, and an antigen is chosen specifically for its production and analysis. As an example of the second type of analysis, antiserum is produced against the well-characterized antigen chicken egg albumin. Then it can be analyzed for total antibody content with homologous antigen, for antibody microheterogeneity by its reactions with closely related antigens such as duck ovalbumin or turkey ovalbumin, for avidity with homologous or heterologous antigen, for its combining characteristics with homologous and heterologous antigen under various circumstances, and for immunoelectrophoretic mobility. For these experiments, the antigen should be as pure as possible and readily soluble, and it should be maintained in the same state of purity and integrity throughout the series of experiments.

Ideally, the antigen also should be thoroughly characterized; one

181

may even use partially synthesized antigen whose chemical and physical composition is better understood than it is for natural antigens (cf. experiments of Maurer *et al.*, 1959). In illustration of the first type of analysis, antiserum rather than antibody is studied for such characteristics as broadness of reactivity with a variety of antigens, content of antibodies with particular specificities or characteristics, or merely for ability to precipitate all antigens in a crude mixture. For example, the broadness of antiserum cross-reactivity must be analyzed critically if the antiserum is to be used in medico-legal work. Here antigen used from one test to another should be preserved as nearly intact and as close to its native state as possible; one need know very little about its chemical or physical composition.

Antiserum

For most immunodiffusion studies, antiserum has been the chief analytic reagent. Although it is relatively easy to produce, its characteristics, unfortunately, are far more variable than those of an antigen (cf. Smith and Jager, 1952). A single antiserum giving only one precipitin band with a highly purified antigen contains individual antibodies with varying avidity for the antigen, varying specificity, and varying physical properties (Crowle, 1960c; Jennings, 1959a), and apparently no two animals of the same species vaccinated with the same antigen under identical conditions will give identical antibody responses (Crowle, 1960c; Jennings, 1959a; Williams and Grabar, 1955a). It is not surprising, then, to find that different animal species can produce antibodies of very different characteristics against a given antigen. Hence, an antiserum and ways for preparing it should be selected very carefully for many types of experiment.

From the characteristics of the precipitates which they produce, two types of precipitins can be identified: the R-type whose precipitates are virtually insoluble in antibody excess and poorly soluble in antigen excess, and the H-type whose precipitates are readily soluble in either antigen or antibody excess. Each has its virtues and disadvantages in immunodiffusion tests. H-type antibodies, for example, offer better antigen resolution, but they also are more likely to produce spurious secondary precipitates due to temperature and concentration changes, but not readily identifiable as such (Crowle, 1960c). Since they have a high molecular weight, they are better for analyzing heavy molecular weight antigens in double diffusion tests than the usually smaller R-type antibodies. Conversely, R-type antibodies may be superior for analyzing low molecular weight antigens which might "overrun" H-type antibody at its origin at the cost of resolving power. Being less susceptible to temperature and concentration artifacts, R-type antibody diminishes chances of misinterpretation due to these in both single and double diffusion tests (Crowle, 1960c; Hayward and Augustin, 1957; Kaminski, 1954a). The resolution offered by these antibodies often is inferior, especially in single diffusion tube tests, to that obtained with H-type antibodies, because undissolved trailing precipitate from one band can overlap proximate bands (Crowle, 1960c). In double diffusion analyses of complex mixtures of antigens in which some constituents may be excessive and others occur only in trace quantities, R-type antibody usually excels over H-type, because reactant concentration extremes, while they may cause confusing blurring and loss of resolution, do not as readily prevent or reverse specific precipitation. For example, in serum immunoelectrophoresis, use of whole serum which has been concentrated in attempts to detect the trace β_{2M}-globulin with H-type antiserum may result in the appearance of the serum albumin band early in development of the test followed later by its complete dissolution. If only one reading is made late in reaction development, this antigen would not be detected (Grabar et al., 1958; see also Fig. V-3). Under similar conditions in which R-type antibody is utilized, the albumin band will be very broad, but at least it is present.

Aside from a consideration of the type of precipitate which may form, selecting an animal species for antiserum production depends upon such factors as the quantity of antiserum desired, the responsiveness of a given species to a certain antigen, the relationship between the species and antigens it might be likely to encounter in disease, the relationship between the species' own antigens and the injected antigens, the specificity of antibody needed, and miscellaneous considerations such as ability to react well with antigen which can be dissolved only in a certain kind of solvent.

Purely for quantity antiserum production, several large animals beside the horse have been used. The sheep has been employed to produce *Clostridium* antitoxin (Schuchardt et al., 1958), the goat for antiserum against rat plasma lipoprotein (Marsh and Whereat, 1959) and to rabbit (Grabar and Courcon, 1958; Kaminski, 1957c), horse, human, pig, and sheep sera (Kaminski, 1957c), the mule for antiserum to human serum (Kaminski, 1957c; Robert et al., 1959; Uriel, 1957; Vaux Saint-Cyr, 1959; Vaux Saint-Cyr et al., 1958) and to clostridial toxins (Guillaumie et al., 1954), and the donkey for anti-human serum antibodies (Bussard, 1954). Antisera to clostridial antigens (Guillaumie et al., 1954) and foot-and-mouth disease virus (Brown and Graves, 1959) have been obtained from cows. In several of these instances, a particular animal was not used for antiserum quantity alone but also for some particular relationship to the antigen. For example, as a natural host to infection with foot-and-mouth disease the cow provides a good source of convalescent precipitating serum (Brown and Graves, 1959). Antiserum for immunoelectrophoretic analysis of human serum is produced in quantity from horses by the Pasteur Institute in France and from goats by Hyland Laboratories in this country.

Animals of intermediate size used for precipitin production include the monkey for antibody to *Staphylococcus* enterotoxin (Bergdoll *et al.*, 1959), polio virus (Grasset *et al.*, 1958; Polson, 1958), and human γ-globulin (Dray, 1960), and the dog for producing antibodies to human macroglobulin (Cleve and Schwick, 1957). The monkey was chosen to produce anti-enterotoxin as an animal species other than man susceptible to its toxicity, for the production of antibody to polio virus as a ready victim of the disease, and for antibody to human γ-globulin for its taxonomic closeness to man and ability therefore to produce more discriminatory antibodies against human serum proteins.

Small laboratory animals are popular because they are so easily handled and are more readily available and less expensive than the larger animals. Although certain of them such as rats, mice, and guinea pigs often are called poor precipitin producers, available evidence clearly indicates that properly vaccinated, these species of animals will produce potent precipitins useful for immunodiffusion investigations. The surest vaccination procedure, incidentally, seems to be to use Freund's adjuvant (see Appendix I). Guinea pigs have provided antibodies to tubercle bacilli and their constituents (Crowle, 1954, 1958a, 1960a,b; Smith, 1956), polio virus (Grasset *et al.*, 1958), foot-and-mouth disease virus (Brown and Crick, 1957, 1958, 1959), streptolysin (Halbert *et al.*, 1955b), chicken ovalbumin and bovine γ-globulin (Crowle, 1960b), rabbit tendon (Heller *et al.*, 1959), diphtheria bacillus culture filtrates (Branham *et al.*, 1959), and to serum constituents taken from other guinea pigs (Oudin, 1957). Rats produce strong precipitins to bovine serum albumin and to tuberculoprotein (Crowle and Lueker, unpublished), mouse serum antigens (Gengozian, 1959), and their own kidney antigens (Heymann *et al.*, 1960). Mice and hamsters likewise produce precipitins to such antigens as chicken ovalbumin, bovine serum albumin, and tuberculoprotein (Crowle and Lueker, unpublished), and mice have been employed to produce highly discriminatory anti-rat serum antibodies (Gengozian, 1959), as well as antiserum to human serum antigens (Riley, personal communication). Ferret precipitins have been utilized to type influenza virus (Jensen and Francis, 1953). Chickens produce precipitins to *Staphylococcus* enterotoxin (Surgalla *et al.*, 1952), human serum constituents (Goodman *et al.*, 1957, 1958a,b), rat serum (Weyzen and Vos, 1957), bovine serum albumin and tuberculoprotein and occasionally chicken ovalbumin (Crowle and Lueker, unpublished). Thus, there seems to be no practical limitation to the species of small laboratory mammals and fowl that can be chosen for producing precipitins for immunodiffusion tests.

Antisera from some of these species have special uses. For example, rat anti-mouse and mouse anti-rat antisera are more discriminatory than rabbit antiserum for mouse and rat serum antigens, respectively. Thus, mouse anti-rat sera having been produced in the mouse will not react with mouse serum antigens and hence are ideal for detecting the potential production in mice of rat serum proteins after they have been irradiated and subsequently treated with rat bone marrow to permit their survival of this irradiation (Gengozian, 1959). Guinea pigs can be infected with foot-and-mouth disease and ferrets with influenza virus; consequently both are convenient sources of convalescent antiserum. Chickens have a possible advantage in precipitin production over laboratory mammals in being taxonomically distant from the various mammals; their own serum protein antigens are far more dissimilar antigenically than those of one mammal to another, so that chickens may be able to produce antibodies to a greater variety of constituents in the serum of some mammal than another mammal would. Another advantage apparently peculiar to fowl antiserum is that usually it will specifically precipitate antigens at high salt concentrations sometimes required for solution of some of these antigens, e.g., edestin (Munoz and Becker, 1952), while these high concentrations tend to inhibit or reverse specific precipitation by mammalian antisera.

Antibodies from human beings are commonly used in immunodiffusion experiments. Often, they are obtained from persons with clinical or subclinical infection or from convalescents, and are used against infecting agent antigens. With one known exception (Roitt *et al.*, 1958), these antibodies have proved to be of the R- rather than H-type. Such human antibodies as those directed against human thyroglobulin (Doniach and Roitt, 1957, 1959; Goudie *et al.*, 1959; Pressman *et al.*, 1957; Roitt and Doniach, 1958a,b; Roitt *et al.*, 1958), against deoxyribonucleic acid (Deicher *et al.*, 1959; Seligmann, 1958a), against various human tissues (Liu and McCrory, 1958), against streptococci (Halbert, 1958; Hanson, 1959; Harris *et al.*, 1955), staphylococci (Beiser *et al.*, 1958), *Mycobacterium* constituents (Burell and Rheins, 1957; Inoue, 1957; Parlett *et al.*, 1958; Parlett and Youmans, 1959), against *Histoplasma* (Heiner, 1958, 1959), *Toxoplasma* (O'Connor, 1957a,b); *Trychophyton* and *Aspergillus* (Pepys *et al.*, 1959a), and against various danders (Frandsen and Samsøe-Jensen, 1955) have been used in immunodiffusion experiments.

Unaccountably, some animal species respond to produce antibody to certain antigens only poorly, if at all (Buchanan-Davidson, 1959b; Goodman *et al.*, 1958a; Kaminski, 1957c; Scheiffarth *et al.*, 1958a; Williams and Grabar, 1955a). Moreover, as has been mentioned before, individual members among a species often fail to form precipitins to a given antigen. Hence, it is sometimes necessary for one to try more than a single species to obtain adequate antisera, and to select among these antisera by actual test after immunization in order to obtain immunodiffusion antisera capable of comprehensive analyses of complex antigen mixtures. Frequently, antisera from several individual animals are pooled as, for example, to prepare commercially antisera for immunoelectrophoretic analyses of human serum. Characteristics of antibodies from certain animal species sometimes make them preferable to other superficially superior ones obtained from another species. For example, rabbit antiserum readily shows a reaction of partial identity between human β_{2A}- and γ-globulins in immunoelectrophoresis while horse antiserum does so poorly, or not at all (Heremans *et al.*, 1959b). Guinea pig antisera are more sensitive to the enhancing effects of certain cations than rabbit antisera (Crowle, 1958a). Horse antisera appear to be somewhat more satisfactory for studying the phenomenon of secondary (periodic) precipitation in single diffusion tubes than rabbit antisera (Crowle, 1960c), and chicken antisera are especially useful for experiments with gaps and striae (Crowle and Lueker, unpublished).

Perhaps more important than selecting the animal species for antibody production is selecting the antigen to inject and the procedure for immunization. Generally, the most effective vaccination procedure consists of injecting the antigen subcutaneously in complete Freund's adjuvant (water-in-oil emulsion containing mycobacteria), in the sense that with this procedure a greater variety of antigens will provoke antibody formation in more species of animals than any other procedure presently known, and higher titers of precipitins usually are obtained than by methods not employing the adjuvant. Moreover, few injections usually are required, multiple or frequent injections not being particularly advantageous. In the writer's laboratory, excellent responses have been obtained in chickens, rats, mice, guinea pigs, hamsters, and rabbits, against various antigens after one or two such injections, the spacing between the first and second injection being from 1 to 3 weeks, and bleedings being made 2 to 4 weeks after the last injection. Intraperitoneal injection has proved nearly as effective as subcutaneous injection. Occasional booster injections of antigen in complete Freund's adjuvant can be given without prior desensitization or fear that the injected animals will die from an allergic reaction. Incomplete Freund's adjuvant (water-in-oil emulsion without mycobacteria) also can be used, although generally it tends to be less stimulatory than the complete variety. Formulas for these adjuvants are given in Appendix I. A course of multiple, simultaneous injections has been proposed to increase the efficacy of immunization (Hayward and Augustin, 1957), but this method has been tried in the author's laboratory in several species of animals and has not proven superior to a protocol of two or three single injections of antigen in water-in-oil emulsion spaced 2 to 4 weeks apart.

The older methods of immunizing animals with several closely spaced injections of dissolved antigens or of injecting them with antigens adsorbed to particulate material such as alum should not be displaced offhandedly. Rabbits vaccinated with human white blood cell lysates have been found to produce distinctly different antibodies depending upon whether this antigen is administered intravenously without adjuvant or injected subcutaneously in Freund's adjuvant (Grabar *et al.*, 1955a). Immunization with antigen in Freund's adjuvant is a form of hyperimmunization, and when hyperimmunization is a disadvantage, as in medico-legal or other work where species specificity is so important, conventional methods of immunization may be preferable. This point leads to the logical conclusion that for a particular experiment better results may be obtained with antiserum from one bleeding than from another taken from one animal at different stages in immunization, and that for some critical studies antisera should be analyzed for the type, quantity, quality, and specificity of antibodies which they contain before they are pooled. The very evident differences in types of precipitins produced by horses during an immunization period (γ-globulin R-type early, β_{2M}-globulin H-type later) already have been cited. Another striking example has been found among sera of different bleedings from cattle convalescing from foot-and-mouth disease (Brown and Graves, 1959). Serum obtained 7 days after the infection reacts with homologous and heterologous sub-types of this virus equally well. However, serum taken from the same cattle 14 and 21 days after infection precipitates only the homologous sub-type. Moreover, immunoelectrophoretically, the 7-day antibodies are β-globulins, while the 14- and 21-day antibodies are γ-globulins. Such evidence as this, showing that antibodies may be β- as well as γ-globulins along with their respective marked physical differences, suggests caution in assuming that γ-globulin obtained by physical or chemical fractionation of antiserum represents this serum's total or even major antibody (Crowle, 1960c). Neither should one assume that precipitins are uniformly stable so that, for example, any antiserum can be heated at 56°C. for half an hour to inactivate complement without impairing its precipitin titer. In some instances such treatment may transform precipitating into coprecipitating antibody, that is, one which by itself is unable to precipitate antigen (Pruzansky et al., 1960). Most precipitins remain intact for many months or sometimes years kept in the refrigerator at about 4°C. either sterile or together with a germicidal additive and may remain less unchanged during this kind of storage than when they are frozen or lyophilized (Crowle, 1960c), but the precipitins of sera from some species of animals, such as mice, apparently deteriorate relatively rapidly when stored unfrozen in the refrigerator (Crowle, unpublished).

A last word concerning precipitins which often is overlooked: the most specific and discriminatory antibodies for antigens from a given animal will be produced, if they can be, by that species itself (Dray and Young, 1958, 1959; Oudin, 1957; Witebsky and Rose, 1959). Barring the feasibility of producing such auto- or iso-antibodies, the next greatest specificity will be obtained by using as antibody producer that species of animal taxonomically most closely related to the one being studied (Crowle, 1960c).

Gel Solvents

Simple physiologic sodium chloride solution usually suffices for good results in immunodiffusion tests, but maximum reproducibility and versatility in any kind of experiment is likely to be obtained when control is exerted over the largest number of factors, any of which can subtly or obviously affect reactant solubility and diffusion, and the antigen-antibody reaction itself. Hence, it is important to turn some attention to gel solvents, their pH, ionic strength, and electrolyte and nonelectrolyte solutes.

Single and double diffusion tests have been carried out in distilled water (Crowle, 1960c; Matthews, 1958; Wilson and Pringle, 1954), isotonic sodium chloride solution (Crowle, 1960c; Hanson, 1959), or with this salt at varying concentrations (Hanson, 1959) up to 13% (Goodman et al., 1957, 1958a; Wilson and Pringle, 1954), in solutions buffered with sodium barbital (Crowle, 1958a, 1960a,c; Halbert et al., 1955b; Halbert, 1958; Lacko et al., 1959), sodium citrate (Crowle, 1960c), citrate-phosphate (Dike, 1960), phosphate alone (Frick and Scheid-Seidel, 1957; Goudie et al., 1959; Grasset et al., 1958; Halbert, 1958; Korngold and van Leeuwen, 1957a; Le Bouvier, 1957; Leone et al., 1955; Parlett and Reher, 1959), sodium azide (Feinberg, 1957), aminoacetic acid (O'Connor, 1957a), tris(hydroxymethyl)aminomethane and acetic acid (Heit-fuss *et al.*, 1959), sodium borate (Finger and Kabat, 1958; Kuhns, 1955; Morton and Deutsch, 1958), sodium carbonate (Dike, 1960), and sodium bicarbonate (Naylor and Adair, 1959). From the references given here can be obtained numerous formulas for immunodiffusion gel solvents; five are described in Appendix II. Since in antigen-antibody precipitation reactions electrolytes seem to play an essential role related to their properties of being charged, these solutions are formulated to conduct the same amount of direct current at a given voltage as physiologic sodium chloride. That is, their actual (although not necessarily calculated, according to presently available formulas, see Chapter II) ionicity is the same as that of physiologic sodium chloride.

Each of the four solutions listed in Appendix II in addition to physiologic sodium chloride, has some particular use or advantage over one or more of the others, so that not all are usable interchangeably. The buffering capacity of barbital is not particularly strong at physiologic pH (7.4), but this buffer is compatible with solubility of more different cations than other commonly employed buffers (Crowle, 1960a). However, barbital buffer may precipitate some antigens (Korngold and van Leeuwen, 1957a) and although it does not seem to affect antisera from certain species of animals (most laboratory animals, for example), it does tend to precipitate some nonantibody human serum constituent (probably immunoelectrophoretic α_2 lipoprotein) which may result in formation of a nonspecific, ill-defined ring of precipitate around a human antiserum depot in agar and other media. The phosphate system is a far stronger buffer than barbital at pH 7.4, and does not elicit as much nonspecific serum precipitation, but agars containing free calcium will give turbid gels with it due to precipitation of calcium phosphate. Neither phosphate nor barbital acts as both buffering and chelating agents as may, for some experiments, be required. Tris provides a convenient alternate for barbital, and it has moderate chelating activity permitting it to remove from activity traces of heavy metal ions often found in agar. Ethylenediamine-acetic acid buffer is a strong chelator and hence can serve as an excellent buffer for metal ions (pM) as well as pH. It also has a uniquely wide range of buffering effectiveness, a range from pH 9 to pH 3, more than bracketing the limits normally usable in immunodiffusion experiments. It is completely volatile, and since both acid and alkali constituting it evaporate at equal rates, it will maintain its original pH through any degree of evaporation (Fasella *et al.*, 1957).

Buffer solutions required for immunoelectrophoresis differ from those of single and double diffusion tests because their pH usually must be more carefully controlled, their ionicity must be lower, and for poorly understood reasons certain electrolytes offer better fractionation than others for given substances, even though they are used under identical conditions. An immunoelectrophoresis buffer usually is composed as a compromise between the quantity of electrolyte permissible during electrophoresis and that compatible with adequate antigen-antibody precipitation, as well as between the pH needed for optimal electrophoretic separation and one at which specific precipitation is not adversely affected. The buffer also must be adjusted between high ionic strength to prevent pH changes during electrophoresis and low ionicity to permit reasonably rapid fraction migration. Generally, immunoelectrophoresis buffers will have pH values between 8.2 and 7.0 and ionicities ranging from 0.025 to 0.1. Most immunoelectrophoretic analyses so far have been applied to sera, and for these a pH of 8.2 and ionicity of 0.05 seem to be about the best. Barbital buffer is eminently suited for use under these conditions.

There are methods for circumventing compromise conditions when this is necessary. For example, if buffer ionicity must be low for electrophoresis, but for subsequent antigen-antibody precipitation it must be high, agar in which electrophoresis has been completed at low ionicity can be soaked in buffer of high electrolyte concentration for a few minutes (Grabar, 1959a). Alternatively, one can use the indicator reactant in a solution of high ionicity, or one can electrophorese a substance in a column of agar and later embed this column in agar of satisfactory composition in which are cast simultaneously troughs running parallel to the column of agar being embedded and to be charged with indicator reactant (Crowle, 1956). These devices also solve problems of unsatisfactory pH or kinds of electrolytes for either electrophoresis or specific precipitation. In short, at a small inconvenience one can, when necessary, dissociate the electrophoresis and antigen-antibody precipitation stages of immunoelectrophoresis.

With so much importance placed on the type of buffer employed in immunoelectrophoresis, it is convenient to have on hand formulas for several different kinds and some knowledge of advantages that one may have over another. The sodium barbital-hydrochloric acid buffer originally described for immunoelectrophoresis by Grabar and Williams (1955) has proved useful and versatile in analyses of various antigens, particularly serum proteins. It also is used in combination with acetate (Bird and Jackson, 1959; Crowle, 1960b; Wunderly, 1957) and with calcium lactate (Hanson, 1959; Hanson and Johannson, 1959a). Borate buffer is used alone (Gitlin et al., 1956; Havez and Biserte, 1959a; Schmid and Macnair, 1956) and in combination with phosphate (Pereira *et al.*, 1959). Tris(hydroxymethyl)aminomethane (TRIS) and ethylene-diaminetetraacetic acid have been employed with borate (Wieme, 1959a). Other buffers such as phosphate and carbonate can be utilized alone (Smith, 1956). Formulas for five immunoelectrophoresis buffers are given in Appendix III.

Selection of appropriate buffer electrolytes for immunoelectrophoresis largely is empirical. Complex buffers may give no better results than the simple ones. For example, using simple barbital buffer, Wieme (1959a) obtained separation of serum antigens in agar which was just as good as he could get with a buffer made up with boric acid, ethylenediamine tetraacetic acid, and TRIS. Nevertheless, different electrolytes do not yield equivalent results under equivalent conditions. Thus, phosphate buffer at pH 7.5 permits only poor separation of human serum; borate buffer at pH 9.0 may yield better separation of serum β-globulins than barbital (Gitlin *et al.*, 1956; Wieme, 1959a). However, separation of serum α globulins seems to be less satisfactory in borate buffer than in barbital (Gitlin *et al.*, 1956). Improved separation of α_2-globulins is obtained by using barbital lactate buffer (Hirschfeld, 1959a). Borate buffers may give results different from other types of buffers if a constituent being separated contains significant quantities of carbohydrate, for borate forms complexes with these tending to change their net mobility during electrophoresis. Hirschfeld reports (1960b) that superior immunoelectrophoretic resolution of human serum antigens can be obtained by using a discontinuous buffer system in contrast to the usually used continuous system. Unfortunately, he does not detail in this or in previous publications how this is used. There are at least two forms of discontinuous buffer systems. For the first, ionicity and pH are the same in the agar strip and its electrode vessels, but different electrolytes are used for each of these. For the second, the pH or ionicity or both in the two electrode vessels differ, and the variable factor in the agar gel can be intermediate between the two extremes of these vessels. The effects of discontinuous buffer electrophoresis are to cause fraction separation in a changing rather than stable environment which, for reasons unknown, may result in improved separation of electrophoretic constituents (Wieme, 1959a).

Barbital buffer, as has been remarked in connection with immuno-diffusion tests, tends to cause precipitation of β-lipoprotein (α_2-lipo-protein, immunoelectrophoretically) in media not containing protective amino acids. This fraction is seen as an opaque area in both agar and Cyanogum 41 immunoelectrophoresis (see Figs. V-1 and V-2) but not in gelatin immunoelectrophoresis (Fig. V-3). Apparently, it remains soluble in the protective gelatin.

Borate and barbital buffers are best used in pH ranges between 8 and 9 where their buffering capacity is strong. For substances which should be electrophoresed in the pH 7–8 range, phosphate buffers excel.

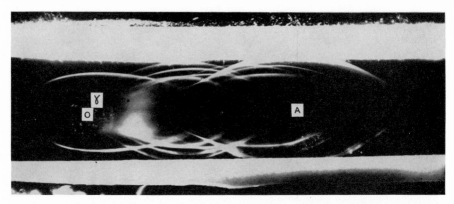

FIG. V-1. Micro immunoelectrophoresis of human serum in 5% Cyanogum 41 gel under conditions similar to those employed with gelatin (Fig. V-3). Immunoprecipitation required 72 hours. Compare positions of albumin (A) and γ-globulin with those in Figs. V-2 and V-3, and note both the lack of electroosmosis and the unusual clarity of the gel.

Ethylenediamine-acetic acid buffer is suitable for both ranges and has the added advantage of volatility mentioned previously.

Immunodiffusion buffers and immunodiffusion tests themselves readily become contaminated with microorganisms. Refrigeration re-

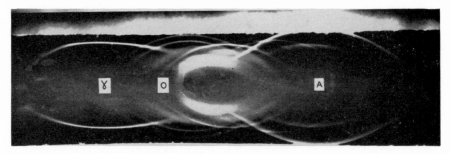

FIG. V-2. Micro immunoelectrophoresis of human serum in 1% agar gel (same "deionized" agar employed for electrophoresis shown in Fig. V-4) under conditions similar to those used with gelatin and Cyanogum 41 (Figs. V-1, V-3). Note electroosmosis and consequent positions of albumin (A) and γ-globulin relative to origin.

tards this contamination, but it can be prevented more readily by the addition to buffers of preservatives which actively oppose microbial contamination. Thimerosal (Merthiolate®) seems to be the most often used preservative. Generally, it is employed at 0.01–0.02%. Only once has it been reported to interfere with immunodiffusion reactions (Le Bouvier, 1957). In this instance it apparently tended to precipitate polio virus antigen causing agar turbidity which was sufficient to interfere with readings. Penicillin and streptomycin used in place of thimerosal in these experiments caused the same difficulty. Borate salts act as their own preservatives (Schmid and Macnair, 1956). Sodium azide can be used at 1% not only as a preservative but also as the principle electrolyte in double diffusion tests (Feinberg, 1957). Solely as a preservative, it is used at approximately 0.02% (Augustin *et al.*, 1958). Phenol has been used (Lebedev and Tsilinskii, 1958), at 0.5% (Toda,

Fig. V-3. Micro immunoelectrophoresis of human serum in 2% gelatin gel, made up in barbital buffer at pH 8.2, ionicity 0.05. Serum was allowed to soak into 1 mm. thick layer of gelatin on microscope slide for 20 minutes from a piece of filter paper at origin (O). Then the filter paper was removed, and 50 volts of direct current were applied for 1 hour and 45 minutes. Finally, strips of filter paper soaked with Pasteur Institute horse anti-human serum were placed parallel and to either side of the expected path of electrophoretic separation, and immunoprecipitation was allowed to develop for 48 hours. Albumin (A) and γ-globulin areas are indicated for comparison with immunoelectrophoretic patterns in other gels (see Figs. V-1 and V-2). Note lack of electroosmosis. All procedures were carried out at 4°C.

1957) or 0.1% (Vyazov *et al.*, 1959); at the latter concentration it slightly lowers the pH of the agar in which it is used, but apparently it does not interfere with immunodiffusion reactions. Penicillin at 1,000 units and streptomycin at 500 units per milliliter are effective (Lebedev and Tsilinskii, 1958). If a reactant to be employed is suspected of being heavily contaminated, it can be sterilized without apparent harm before it is used by adding liquid ethylene oxide to it to a final concentration of 1% (Hanson, 1959a).

Other substances are added to agar solvents used in immunodiffusion tests for any of various reasons. Sodium ethylenediaminotetracetate (NaEDTA) has been used at 30 mg. to the liter to chelate calcium and thus to prevent precipitation of its salts in agar containing it (Feinberg,

1957). This chelating salt also has been employed at 0.5 mg. per liter of veronal buffer to scavenge trace metal ions in experiments where their normal presence in agar could affect results (Crowle, 1960a). Cadmium, nickel, and lanthanum salts can be incorporated in agar gels at concentrations ranging from 0.05% to 0.00005% to increase the sensitivity of immunodiffusion tests (Crowle, 1958a, 1960a). Unstable antigens can be employed without gross denaturation in agar diffusion tests in which as much as 25% glucose, glycerine, or other polyhydroxy compounds are added to the agar (Heitfuss *et al.*, 1959). Glucose and glycerine also have been used to increase viscosity and osmotic pressure in agar during double diffusion experiments (Crowle, unpublished). The confusing nonspecific precipitate formed by some antisera, after diffusing a short distance into agar gel made up in barbital buffer can be prevented, without adversely affecting specific precipitation itself, by incorporating glycine at 7.5% in the agar (Halbert *et al.*, 1955b). The turbidity also is diminished or prevented by lowering the concentration of sodium barbital used to buffer the agar solvent (Crowle and Lueker, unpublished) or by replacing it with sodium phosphates as buffer salts (W. T. Kniker, personal communication). However, additives should not be employed indiscriminately in tests in which precipitin band density is an important measurement. Thus, Glenn (1959a) has shown that such additives as serum proteins, dextran, or even sodium chloride can have significant effects on band density. Serum proteins, salts, or nonpolar solutes are added to the antigen layer in single diffusion tests to make the specific gravity of this layer equal to or above that of the antiserum layer (Buchanan-Davidson and Oudin, 1958; Rubinstein, 1954). Generally, additive concentrations for this purpose should be at least 2%. Indicators for pH have been included in agar without detriment to immunodiffusion reactions (Goudie *et al.*, 1959).

Gelling Agents

Although agar is undoubtedly the most popular gelling agent for immunodiffusion tests, remarkably little is known about its chemical and physical properties, considering its wide use. Disappointingly small effort has been expended toward production and marketing of a standard, highly purified agar analogous to a "reagent" grade chemical. Consequently, individual laboratories often have had to devise their own agar purification procedures for immunodiffusion tests.

Agar is a polysaccharide obtained from any of several red algae (Wieme, 1959a), usually as calcium or magnesium salts of a mixture of polysaccharide sulfuric esters (McIlwain, 1938). Crude agar contains silicates, ferric oxide, aluminum oxide, calcium oxide, magnesium oxide, calcium iodide, borate, and arsenate (McIlwain, 1938). Laboratory grade agars employed in this country for bacteriologic culture medium can be reduced by incineration to an ash content averaging 3%, in which can be identified copper, cadmium, iron, manganese, zinc, nickel, barium, calcium, strontium, and magnesium (Crowle, 1960a). However, contaminants of this kind can be eliminated, and the calcium or magnesium salt apparently transformed into a monovalent ion agar salt (Crowle, 1960a; McIlwain, 1938), and the ash content can be reduced to as low as 0.01% so that none of these contaminants is detectable by ordinary qualitative chemistry (Crowle, 1960a). The simplest procedure for agar purification, which suffices for most immunodiffusion tests, providing one starts with a laboratory grade agar (e.g., Difco, BBL), is to melt the agar in its buffer at the final concentration desired (for immuno-electrophoresis and double diffusion tests 1%; 0.6% for single diffusion tests in which the melted agar later must be diluted with an equal volume of reactant), insuring that this solution is complete but avoiding prolonged heating, and then to filter it through several layers of lintless cloth (gauze), coarse filter paper, or any of various inert powdered filtering agents such as shredded paper, diatomaceous earth, or asbestos. This process removes lint and other gross insoluble particles and may clarify the agar slightly (Augustin et al., 1958; Dike, 1960; Feinberg, 1956; Grabar, 1959a; Grabar and Williams, 1955; Grant, 1959; Ouchterlony, 1948a; Oudin, 1952; Rubinstein, 1954; Wunderly, 1957). A certain amount of soluble contaminating material can be removed by dialyzing undissolved agar granules (Grabar, 1959a; Grabar and Williams, 1955; Harris et al., 1955); more is eliminated by dialysis (Crowle, 1960c; Grabar and Williams, 1955; Itano, 1933; Ouchterlony, 1948a; Seibert and Soto-Figueroa, 1957; Williams and Grabar, 1955a) and much more by electrodialysis (Wieme, 1959a) of the agar in diced gel form. Hot agar solution can be centrifuged clear (Munoz and Becker, 1950; Oudin, 1952) without prior treatment, yielding essentially the same product obtained by simple filtration. Alternatively, prior to centrifugation, agar solution can be treated with alcohol or acetone to precipitate the agar itself (Fairbrother and Mastin, 1923; Grabar, 1959a; Itano, 1933), with a soluble calcium salt to precipitate calcium sulfate (Björklund, 1952a; Leone et al., 1955), or with charcoal or egg albumin for clarification (Grabar, 1959a; Grasset et al., 1958). If, first, a gel is made by dissolving the agar and then chilling it, and this gel, next, is frozen and finally is thawed, the gel is broken physically, and shreds of agar can be centrifuged out leaving behind dissolved impurities (Grabar, 1959a; Popovich, 1935). By chemical treatment the agar can be changed to its potassium salt and freed of most inorganic constituents (Fairbrother and

Mastin, 1923; McIlwain, 1938). The agar gel can be dialyzed as a thin layer on a glass plate and then dried (Wieme, 1959a).

If for some reason an entirely soluble grade of agar is not available with which to begin, then its hot solution must be filtered or otherwise cleared of insoluble particles prior to subsequent purification. The next stage of purification is attained by dialyzing the agar gel prepared from the hot filtrate. Although further purification can be achieved using one of the methods for re-melting and precipitating the agar, re-melting and gelling cycles and retaining the agar in hot solution for very long should be minimized or avoided, since these treatments tend to alter the physical and chemical nature of agar and hence require careful control (Crowle, 1960c). Highly purified agar can be obtained from laboratory grade agar using the following procedure (Crowle, 1960a).

Agar granules are mixed well with 20 times their own weight of 1% racemic tartaric acid in distilled water, neutralized to pH 7.0 with ammonium hydroxide, and allowed to stand with occasional agitation for at least 45 minutes. They are filtered free from this solvent on a coarse filter and then partially dried by washes of anhydrous methanol. Next, they are stirred into 20 times their own weight of 1% salicylic acid in 95% ethanol and permitted to stand in this bath with occasional shaking for at least 45 minutes and then again recovered on a coarse filter. Finally, they are rinsed 4 times with 1% ammonium hydroxide in deionized water and then repeatedly with deionized water alone until the washings are of neutral pH. This final rinsing procedure is facilitated if the agar is mixed with the water, then filtered through several layers of gauze, and, lastly, gathered into the center of the gauze which is closed and strongly twisted and compressed to express the fluid. The still moist washed agar is dried in a 37°C. dry air oven, a process which can be accelerated if it first is rinsed twice in acetone. From an agar originally containing 3–4% ash on incineration, this method yields one with an ash content as low as 0.01%, free of calcium or other divalent ions, and apparently in a form in which calcium has been replaced by ammonium ions. It appears to form a somewhat firmer gel than that formed by presently available laboratory grade agars when equal concentrations are compared.

Since the properties of an agar gel can markedly affect results from immunodiffusion and immunoelectrophoresis tests (Crowle, 1960c; see Fig. V-4), to prepare a large batch for use in subsequent series of experiments is desirable.

The next most popular gelling agent for immunodiffusion tests has been gelatin, but before this substance is considered, another nearly the same as agar and with some usefulness should be mentioned. This is a polysaccharide of carrageenan obtained from algae different from those yielding the usual agar. It has a lower melting point than agar, but a higher gelling point, and its gellation is promoted by potassium ions, although these are not absolutely required. As it is supplied commercially, it is known as "K-agar" (Baltimore Biological Laboratory, Inc.). It forms a good gel equivalent in stiffness to that of 1.5% agar when it is used at 1.5% in a solution containing 0.5% potassium chloride; twice as much is required to give a gel of nearly equal stiffness if sodium chloride is substituted for potassium chloride (Baltimore Biological Laboratory, Inc., 1960; Crowle, unpublished). In potassium chloride solution it melts at 66°C. and gels at 55°C.; in an equivalent sodium

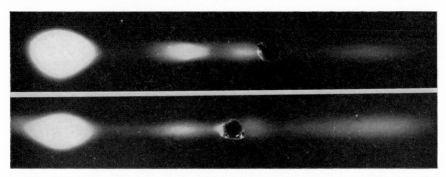

Fig. V-4. Electrophoresis of human serum under similar circumstances in two different batches of agar, especially deionized agar (above) and laboratory grade agar from which the deionized agar was prepared (below). In particular, these two photographs of thiazine red R-stained serum proteins demonstrate differences in fraction position relative to an origin which are common among different batches of agar and which are due to varying degrees of electroosmosis. Electroosmosis is responsible for the shift, observed in both photographs, of all serum components toward the cathode (right), even though several have sufficient repulsion for the cathode to remain on the anodic side (left) of the origin (hole).

chloride solution it melts at 59°C. and gels at 40°C. Complete melting and congealing temperatures vary somewhat with the actual concentration of this polysaccharide. As it is supplied at present, it forms a turbid solution and gel. However, it is clarified readily by filtration while liquid through coarse filter paper (Crowle and Lueker, unpublished). Since a considerable amount of the original powder is insoluble, the gel should be prepared at perhaps 0.5% higher concentration than the concentration finally desired. It is useful for immunodiffusion tests, but for several reasons it seems impractical for immunoelectrophoresis (Crowle and Lueker, unpublished).

As has been indicated in Chapter I, gelatin was the first gelling agent employed in immunodiffusion (Bechhold, 1905). It also has the distinction of having been used in the first double diffusion tube tests described in publication (Pope *et al.*, 1951). Its biggest disadvantage by comparison with agar is that its gels must be kept cool or they will melt. When it is made up in physiologic barbital buffer, about twice as much is required as agar to give a gel of equal firmness; that is, 2% gelatin is required to produce a gel equivalent at refrigerator temperature to 1% agar gel at room temperature (Crowle, unpublished). It is not merely a sometime substitute for agar, but rather it is an alternate and different type of gel, not being a polysaccharide but consisting purely of amino acids. When immunodiffusion reactions must be carried out in the refrigerator, such as when one or more of the reactants is heat-labile, gelatin has the advantage over agar of producing a gel which remains completely clear at refrigerator temperature (Oakley and Fulthorpe, 1953). It also tends more than agar to stabilize particularly labile antigens against denaturation. Heitfuss and co-workers (1959) employed it for this reason to study delicate cabbage proteins. Sometimes, as in determining molecular weights, it is necessary to impede diffusion of molecules of various selected sizes in immunodiffusion tests. This can be done over a wider range of molecule sizes with gelatin rather than with agar (Allison and Humphrey, 1959). Some antigens, such as thyroxine, cannot be studied very well in single diffusion tests employing agar because they seem to complex with this gel. Perhaps gelatin might be useful as a substitute which is inert to these antigens. Despite its evident utility, gelatin has not seen much use in immunodiffusion tests and appears never to have been reported used for immunoelectrophoresis. Gelatin might be particularly useful in experiments utilizing sensitive polysaccharide stains which might stain agar so heavily that precipitin bands taking them up would not be evident in the agar but would in gelatin. Figure V-3 clearly demonstrates its utility for both immunodiffusion and immunoelectrophoresis.

Pectin has been used as a gelling agent in immunoelectrophoresis of human serum (Grabar *et al.*, 1956b). However, it has proved to be difficult to work with both in this laboratory and in Grabar's (1959a) where it was originally used. It is possible to obtain precipitin reactions in rather poor but usable (mostly for simple diffusion tubes) pectin gels prepared as follows (adapted from Paton, 1959). Two grams of citrus pectin (Eastman Organic Chemicals) are mixed into enough absolute alcohol to form a thin paste, and then this is dissolved in 45 ml. of distilled water by heating it at autoclave temperature for just a few minutes (excess heating causes considerable hydrolysis). Then, to the solution while it still is quite hot are added 5 ml. of 0.05 M CaCl$_2$

with rapid and complete mixing. Upon refrigeration this solution forms a soft, clear gel with a strength about equivalent to that of 0.5% agar.

A new gelling agent promising to be very useful in immunodiffusion tests yields water-clear, colorless gels chemically entirely different from those described above. This is Cyanogum 41®, a product of American Cyanamid Co., which is a mixture of two organic monomers (acrylamide and N, N¹-methylenebisacrylamide) in proportions able to produce stiff gels under the influence of the proper catalysts (American Cyanamid Co., 1959; Raymond and Wang, 1959; Raymond and Weintraub, 1959). Methods for using Cyanogum in immunodiffusion tests have been worked out in the writer's laboratory (Crowle, unpublished). Cyanogum is dissolved in physiologic sodium phosphate buffer at pH 7.4 (Appendix II) to make a 5% solution and filtered through Whatman #1 filter paper. Then DMAPN* (β-dimethylaminopropionitrile) catalyst is added at a proportion of 1.2 ml. of a 10% solution for 300 ml. of the Cyanogum solution and is followed by a second, ammonium persulfate (AP), at the same concentration. This mixture will gel after several hours at room temperature providing it is kept free of atmospheric oxygen and is not used in very thin layers. A more convenient and rapid method for gelling it in layers as thin as 1 mm. on top of microscope slides placed in Petri dishes consists of covering the surface of the freshly poured monomer-catalyst solution with an inert organic solvent such as light mineral oil (n-heptane is particularly convenient because it has a high boiling point and yet is easy to wash from the surface of the gel after it has formed with petroleum ether, ether, or a similar solvent) and placing this Petri dish with its lid on over a steam bath for 5 minutes. A sturdy gel will form in about 4 minutes. The inert organic solvent (whose purpose is to exclude oxygen during gellation) is washed from its surface, and the gel is ready for use. The slide immersed in gel is cut free and used for microimmunodiffusion or microimmunoelectrophoresis tests (Fig. V-1). The gel resulting from this procedure is about equivalent in stiffness to a 1.5% agar gel, but it is completely clear and colorless. It is far more flexible and is difficult to crack by rough handling. However, somehow it seems to impede diffusion of reactants so that precipitin reactions in it may take two to three times longer for full development than they do in agar. Although the gel is said by its manufacturers to be nontoxic, sufficient traces of its original toxic monomer form apparently remain in it to prevent its contamination by microorganisms. Protein stains of the same kind as used in agar (Crowle, 1958c) can be applied to this type of gel providing it is not dried first. Destaining

* Cyanogum 41 and the two catalysts generously were supplied by the American Cyanamid Co., 30 Rockefeller Plaza, New York.

must be somewhat more prolonged. The gel can be dried to a thin film after staining if it is first soaked in 1% acetic acid containing 10% glycerol. The gel is sticky to the touch so long as it is moist, so that for

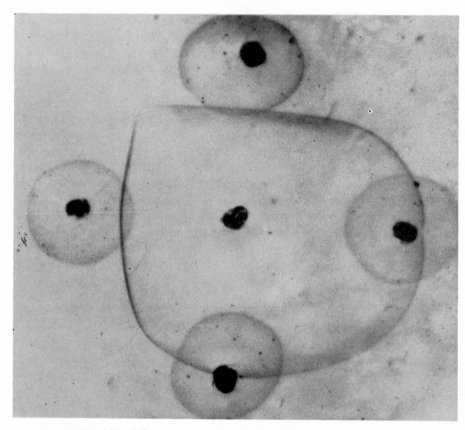

FIG. V-5. Double diffusion test carried out in cellulose acetate membrane. Bovine γ-globulin antigen at 0.02% was applied in the center, and guinea pig antiserum around this in four different spots: undiluted, 1:2, 1:4, and 1:8 (counterclockwise, starting from top). Reactions were allowed to develop for 3 days at room temperature and then were made visible by staining with thiazine red R. Note antigen-antibody equivalence at 1:2 antiserum dilution signified by sharp precipitin line. (Courtesy C. W. Fishel.)

convenience any object touching it should be water-proofed with petrolatum if any sticking is to be prevented. Slides on which the gel is employed need not and, indeed, are better not coated with any water-repellent as are slides used for agar gels.

Double diffusion tests can be performed in cellulose acetate "paper" of the type used for filtration (Fig. V-5) (Consden and Kohn, 1959).

This type of paper is wet readily and apparently permits large molecules to diffuse through it freely without adsorbing them.* Unmarked circles of membrane usually employed for filtration are satisfactory for this kind of test. The membrane is soaked in the buffer to be used, blotted free of excess, and then, while supported on a bed of pins, or similar object, touched with 1 to 5 microliter droplets of antigen and antibody, the respective reactants usually set about 1 cm. from each other. The droplets are allowed to sink into the paper while it is kept in a moist chamber, and then to prevent evaporation the membrane is immersed in a bath of mineral oil for immunodiffusion reactions to occur. After about two days' standing in oil at room temperature, the membrane is removed and washed free of oil with petroleum ether, and its water-soluble constituents next are leached away by a 1 to 3 hour soaking in buffered saline. Since the membrane is opaque, precipitates will not be visible until they are stained (see Appendix III) or the membrane is cleared after washing and drying by a soaking in mineral oil. Stained precipitin bands can be viewed with or without oil clearing. Cellulose acetate membrane also is used for immunoelectrophoresis (Condsen and Kohn, 1959).

This type of membrane compares favorably with agar, gelatin, and Cyanogum 41 as a medium for immunodiffusion tests. With it, as also with gelatin and Cyanogum, electroosmosis is negligible in immunoelectrophoresis. A big inherent advantage to it is that it requires only very small quantities of reactants, but unfortunately, this advantage tends to be offset by several disadvantages. The membrane is extremely fragile and hence must be handled and stored carefully. Since it is opaque, one cannot observe the progress of an immunodiffusion test during development of its precipitin bands, or the effects of various treatments on these bands, and one cannot observe final precipitates without first washing the membrane. This washing can remove some precipitin bands (Crowle, unpublished).

Cellulose acetate strips on which simple serum electrophoresis has been carried out (Smith and Murchison, 1959) can be used in a form of immunoelectrophoresis, in which one of these is laid upon agar gel so that electrophoresed serum components diffuse into the gel to react with antibody diffusing simultaneously either from a trough cast parallel to the membrane strip or from another antibody-soaked membrane laid parallel to the first (Bodman, 1959; Kohn, 1957). The same method employing filter paper strips rather than cellulose acetate is reported by

---

* It can be obtained from Oxo, Ltd., London, or its agent in this country, Consolidated Laboratories, Inc., Chicago Heights, Illinois. Cellulose nitrate filter paper is not satisfactory for immunodiffusion tests.

Scheiffarth and co-workers (1957) to yield excellent results. Although precipitin reactions apparently cannot be carried out in starch gels, starch columns used for electrophoresis can be embedded in agar so that fractions in them can diffuse against antibody which itself diffuses from another source in the opposite direction (Goodman et al., 1958b; Havez and Biserte, 1959a; Moretti et al., 1959; Poulik, 1952, 1956, 1959; Poulik and Poulik, 1958). Filter paper appears to have too coarse a texture for use in immunodiffusion (see Ouchterlony, 1958). A technique resembling immunoelectrophoresis but in which antigen and antibody simultaneously are electrophoresed so that during electrophoresis they cross and react on the paper has been described (Machboeuf et al., 1953; Nakamura et al., 1959a,b), although it seems to be more a curiosity than a practical method. Even more distantly removed from "legitimate" immunoelectrophoresis is the method of electrophoresing antiserum on paper and afterwards spraying the paper strip with antigen which combines with antibody wherever it is located in the serum pattern. This method has been utilized to show that anti-typhoid antibody in the human being is primarily a γ-globulin (Bustamante, 1957). Precipitin or agglutinin reactions on paper, as those in cellulose acetate, are detected by staining after inert stainable materials have been washed from the paper; specific aggregates remain fixed to the paper without special treatment during this washing.

Cells

In this section will be described various reaction containers, chambers, or cells and patterns for reactant arrangement, and the relative merits of the more distinctive methods which have been described in the literature will be discussed. To consider every method used in immunodiffusion would be impractical, and therefore this discussion is limited to representative methods, or methods of some particular advantage or significance.

Single Diffusion

Single diffusion techniques probably have their greatest utility for studies on the nature of antigen-antibody reactions, since for most qualitative and quantitative analyses some double diffusion technique can be used which equals or betters any single diffusion method. Single diffusion tests can be carried out in tubes or on plates. Single diffusion plate tests receive little contemporary attention, but in the early days of immunodiffusion they proved practical for typing bacteria (see Chapter IV).

The plate single diffusion test is set up in one of two ways. For the first, agar containing one reactant is poured around molds which, after the agar has gelled, are removed, and the wells they leave are charged with the other reactant (Ouchterlony, 1949c; see Fig. I-1). In the second, external reactant is placed upon already gelled agar containing the internal reactant. For example, one can inoculate bacteria to the surface of nutrient agar containing specific antibody for antigens produced by the bacterium (Chen and Meyer, 1955; Ouchterlony, 1948b, 1949c), or place upon such agar containers for antigen like glass cylinders (Ouchterlony, 1958), Plexiglas templates (Crowle, 1960b; Fig. V-6:19; Fig. V-7:14), or filter paper. Aside from the fact that diffusion is radial rather than confined to a column in plate single diffusion tests, these can be used and interpreted in much the same way as the single diffusion tube test. Radial diffusion is more difficult to handle in mathematical analyses than the essentially linear diffusion in tube tests, and this probably accounts primarily for the plate test's current low popularity. Although the plate test can be employed to compare two external reactants (Feinberg, 1957; Oudin, 1955; Petrie, 1932; Fig. I-1), single diffusion comparator tubes offer somewhat finer discrimination, and double diffusion tests far better resolution. The plate method does seem to have valid use as a quantitative technique (Crowle, 1960b; Feinberg, 1957; Hayward and Augustin, 1957). Using it, one determines the minimal concentration of an antigen which is capable, by exceeding antibody present in surrounding agar, of diffusing from its origin to form a visible precipitin disk around the origin, that is, the concentration of antigen which is just slightly more than required for dynamic equilibrium at its interface with antibody. In this kind of test, a series of wells in the antibody-containing agar (Feinberg, 1957; Hayward and Augustin, 1957) or holes in a plastic matrix laid upon this agar (Crowle, 1960b) are charged with decreasing quantities of antigen in constant volumes. At the higher concentrations, antigen will exceed the amount which antibody in the agar can precipitate, and it will form a disk of precipitate around its origin. Succeedingly more dilute antigen concentrations will form succeedingly smaller diameter circles until, at equivalence, no visible circle will be formed. The meaning of this test is tempered by the fact that equilibrium between antigen and antibody is established by piecemeal mixture of the two reactants being fed into the reaction area by diffusion and hence is governed by their respective molecular weights and diffusion coefficients (Crowle, 1960b; see Chapter III).

For the macro single diffusion plate test in which molded wells are to be used, one first pours sufficient 2% agar mixed at just above its gelling point (46–48°C.) with an equal volume of internal reactant (usually antiserum) to cover the bottom of the vessel being used (e.g., a Petri dish). After this layer has gelled, the molds (glass cylinders preferably made water repellent with a silicone, paraffin, or some such agent; chilled, waterproofed metal bars with air holes drilled through them; plastic bars, cylinders, or tubes) are placed on it in a predetermined position, and then a second agar layer two or three times thicker and containing internal reactant is poured upon the first. After this has solidified, the molds are removed without disturbing the contact between the two agar layers, a process facilitated by first chilling the plates. Alternatively, a layer of agar and internal reactant of full thickness can be poured and wells can be punched out of the gelled agar with cork borers, or with special cutters (Feinberg, 1957). The bottoms of holes made in this way should be sealed against reactant leakage with a drop of molten agar. The wells, however formed, are filled with appropriate external reactant solutions, which can contain agar so that they gel later, and the plates are incubated at a selected constant temperature for several days for full precipitin band development.

When cylinders are to be used as external reactant containers by being placed upon the agar gel, one simply pours agar to the thickness required and then drops these cylinders in place on the solidified agar and charges them with liquid reactant. Maximum resolution and easy reading are achieved by using thin layers of agar.

Micro single diffusion plate tests are set up in essentially the same fashion but with all apparatus miniatured. For example, a microscope slide is coated with agar solution made up in distilled water (concentrations ranging from 0.2% to 3.0% have been used by various workers to coat glassware to be used in immunodiffusion tests) and then dried. This coating minimizes movement of agar gel later poured onto the slide and chances of reactant leakage between the gel and the slide (Oudin, 1955). Then, enough molten 1% agar is poured over the entire slide to form a layer 1 to 2 mm. thick; surface tension keeps the agar from running off the slide. Wells are punched in the agar with capillary glass tubing or with a large gauge hypodermic needle which has had its point filed off, and the wells are charged with reactant. Placing cylinders upon agar in a micro adaption of the single diffusion plate and using these to contain external reactant is impractically difficult. Instead, a sheet of Plexiglas with funnel-shaped wells bored through it (Fig. V-6:19; Fig. V-7:14) is laid upon still molten agar poured between two layers of waterproof tape on a glass slide, so that this template lies on the tape in intimate contact with the soon solidified agar (see Fig. V-13). The bored holes serve the same function as individual cylinders, but they are held rigidly in evenly spaced positions. With such a Plexiglas

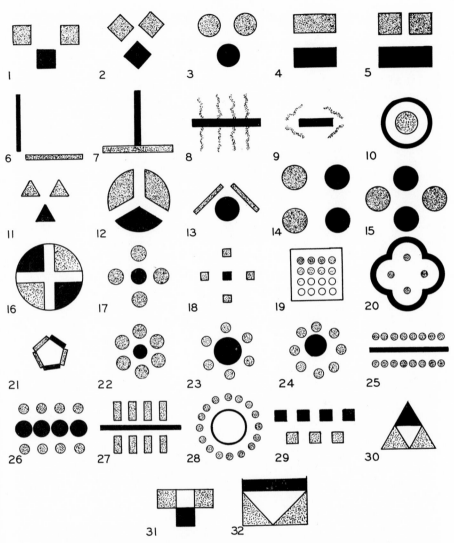

Fig. V-6. Schematic representation of various forms of double diffusion tests (excepting form 19) which have been used by various experimenters and which are referred to in text. Solid black shading represents antibody, while stippled areas represent antigen.

template, 16 individual sources of external reactant have been used on agar 2.5 cm. square and 0.6 mm. thick (Crowle, 1960b). Micro tests have the obvious advantage over macro tests of requiring much less of the reactants; they also tend to be more sensitive.

Single diffusion tube tests probably have their greatest utility in

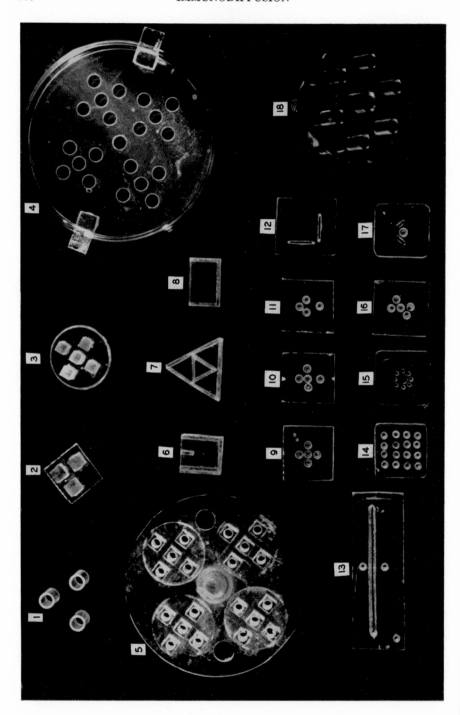

studies of one or another phase of the antigen-antibody precipitin reaction. Although they have been employed for elementary quantitation, double diffusion techniques are available for this purpose which are simpler, more sensitive, and more reliable than single diffusion tube tests at their present state of development (Crowle, 1960c). Single diffusion tube tests generally are set up in tubes with 2–3 mm. internal diameter by methods which do not vary much in different laboratories. First, the tubes are rinsed in agar solution in distilled water and then drained and dried; this applies their protective agar coating. Sometimes this coating is neither needed nor desirable. Thus, columns of agar in which reactions have taken place can easily be slipped from the tubes for various supplementary analyses (Glenn, 1959a; Jennings, 1959d) only if the tubes are not previously coated. On the other hand, if the agar used to gel the reactant(s) is 1% or more, the gel's shrinkage is so small that no coating actually is needed (Augustin et al., 1958). Next, the tubes, which usually are 6–8 cm. long, are filled to about half with antiserum-agar mixture made by mixing one volume of warmed antiserum with an equal volume of 0.6% agar cooled to just above its gelling point. Finally, antigen solution or gel is layered upon the antibody gel. If the rate of movement of a precipitin band is of primary importance to a single diffusion tube experiment, then for consistency antigen should be incorporated in agar in the same way as its antiserum is. This avoids convection currents due to differences in specific gravities of antigen and antibody layers (Preer and Telfer, 1957). Sometimes, however, observation of the number or characteristics of various precipitin bands suffices, and the simpler procedure of using liquid antigen can be employed or may even be preferable.

There are certain details in setting up single diffusion tubes which facilitate the procedure. Dried, agar-coated tubes can be stored at 4°C. indefinitely (Glenn, 1956a), and indeed tubes with the antiserum layer in place also can be stored at 4°C. for at least 5 weeks without deterioration, provided that this layer has an antiseptic added (Glenn et al., 1958b). Should agar not be used to line the tubes before the

---

Fig. V-7. Photograph of various cells and templates used in double diffusion experimentation and immunoelectrophoresis (No. 13). Forms 1 through 5, and 18 are used for macro tests, and templates 9 through 17 for micro tests. Cells 6, 7, and 8 have special uses (see text). No. 18 is a cutter used to punch a pattern of holes in an agar gel, while No. 4 is a pattern used temporarily to locate cylindrical molds (No. 1) in the desired pattern before melted agar is poured around them. Forms 1, 2, 3, and 5 are molds which are removed from solidified agar leaving patterns of wells. Templates 9 through 17 feed reactants into very thin layers of agar gel upon which they rest.

antiserum layer is added, then if liquid antigen is employed, one should make up the antibody in 1% or more agar and allow it to gel in the tube at room temperature; one should not refrigerate these tubes later since this tends to shrink the gel (Augustin et al., 1958). Pre-coating the tubes with agar is unnecessary if agar is used to gel both antibody and antigen layers, for there will be no liquid to seep between the tube walls and the agar, and any shrinkage will occur uniformly throughout the entire column. This would not necessarily hold for other gelling agents subject to syneresis. The meniscus between antigen and antibody can be flattened somewhat by slightly overcharging a tube with antibody and immediately withdrawing the excess antibody so as to wet the sides of the tube above the meniscus plane (Oudin, 1952). Bubbles at the meniscus sometimes present a problem. With small internal diameter tubes they can be removed merely by inverting the tube immediately after the agar layer has been poured and while the agar still is liquid and then keeping the tubes upside down until the agar has gelled (Munoz and Becker, 1950). Tubes with parallel walls are more expensive and harder to obtain than those made from glass tubing, but they permit better observation and photometric recording (Oudin, 1952). The best precipitin band resolution and least chance of false band differentiation or formation in single diffusion tube tests is obtained when the least antibody is used which will yield a visible precipitate (Crowle, 1960c). Secondary precipitate artifact bands are the most readily recognized if precipitating- rather than flocculating-type antibody is employed (Crowle, 1960c).

Once single diffusion tubes have been set up, they can be stoppered against evaporation with vaccine bottle caps which also are convenient objects for handling and labeling (Glenn, 1956a), with waxes or gums, or by pouring mineral oil on top of the antigen layer (Lebedev and Tsilinskii, 1958; Telfer and Williams, 1953). Since these tests are so sensitive to temperature changes which cause secondary precipitates to appear in them, they must be kept at constant temperature. Hence, preferably they should be immersed in water during reaction development, regardless of the temperature used, since water offers greater inertia to temperature change than does air. Temperature changes of several degrees, such as those which occur in most kitchen refrigerators, usually will be sufficiently dampened in this way not to cause any difficulties.

Occasionally, one may wish to use a single diffusion tube test in which several antigens can be compared at one time. This is accomplished in specially made cells called "comparator cells" (see Fig. V-7:6). The first of these described (Surgalla et al., 1952) was used to compare the reactions of each of four antigens with a single antiserum. An outstanding shortcoming of these comparator cells (and also of their double diffusion variations) is that since diffusion of compared antigens is parallel, comparing closely situated pairs of antigens originating from separate depots may become impossible; on some occasions experimental circumstances may lead one to conclude that a given antigen is diffusing from two sources when really it is diffusing only from one (Crowle, 1958b). A new form of single diffusion comparison has been described recently (Bergdoll et al., 1959) which does much to overcome this difficulty. Actually, it is a hybrid single-double diffusion test. In this modification, if cell No. 6, Fig. V-7, were employed, to the Plexiglas partition would be appended one of an equally thin layer of agar, without added reactant extending between the end of the Plexiglas partition and the bottom of the cell. This agar partition would have on either side of it two internal reactants to be compared; external reactants would, as usual, be placed on opposing sides of the upper short Plexiglas partition.

A unique application of the single diffusion comparator cell is exemplified by studies showing that certain *Pasteurella pestis* antigens diffuse more slowly when mixed with rabbit serum or serum albumin than when this serum is not used, and that rabbit globulin has an opposite effect (Ransom et al., 1955). This was illustrated without direct measurements and under identical, rather than just similar, experimental conditions using a single diffusion comparator cell in place of several single diffusion tubes: the relative positions of precipitin bands produced by one antigen from a source containing one or another additive were compared directly and specifically with those from the source without additive. Differences in diffusion rates would have been more laborious to demonstrate using double diffusion tests or series of single diffusion tests.

Double Diffusion

Double diffusion tests are used more often than single diffusion tests primarily because analytically they are more versatile, and generally they require less experience and care to set up adequately. They tend to be easier for the occasional user of immunodiffusion tests to interpret correctly, and they are less subject to variability, such as induced by sudden temperature changes, which complicate interpretations of immunodiffusion tests (Crowle, 1960c).

Double diffusion techniques, like single diffusion methods, are either of the tube type or the plate type, and they can be macro- or microscale. Double diffusion tube tests are set up in the same way as single

diffusion tube tests, except that agar containing no reactant is inter-
posed at proper thickness between antigen and antibody layers and reactions rarely are permitted to occur outside of this layer. The tube test
used to have the particular advantage over plate tests of a somewhat
greater resolving power for individual antigens in complex systems, but
refinements in existing plate techniques as well as development of micro
plate methods of high sensitivity has reduced this advantage leaving
only one other: the micro tube test is probably somewhat more sensitive than the best available plate test. Double diffusion plate tests are
set up either in Petri dishes or similar containers using virtually the
same procedures as described above for single diffusion plate tests but
without incorporating any reactant in the agar before it is poured, or
they are set up in one of several different kinds of cells. Micro double
diffusion tests can be carried out in capillary tubes, on microscope
slides, or even on microscope cover slips, also by the same basic procedures already described.

Double diffusion tube tests have been carried out in small test tubes
of 8 or 9 mm. internal diameter (Oakley and Fulthorpe, 1953; Relyveld
and Raynaud, 1959), glass tubing made into tubes with approximately
2 or 3 mm. internal diameter (Parlett and Reher, 1959; Preer, 1956; Rose
and Witebsky, 1959), and in capillary tubing of 0.7 mm. mean internal
diameter (Vyazov et al., 1959). By using special adaptions, Easty and
Ambrose (1957) were able to observe double diffusion tube reactions
under the interference microscope (see Fig. V-14). Wilson (1958) cut
tube-like troughs into thick Plexiglas sheeting for setting up and directly comparing single and double diffusion tube reactions under
identical conditions. Several laboratories have adapted comparator cells
of the type used for single diffusion to double diffusion analyses (Bergdoll et al., 1959; Crowle, 1958b; Oudin, 1955). From descriptions given
of these various techniques and others, not mentioned here, some generalities can be drawn.

The thickness of the layer of gel separating antigen and antibody in
double diffusion tube tests and in which precipitin bands are to develop
must be selected in a compromise between test sensitivity and band
resolution. The thinner it is, the more crowded will be the bands, but
also the more likely that one or both of the reactants will not be diluted by diffusion beyond ability to form a visible precipitate. The
thicker the layer, the longer time will be required for full development
of all reactions. A chief disadvantage of double diffusion tube tests
judged in comparison with several types of plate test is that occasionally
two precipitin bands will overlap, appearing to be one, so that the
potential resolution of this type of test always is less than that of the

gradient double diffusion plate test, for example. On the other hand, the double diffusion tube test's greatest advantage probably is its high sensitivity. This makes it potentially a very useful quantitative technique, as has been mentioned before (see Chapter III).

The most frequently used double diffusion tube test has been the semi-micro type described by Preer (1956). It serves as an example of methods generally used for this type of test. Glass tubing with an internal diameter of about 2 mm. is cut into lengths of between 6 and 10 cm., fused at one end, and then coated internally with 0.1% agar by being filled momentarily with this solution which immediately afterward is poured out. The coated tubes are dried and then charged with the reactants. Warm antiserum is mixed with an equal quantity of agar at double (1.2%) its finally desired strength, and this mixture is deposited in the bottom portion of the tube with a capillary tube or a syringe and 26 gauge needle. Then, the intermediate layer of warm 0.6% agar solution is poured upon the antiserum layer, and when that layer has gelled, a final layer of antigen, in 0.6% agar or without gelling agent, is deposited upon the intermediate layer. The sequence of reactants can be reversed without any change in results, that is, antigen poured first followed by intermediate and antiserum layers above it. The intermediate layer usually ranges from 5 to 10 mm. in thickness; the best thickness is determined experimentally for any antigen-antibody system. Tubes of internal diameter as small as 2 mm. should be kept warm during addition of each layer so that premature agar gelling will not take place. Preer trains a thermostatically controlled infrared lamp on the apparatus maintaining its temperature at 60°C. The same result can be accomplished somewhat less conveniently if the tubes are kept in warm water. Results are read under a stereoscope with the aid of dark-field illumination (see below).

Reactants in such small volumes as 0.001 ml. can be employed in double diffusion capillary tube tests such as described by Vyazov and co-workers (1959). The end of a capillary tube with internal diameter between 0.6 and 0.8 mm. is immersed in hot 1% agar and allowed to draw up a column of predetermined length to act as the intermediate layer in which reactions will take place. Then this gelled agar column is moved into the tube to leave a 15–20 mm. space at one end, and the tube is cut at the other end to leave a similar length of free space. Lengths of 4–8 mm. of liquid antigen and antibody are injected through fine capillary tubing into the opposing ends of this tube. Finally, both ends are sealed with paraffin, and the tubes are attached to glass slides for easy handling. Very accurate objective recordings of precipitin bands which develop can be obtained by using a specially modified microscope with a photometer attached to it to measure transmitted light as one of these small tubes is moved across its field of vision.

Improvements on existing tube double diffusion methods, aside from miniaturation, have consisted of devising various comparator cells such as No. 6, Fig. V-7. Since they do not seem to offer any particular advantages over various double diffusion plate tests they will not be considered in any detail. In these cells, the opposing reactants diffuse face-to-face and, as mentioned in connection with single diffusion comparator cells, the relationship between precipitin bands formed by two different depots cannot be determined readily in many instances because these lines do not tend to cross at acute enough angles. Moreover, antigen diffusing from one depot may form a line which suggests that this antigen also is diffusing from the other depot, or antigen may diffuse from two depots but appear to be diffusing from only one by the form of line appearing (Crowle, 1958b).

Since it is impractical to describe in detail here the many variations of plate double diffusion tests, the following discussion includes key references from which the reader can obtain details as he desires. However, to help him in selecting some reactant arrangement for his own experiments, diagrammatic and photographic summaries of various arrangements are shown in Figs. V-6 and V-7.

Double diffusion plate tests still are carried out most commonly in Petri dishes (Björklund, 1956; Efford, 1952; Elek, 1949a; Gell, 1955a; Jennings, 1959c; Miller and Heckly, 1959), but since most Petri dishes have uneven bottoms which can create difficulties in observing or photographing precipitin bands, and since they do not readily adapt themselves to any of the various staining procedures used for precipitin reactions, these vessels are being and should be superseded increasingly with various types of containers optically more suitable. Thus, tests can be carried out in agar poured onto photographic glass plates, the agar being confined only by its surface tension at the plate edge (Kaminski, 1954c; Wodehouse, 1955a), by waterproof tape (Wadsworth, 1957), by a stainless steel ring (Rose and Witebsky, 1959), or by a plastic ring bonded to the glass (Wilson and Pringle, 1956). Micro tests are set up on microscope slides in similar fashion (Biguet et al., 1959; Crowle, 1958c, 1960b; Grasset et al., 1958; Hartmann and Toilliez, 1957; Yakulis and Heller, 1959). Occasionally, plastic Petri dishes have been employed (Jennings, 1954b). Under the category of cells for double diffusion plate tests are included several specially prepared containers usually made of plastic, and whose purpose it is to confine diffusion of reactants and direct most of it into a reaction arena (Crowle, 1958b; Jennings and Malone, 1954a; Oakley, 1954; Sang and Sobey, 1954).

A wide variety of reactant depot arrangements is available from which to choose. For comparing two reactants with respect to a third, there is the basic arrangement of three cubic wells cast in agar (Björklund, 1956; Wilson and Pringle, 1954, 1956; Fig. V-6:1,2; Fig. V-7:2) or of three circular wells (Jennings, 1954b; Wadsworth, 1957; Wodehouse, 1955a; Fig. V-6:3; Fig. V-7:1); and of two short rectangular wells facing a third trench-like well (Bergdoll, *et al.*, 1959; Kleczkowski, 1957; Fig. V-6:5). The shapes of these wells has been altered in some instances for purposes of clearer differentiation (Björklund and Björklund, 1957; Crowle, 1960b; Ouchterlony, 1958; Fig. V-6:11, 12, 13), as has their actual spatial relationship to each other (Wilson and Pringle, 1954, 1956). In these various forms, most of each of the opposing reactants diffuses face-to-face. However, it is the small area in which reactants encounter each other at angles less than 180° that many of the most revealing precipitin band formations take place and where degree of line crossing and differentiation is most readily observed. Some arrangements take advantage of this less-than-180° diffusion path and become double diffusion gradient tests in which, for example, antigen and antibody fronts are forced to move at right angles to each other. Double diffusion gradient tests include set ups in which troughs are cast in the agar or cut out of it (Allison and Humphrey, 1959, 1960; Elek, 1949a; Ouchterlony, 1948a; Fig. V-6:6), plastic templates with slots are laid on the agar in this right-angle form (Crowle, unpublished; Fishel, personal communication; Fig. V-7:12), reactant-soaked filter paper strips laid out in the form of a "T" or an "L" (Elek, 1949a; Fig. V-6:7), or troughs or filter paper strips charged with antibody are overlaid with bacterial culture streaks (Elek, 1948; Ouchterlony, 1948b; Fig. V-6:8), or placed at angles to them (Marcuse and Hussels, 1955; Fig. V-6:9). Two simple forms of double diffusion plate tests which should not be superior to comparable double diffusion tube tests are (1) an arrangement where one trough faces another (Ouchterlony, 1948a; Fig. V-6:4) or (2) one in which a circle of bacterial growth surrounds a source of antibody diffusion or vice versa (Chen and Meyer, 1955; Fig. V-6:10).

Other arrangements allow one to compare simultaneously several antigens, several antisera, or both, although with less discrimination than can be obtained by the simpler tests, since experimental conditions necessarily must be adjusted to the average requirements of many antigen-antibody systems. These arrangements include four circular wells disposed as corners of a square (Shandon Scientific Co., 1959; Fig. V-6:14), a diamond (Feinberg, 1957; Shandon Scientific Co., 1959; Fig. V-6:15), five circular or square wells with four forming the corners of a square and one the center of it (Crowle, 1958c; Efford, 1952; Hartmann and Toilliez, 1957; Jennings, 1956; Korngold, 1956a; Korngold and Lipari, 1955a; Leone *et al.*, 1955; Shandon Scientific Co., 1959; Yakulis and Heller, 1959; Fig. V-6:17,18; Fig. V-7:3,4,5,9), six or eight satellite wells around the same size or larger centrally or eccentrically placed well (Crowle, 1960b; Feinberg, 1957; Gell, 1955a; Grasset *et al.*, 1958; Hayward and Augustin, 1957; Shandon Scientific Co., 1959; Fig. V-6: 22,23,24; Fig. V-7:15,18), a large number of satellite wells ranging around the outside of a circular trough cast in agar with the rim of a plastic Petri dish (Crouch, 1958; Fig. V-6:28), and a line of wells on either side of a trough (Biguet *et al.*, 1959; Kaminski, 1954c; Fig. V-6:25,27), or a similar line of slightly larger wells (Wright, 1959; Fig. V-6:26). The wells also have been arranged in zig-zag disposition (Gell, 1955a; Fig. V-6:29). Some unusual forms include triangular depots placed at 90° intervals around a Petri dish to leave a cross of agar in which reactions take place (Parlett and Youmans, 1956; Fig. V-6:16), and placement on nutrient agar of a rounded hollow square of filter paper soaked with antibody on which in the corner of each rounded square is spotted a bacterial culture (Chen and Meyer, 1955; Fig. V-6: 20). A pentagonal reaction arena with a specially formed depot for each side of the pentagon has been found useful in studying precipitin band cross reactions (Jennings, 1959c; Fig. V-6:21). Especially made plastic cells have been used to obtain an equilateral triangular reaction area (Crowle, 1958b; Jennings, 1958; Jennings and Malone, 1954a; Fig. V-6:30; Fig. V-7:7) or a right-angled triangular area whose acute angles can be varied according to experimental requirements (Crowle, 1958b; Fig. V-6:32; Fig. V-7:8; Fig. V-11), or in which the reaction arena is square (Crowle, 1958b; Oakley, 1954; Sang and Sobey, 1954; Fig. V-6:31). Among the various arrangements shown in Fig. V-6, the following have been adapted successfully to micro scale use: forms 3 (Wadsworth, 1957), 5 (Crowle, unpublished; Fishel, personal communication), 6 (Crowle and Leuker, unpublished), 13 (Crowle, 1960b), 17 (Crowle, 1958a; Hartmann and Toilliez, 1957; Wadsworth, 1957; Yakulis and Heller, 1959), 22 (Grasset *et al.*, 1958), 23 (Crowle, 1960b), 25 (Fishel, personal communication). Figure V-7 shows Plexiglass templates used for making some of these adaptions.

Reactant depots are arranged in or on agar with any of several devices. These include metal rods coated with paraffin (Björklund, 1956; Ouchterlony, 1948a; Wilson and Pringle, 1954), plastic rods glued to plastic sheeting in a desired form (Crowle, unpublished; Leone *et al.*, 1955), plastic cylinders, metal cylinders (Miller and Heckly, 1959; Rose and Witebsky, 1959), and glass cylinders (Chen and Meyer, 1955; Efford, 1952; Wodehouse, 1955a). These instruments are used as molds, placed in the container into which agar will be poured and then removed after the agar has gelled. Jennings' (1959c) special pentagonal pattern with arms for each side of the pentagon is prepared by pouring melted paraffin into a Petri dish, allowing this to solidify, and then carving portions of this pattern from the paraffin and charging each freshly carved cavity with the appropriate agar mixture. Other unusual patterns suited to the particular purposes of a given experiment could be obtained using this technique. Instead of molding wells in agar, one may employ cutting or coring instruments to make troughs or holes in already gelled agar. The cork borer is most commonly used (Matthews, 1958; Yakulis and Heller, 1959), but cutters—especially made for this purpose and affixed to metal back-plates—(Shandon Scientific Co., 1959; Fig. V-7:18) which will produce very accurately any of several patterns can be purchased. These are made for use in special 4.5 cm. diameter Petri dishes (Feinberg, 1957; Shandon Scientific Co., 1959). For micro tests, one may also employ cork borers (Yakulis and Heller, 1959) and hypodermic needles (Hartmann and Toilliez, 1957) held in patterns by a backboard (Grasset et al., 1958), or capillary glass tubing (Crowle, 1960b).

Rarely, in the macro double diffusion plate test, some open-bottomed container, such as a glass cylinder, resting on the surface of agar gel is used as reactant depot (Wodehouse, 1955a). This is satisfactory only if the agar layer is thin (no more than 2 mm. thick); slanted ribbon-like precipitates will form in thicker agar, because a gradient of diffusing reactant will be established through the depth of the agar as its front advances laterally. The real value of this method emerges from the fact that the potential sensitivity of double diffusion tests depends largely upon how much reactant can be fed into the precipitin zone (see Chapter III). Consequently, a test in which a large volume of each reactant can be fed steadily into a thin layer of agar will be more sensitive than one in which only the volume which can be held in a well cast in such thin agar can be used. Although wells in agar can be recharged, this risks the appearance of artifacts which confuse the results and their interpretation (Crowle, 1960c). One solution to feeding a large reactant volume into a thin layer of agar has been to glue plastic cylinders, each with a small arch cut in its lower end, to the bottom of a plastic dish and then to pour sufficient agar to just cover these arches while the mold rests in a Petri dish (Jennings, 1954b). Then, the plastic cylinders, which are considerably higher than the thickness of the agar and which protrude above it, can be filled with reactant. This particular method also has the advantage that reactant diffusion in a sense is directional, in that reactant can escape into the agar only through the arches which are aimed toward the common reacting arena. Another method which takes advantage also of miniaturation and use of very thin agar gels consists of placing a Plexiglass template directly upon agar just before it gels (Crowle, 1958c, 1959b; Wadsworth, 1957; Fig. V-13). In this plastic template are drilled funnel-shaped holes in any of several patterns. Since the template is as many as six times thicker than the agar, each hole in it holds a relatively large quantity of reactant which it feeds steadily into the agar. The agar is thin enough in this technique to prevent slanting of precipitin bands, since essentially diffusion proceeds from a flat, very small disc-shaped area.

With these many double diffusion plate techniques from which to choose, how is one to decide which would be the most likely to yield the best results for a given problem? Certainly, no single test excels for all purposes. For example, gradient diffusion methods usually are not as satisfactory for comparing complex mixtures of antigens as one of the three-well arrangements, because any single one of the gradient methods is somewhat less versatile than one of the better well methods. To a certain extent, this lack of versatility has been overcome in a gradient technique in which the reaction arena can be made deeper or shallower without changing reaction cells, but rather by changing the way in which one cell is used (Crowle, 1958b; Fig. V-8). Despite the relative ease with which this modification can be used, it is more difficult to set up and takes much more time than well comparison tests. On the other hand, when a relatively simple antigen-antibody system is being studied, more information can be obtained from a single gradient test about antigen and antibody molecular weight, antigen and antibody heterogeneity, characteristics of antigen-antibody combination, and the relative concentrations of these two reactants in their original solutions, than from a single test using any other type of double diffusion technique. As a generality, then, simply enumerating and roughly comparing the individual constituents of complex antigenic mixtures might best be done with one of the well techniques, while for critically enumerating individual constituents of an antigen mixture, or for gaining any of the information mentioned above, one of the gradient methods is preferable. In the author's opinion, the gradient techniques offer the most reliable way among all immunodiffusion methods of enumerating the number of antigen-antibody systems under investigation in any given experiment (Crowle, 1960c). Cells especially made for double diffusion gradient tests have the same uses as gradient tests set up in the Petri dish, but they have the added advantage of utilizing reactants more efficiently, in that these can diffuse only into the reaction area and are not lost to surrounding medium (Crowle, 1958b).

Among the simple three-well set-ups, forms 11, 12, and 13 (Fig. V-6) exaggerate the lack or presence of interaction between individual antigens in two mixtures being compared against an antiserum, sometimes making interpretation of results more obvious (Fig. V-9). Four-well forms such as 14, 15, and 16 (Fig. V-6) are most useful in simultaneously comparing two antisera and two antigens. They will show, for example, which antigen common to two different antigen preparations has not elicited antibody formation in one animal but has in another.

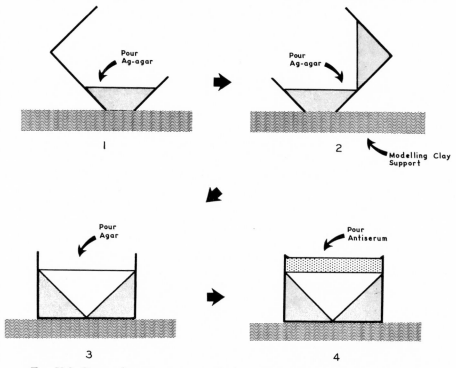

Fig. V-8. Steps taken in setting up double diffusion gradient test in Cell 32 of Fig. V-6 and 8 of Fig. V-7. The angles of the clear reaction arena can be varied, while still using the same type of cell, by varying the angle at which this is held in its modeling clay support during pouring of antigen-agar mixtures.

Form 21 combines some of the virtues of gradient diffusion with the possibility of simultaneously observing the interactions between three antigen mixtures and one or two antisera or vice versa all occurring in the same reaction arena, something not possible with any other technique described. This form might usefully be extended to a hexagon. A reaction area with more sides and therefore more reactants than this would become impractically complex, unless from each of the depots were diffusing reactants capable of forming only one or two lines. This technique probably could be adapted readily to single diffusion comparisons by incorporating antibody in the reaction arena agar.

Arrangements for comparing numerous different antigens or antisera grossly and all at one time are useful and economical in miscellaneous

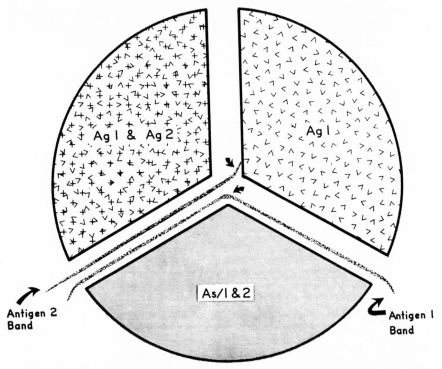

FIG. V-9. A diagram showing how form No. 12 (Fig. V-6) differentiates between an antigen (1) common to two compared mixtures and one found only in one of these mixtures (2), when these two mixtures are compared using antiserum reactive with both antigens (As/1 & 2).

surveys and preliminary experiments. The simplest of these is the five-well set up (Fig. V-6:17,18) in which, for example, four antisera can be compared for antibody content to a given antigen. Fractions obtained from different drip points in electrophoretic curtain separation of an antigen can be tested against antiserum by such forms as 25, 27, and 28 (in Fig. V-6) (Halbert, 1958); such techniques also can be used for simultaneously testing antigens from several species of microorganism against antiserum to one of the species (Biguet *et al.*, 1959). Forms 23, 26, 27, and 29 (in Fig. V-6) have been used for quantitative analyses

(Crowle, 1960b; Feinberg, 1957; Hayward and Augustin, 1957; Gell, 1955a).

Because of their greater sensitivity, economy, rapidity, and convenience in setting up, reading, washing, staining, preserving, and photographing, micro adaptions of the various arrangements probably should be used in preference to macro forms whenever they are available. Templates (Fig. V-7:9,10,11,12,15,16,17) for many variations are readily made from Plexiglas.

To illustrate how most double diffusion plate tests are set up, specific techniques for the macro three-hole test (Ouchterlony, 1958), for one of the triangle cell tests (Crowle, 1958b), and for the micro five-hole test (Crowle, 1958c) will be described. For the first of these (Fig. V-10) one pours into a small Petri dish (4.5 cm. in diameter) a base layer of 1% agar thick enough to give a perfectly level surface. When this has solidified, molds are placed on a predetermined pattern matching one drawn on paper and placed under the Petri dish. Alternatively, the pattern of wells can be prepared by using molds attached to a backboard in this pattern (e.g., Fig. V-7:2). With the molds in place, a second thicker layer of agar is poured and allowed to solidify. If the molds have been treated to be water repellent and have air holes drilled through them, they are not difficult to remove from the agar once it has been chilled. When cutters instead of molds are employed, no base layer of agar is needed, but when the holes have been cut and their agar cores removed, the bottom of each is sealed with a drop of melted agar before reactants are added. When odd-shaped wells are required, they may have to be cut to order with a scalpel or razor blade, or special molds or cutters will have to be made.

The triangle cells originally used by Jennings and Malone (1954a) can be prepared for use in one of two ways. They can be filled with 1% agar solution, and then agar gel from each of the three angles of the triangle can be cut and removed and replaced with reactant mixed with agar so that it will gel. Or, agar solution containing reactants poured into each of those angles of the triangle can be prevented from filling its center by blocking its flow with appropriate inserts placed between adjacent walls of the triangular cell (Fig. V-7:7). The small central triangle resulting is charged with agar having no reactants. There are several disadvantages to the original technique (Crowle, 1958b), one of the chief ones being that with a given cell the shape of the reaction arena always has to be the same. A simplified modification of this technique has been developed in which the geometry of the reaction arena can be changed at will in a single type of cell (Crowle, 1958b; Fig. V-11). A small, flat, rectangular Plexiglas compartment with only one

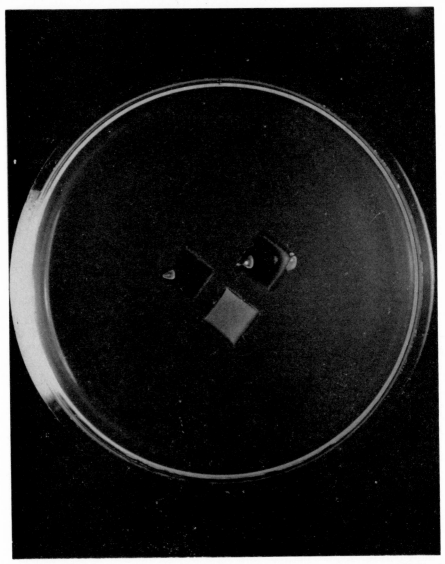

FIG. V-10. Photograph of macro double diffusion test set up in a small Petri dish using Mold No. 2, Fig. V-7. This is often called an "Ouchterlony" test after the experimenter who popularized it. Generally, two antigens (clear solutions) are compared using a single antiserum (turbid solution).

of its long, narrow sides open is used (Fig. V-8). This cell is placed on modeling clay, tilted first to one side and then to the other as, respectively, first one corner and then the other is filled with antigen-agar mixture. Then it is laid flat, and the triangular space between these two filled-in corners is itself filled with clear agar. After this has gelled, it is overlaid with antiserum, either liquid or in agar. The angles of the

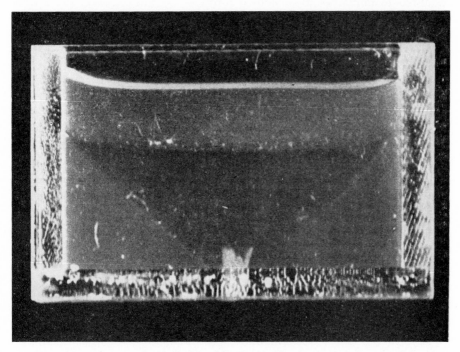

FIG. V-11. Photograph of double diffusion gradient test set up in Cell 8, Fig. V-7 (enlarged 5 times). Usually, corners are charged with antigens to be compared and antiserum is layered on the base of the triangular reaction arena (see Fig. V-8), but this procedure can be reversed, antisera being mixed with agar and placed in opposite corners for comparison using a single antigen.

reaction arena triangle can be made more or less acute, to suit the precipitin band resolution required in an experiment, by varying the tilt of the cell while its corners are being filled.

Micro double diffusion plate tests can be set up in the same way on microscope slides using smaller cutters as they are in Petri dishes. Miniaturing a test in this way gives it several advantages (e.g., economy, rapidity, precipitin band resolution), but it will not be more sensitive than its macro form, since the ratio of reactant volume to the volume of agar surrounding it remains nearly the same. The technique first described by Wadsworth in 1957 of using plastic templates with holes drilled in them for feeding large quantities of reactants into relatively very small cross sections of agar gel at once combines all the advantages of miniaturation and provides greater sensitivity.

Wadsworth's idea of using templates has been adapted with excellent results to use with microscope slides (Crowle, 1958c), and it can be adapted to miniature most known forms of double diffusion plate tests as well as immunoelectrophoresis (cf. Crowle, 1960b; Fig. V-7). The first step in setting up this type of micro double diffusion plate test is to dip a clean microscope slide in hot 0.2% agar in distilled water to coat

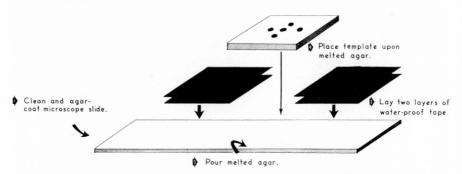

Fig. V-12. Steps taken in setting up a micro double diffusion test using a Plexiglas template (e.g., No. 9, Fig. V-7).

it and then to allow the slide to drain and air-dry. Then, double layers of waterproof, plastic electrical insulating tape* are laid down across the slide parallel to each other and separated by about 2 cm. (Fig. V-12). In the space between the tapes is placed about 0.3 ml. of 1% agar at about 60°C., and upon it immediately afterward is laid a plastic matrix, slightly broader than 2 cm., the underside of which previously has been very lightly polished with a water repellent grease. If this matrix is laid properly across the breadth of the glass slide and upon the edges of the supporting strips of tape, no air is trapped between it and the agar, its funnel-shaped holes make intimate contact with the agar, and between it and the glass slide there will be a uniformly thick agar layer only very slightly thicker than the double layer of tape (i.e., about 0.5 mm.). As soon as the agar has solidified, each hole is filled with reactant, care being taken that in each instance the liquid added touches the agar and that no air bubbles intervene. Then, the glass slide

---

* Some kinds of tape (e.g., adhesive tape used for surgical dressing) contain substances which diffuse into adjoining agar gel and precipitate antiserum. Sears, Roebuck "Homart" plastic tape for electric wiring is used in the author's laboratory.

with its plastic matrix (Fig. V-13) is held at refrigerator or room temperature in a humid atmosphere (e.g., a Petri dish containing a disc of moistened filter paper in it) for from 24 hours to 3 days, depending upon the antigen-antibody system being studied, for complete reactions to occur. The reactions will develop more rapidly if the incubation

FIG. V-13. Photograph of micro double diffusion test (enlarged 1.5 times) set up using procedure shown in Fig. V-12 and template No. 9, Fig. V-7. Template rests directly upon 1% agar gel under it but also is supported, particularly before freshly poured agar solution gels, by edges of tapes on either side of it. Note that holes in template have funnel shape and therefore two diameters, the smaller being in contact with agar and the larger holding reactant solution.

atmosphere is less than saturated with water, but one should take care not to wait too long before terminating incubation, lest the agar under a template dry out too much and shrink away from the template.

Sensitivity and Resolution

Potential sensitivity and resolution may be factors of major importance in selecting an immunodiffusion test for a given problem. A test's susceptibility to artifacts (i.e., formation of secondary precipitates) also may weigh heavily in its possible adoption—and not necessarily against it as, for example, in studies on the mechanisms of antigen-antibody precipitation (Crowle, 1960c). Precipitin band resolution in double diffusion tests is superior to that in single diffusion tests (Wilson, 1958). The latter test also is more prone to the technical difficulty of spurious band formation (Crowle, 1960c). Which test is the more likely to detect the smallest quantity of antigen or antibody is both a controversial and important question; it deserves special discussion.

Basic Considerations in Sensitivity

The intensity of a precipitate, and therefore its potential visibility, depends primarily upon the quantity of antibody forming it (Boyd,

1956; see also Chapters II and III). Hence, logically that test which places the most antibody in the reaction area should be the most sensitive. Since no matter how much antibody is fed into agar by any form of the double diffusion test, its concentration in free form could never exceed that originally present in the depot, and since this concentration is maintained from the beginning of the test in single diffusion techniques, single diffusion tests might appear superficially to be potentially more sensitive than double diffusion tests. However, in the double diffusion test there is a concentrating effect in the forming precipitin band. Thus, if appropriately dilute antigen meets very dilute antibody, it combines with it in a plane of optimal proportions; at first, this will not be noticed because antibody is so dilute. Nevertheless, diffusion of the two reactants into this plane does not stop but, if their sources are relatively inexhaustible, as they can be in the template-fed micro double diffusion test, rather, it continues to form insoluble complexes until, finally, there are enough to become visible. Thus, although soluble antibody in the surrounding agar cannot exceed the original concentration used in its depot, in the plane of precipitation its diffusion is stopped by antigen which combines with it and precipitates it and, as some precipitates, more in soluble form diffuses into the reaction area to replace it and in turn is precipitated. Hence, in its precipitated form, antibody can become many times more concentrated than it originally was. This does not happen in single diffusion tests, for by their basic nature antigen always is kept excessive. Immediately ahead of the advancing precipitate band there actually is an area of antibody depletion (Crowle, 1960b,c), so that in the single diffusion test, precipitates can never form involving more antibody than originally present in the agar, and, indeed, they actually may form in the presence of somewhat less antibody (see Fig. III-1). The single diffusion test inherently lacks the concentration effect found in the double diffusion test (the "sink effect" mentioned by Aladjem and co-workers, 1959).

Another factor diminishing the sensitivity of single diffusion tests is that specific precipitation always takes place under adverse circumstances. It occurs under conditions of antigen excess and, because of continuing and progressively greater excesses developing at any given plane, it cannot consolidate into a precipitate consisting of antigen-antibody complexes arranged optimally into a maximum aggregate.

From this discussion, one can conclude that a constant-feeding type of double diffusion plate or tube test should be more sensitive than any other type of immunodiffusion test. Other types of double diffusion test, however, may or may not equal the single diffusion test in sensitivity. Moreover, if one of the reactants in a double diffusion test serologically is greatly excessive, the test becomes essentially a single diffusion test and generally loses sensitivity and resolution. Comparisons of sensitivity on the basis of experimental data therefore cannot be made haphazardly.

Experiments

The sensitivity of constant-feed double diffusion tests has never been tested with sufficient precautions to clearly verify the above ideas. However, available data from various sources tend to substantiate them. In three instances, experimental comparison of single and double diffusion tube tests on approximately equal terms showed the latter to be the more sensitive (Finger and Kabat, 1958; Preer, 1956; Wilson, 1958), although not always greatly so (Finger and Kabat, 1958). The greatest sensitivity in terms of minimum quantities of either antigen or antibody detected so far has been achieved in the double diffusion tube. Although the limit of sensitivity for such tests has been placed at about 5 μg. of antibody nitrogen (Grabar, 1957a), semimicro double diffusion tube tests have been employed to detect 0.03 μg. of antibody N (Finger and Kabat, 1958); they readily detect quantities of antigen below 1 μg. (Augustin and Hayward, 1955; Hayward and Augustin, 1957), and as low as 0.01 μg. (Preer, 1956). The sensitivity of single diffusion tube tests apparently has not been tested so often. In its semimicro form, it can detect at least 6 μg. of antibody N and 0.8 μg. of antigen N (Rubinstein, 1954).

Vyazov and co-workers (1959) state that their micro double diffusion tube test is more sensitive than either the "ring" precipitin test carried out under the same conditions or the classic precipitin test in aqueous medium. The popular forms of macro double diffusion plate test appear to be less sensitive than either single diffusion or double diffusion tube tests, largely because most reactant from each depot diffuses wastefully into surrounding areas where reactions are not expected to occur. Thus, with a 2.3 cm. separation of cups, the macro Ouchterlony plate has been found to be about one-fifth as sensitive as the aqueous precipitin test (Wilson and Pringle, 1954), which itself is less sensitive than the most sensitive immunodiffusion tests. However, if distances between reactant depots are decreased by a factor of about 3 in this plate, the sensitivity of the test can be increased as much as fourfold (Relyveld *et al.*, 1956) to detect as little as 1.5 μg. of antigen. Micro double diffusion plate tests have shown readily visible precipitates with as little as 1 μg. of antigen (Brown and Crick, 1958; Grasset *et al.*, 1956) and 1 μl. of antiserum (Grasset *et al.*, 1956); these micro tests were not of the constant-feed type, which should be more sensitive.

Auxiliary Methods for Increasing Sensitivity

From published data, then, the potential sensitivity of the most sensitive unsupplemented immunodiffusion tests should be such as to detect about 0.01 μg. of either antigen or antibody. This sensitivity can be increased several-fold by auxiliary methods. Co-precipitating agents can be used to make visible otherwise invisible antigen-antibody aggregates in agar gel; these agents can be either antibody (Goudie et al., 1959), or antigen (Jennings, 1959d). Practically, the diagnosis of histoplasmosis (Heiner, 1958) and of tuberculosis (Parlett and Reher, 1959) has been aided by such intensification. In the first instance, an antiserum known to contain precipitins for Histoplasma antigen was placed in a well in a double diffusion plate next to another well charged with antiserum suspected to contain such antibodies, but if so, containing too few to yield a visible precipitate without prior concentration. Both were allowed to react with Histoplasma antigen placed in a third well. The first antiserum formed a precipitin band which was relatively straight throughout its length except where the weak antiserum diffused across its path. Here it bent sharply away from the source of this antiserum, thus indicating the presence, although invisible, of homologous antigen-antibody reaction in that particular area. Serum containing none of this antibody produced no perceptible bending influence on this line. In the second instance, the diagnosis of tuberculosis, antiserum too weak to give a precipitate in the double diffusion tube test was withdrawn and renewed periodically, supposedly increasing the concentration of antibody in the agar layer where a precipitin reaction was occurring and building it to the stage where it became visible (Parlett and Reher, 1959). The same effect might be obtained by using animal antiserum of known precipitin content purposely diluted below a concentration just capable of giving a visible precipitate. This could be mixed with a suspected positive but weakly-reacting human antiserum, whereupon the added animal precipitins acting together with those already present would be able to form a visible precipitin band (Parlett, personal communication).

More complicated, and usable primarily as a research tool, is interferometric microscopy, which can detect antigen-antibody aggregation in agar too weak to be visible (Ambrose and Easty, 1953). The regular patterns of alternating parallel light and dark bands seen in the interference microscope when clear agar gel is being observed are not disturbed by the presence of either antigen or antibody solutions in this agar. However, when antigen and antibody combine to form an aggregate, this aggregate affects the phases of light passing through it, and along a well-defined plane corresponding to the length of the aggregate as seen through the microscope it induces an irregularity in the pattern (Fig. V-14).

Invisible precipitin band detected.

Visible precipitin band indicated.

Fig. V-14. Pattern seen through an interference microscope examining agar of a double diffusion tube test containing a visible precipitin line and an invisible antigen-antibody aggregate, the latter detected by a regular but not complete disturbance in the pattern of light and dark bands. (Drawn from photograph published by Ambrose and Easty, 1953.)

This and other auxiliary tests suggest that when antigen-antibody aggregates grow to a certain size in agar they are fixed *in situ* by their very size, being unable to diffuse through the "spaces" in the network of the supporting medium. Presumably, the more concentrated and compact a gel is, the smaller antigen-antibody aggregates will be trapped and become susceptible to revelation by an auxiliary technique. Once these aggregates are trapped, they may remain invisible, but they should not diffuse from the area in which they have formed unless their aggregation is readily reversible. Hence, if the agar is washed and then soaked in a protein stain, otherwise invisible precipitates should be detected by the specific strain. On several occasions, in the writer's experience, this has proven to be true (Crowle, 1958c; unpublished). Often, however, with the 1% agar gels ordinarily employed, aggregates may be too small to remain fixed in the gel through washing or are soluble and must be detected before this treatment (Crowle, 1960a). This frequently can be accomplished employing the specific enhancing effects that the cations cadmium, nickel, and lanthanum have upon antigen-antibody aggregation (Crowle, 1960a; see Fig. IV-14). Incorporating cadmium salts at appropriate concentrations in agar in which antigen and antibody are to react has been found, for example, to increase by about fourfold the ability of some antisera to form a visible precipitate (Crowle, 1958a). More simply, one merely soaks agar in which antigen-antibody reactions supposedly have occurred in very weak (e.g., 0.0125%) solutions of a cadmium salt for a few minutes to develop previously invisible precipitin bands, making them visible (Crowle, 1960a). Sometimes, certain types of antisera can be used for the same purpose (Goudie et al., 1959). Some antigen-antibody aggregates form as transparent bands in the normally slightly turbid background of an agar gel. These have been transformed into normal-appearing, light-scattering precipitates by swabbing the surface of the agar gel with mineral acids or exposing the agar to fumes from a volatile acid (Goudie et al., 1959).

A method for potentially greatly increasing the sensitivity of immunodiffusion tests which has only begun to be exploited is to use reactants labeled with radioactive substances. Antigen and antibody may form sub-visible aggregates which, so long as they are fixed by their size in the gel and remain immobile, can be detected by autoradiography (Perlmann and Hultin, 1958). Since exposure of photographic material is cumulative, prolonged exposure of a photographic film to such a precipitate containing labeled antigen could increase the sensitivity of an immunodiffusion test greatly, perhaps within or beyond the range of the most sensitive serologic tests available. This is of double interest because detection of a reaction would be direct, not depending upon complicating secondary serologic procedures such as red blood cell agglutination or lysis. Published illustrations of autoradiographs of immunoelectrophoretic patterns (Hirschfeld and Söderberg, 1960) suggest that precipitin band resolution may be diminished if exposure of photo-

sensitive materials is prolonged to increase sensitivity when two precipitin bands are very close to each other. This is due to scatter of radioactivity, emanating from both bands, which overlaps and adds up to
enough to expose areas of the film between the two bands. For maximum sensitivity in autoradiography of immunodiffusion tests, then, the
precipitin reaction should be carried out in as thin a layer of gel as
possible, which, after reactions can be assumed to have taken place,
should be washed free of uncombined reactants and dried to a very
thin film. Then, this film must be placed under pressure in direct contact with thin-emulsion photographic film capable of recording images
in high contrast and with maximum possible resolution.

Immunoelectrophoresis

The methods and uses of immunoelectrophoresis have been reviewed
very recently by Grabar (1959a); Wieme (1959a) has written an excellent monograph on agar electrophoresis. The reader is referred to
these two comprehensive works and to Chapters II and III in the present
book for detailed description of factors governing immunoelectrophoresis
tests. The following paragraphs will present essential information regarding various methods of immunoelectrophoresis as an introduction
and guide to how to use this potent analytic technique.

The essential requirement of immunoelectrophoresis which differs
from those of double diffusion plate tests is to obtain optimal electrophoretic fractionation of the reactant being analyzed and then to detect
the separated fractions, usually in the same medium in which electrophoresis has been performed, under conditions best restricting undue
spread and overlapping of these fractions by diffusion. Basically, one
needs simply to cover the surface of a glass microscope slide with agar,
punch a hole in the agar, charge this with reactant, pass direct current
through the agar to fractionate this reactant, cut a slot parallel to the
plane of separation, and fill this slot with indicator reactant (usually
antibody) to detect the separated fractions. Familiarity with the niceties
and refinements of each of these steps leads to the best use and proper
interpretation of immunoelectrophoresis tests.

Macroimmunoelectrophoresis

There are macro and micro immunoelectrophoresis techniques, the
latter developed only recently but rapidly becoming more popular
than the former. The original macroimmunoelectrophoresis method described by Grabar and Williams (1953, 1955) is still often used and,
being basically the same as several subsequent modifications not employing templates, exemplifies what might be called classic immuno-

electrophoresis. First, a bed layer of agar is poured in a large, flat container, and then a somewhat smaller glass plate which has been pre-coated with agar and dried is laid upon this level agar gel. Filter paper wicks are placed at each end of the glass plate later to connect each end with its respective buffer vessel, and agar then is poured over the glass plate into the large dish to cover the plate to an even thickness. After this second layer of agar has gelled, the plate and its paper wicks are cut free, the plate is laid upon the facing edges of buffer vessels to form a bridge between them so that the wicks hang into the buffer in each vessel, a hole either cast in the agar slab during its pouring or later punched in it with a cutter is filled with the material to be separated, and direct current is applied for electrophoresis. Constant pH is maintained during electrophoresis in each buffer vessel by directing a constant slow flow of fresh buffer into these to replace that equally slowly siphoned away and removing electrolysis products with it. After electrophoresis, the indicator reactant (usually antibody) is added to a trough cut or cast parallel to the plane of electrophoretic separation, and the plates are incubated at room temperature in a humid atmosphere as double diffusion plate tests until precipitin bands are deemed fully developed. They should be examined during this incubation, since lines may appear and disappear when vastly different quantities of individual antigens are used as, for example, in human serum. Since Grabar and Williams carried out electrophoresis at room temperature and did nothing to protect their agar against drying during this run, they used a buffer of low ionicity and passed only a weak current through it for several hours. For example, agar made up in barbital buffer of calculated ionicity 0.05, pH 8.2, is submitted to an electric potential of 3–4 volts per cm. (40–50 milliamperes running through a 13 by 18 cm. agar plate of agar) for 4 hours (Grabar and Williams, 1955). This method is admirably simple and requires little practice to master. It has yielded excellent results and apparently still is used virtually unchanged at the Pasteur Institute, where it originated, as a favorite technique. However, it has some outstanding handicaps which have been successfully overcome in more recently developed immunoelectrophoresis techniques. It uses reactants very wastefully, requiring quantities of tenths of a milliliter or even milliliters. Excessive amounts of buffer and agar also are expended by it, and large plates of glass must be used as agar supports. Precipitin reactions require many days to develop fully. Once these have developed, if they are to be washed in their agar matrix, and stained and dried, these procedures must be carried out sluggishly because of the agar's thickness. Finally, since the agar is thick and indicator reactant diffuses from a trough whence its diffusion front may be slanted, equally slanted ribbons of precipitate may form which overlap and obscure each other when the agar is dried flat.

Microimmunoelectrophoresis

The increasingly popular microimmunoelectrophoresis technique devised by Scheidegger (1955) has been developed to the point where apparatus necessary for it now is available commercially (e.g., National Instrument Laboratories, Inc., 828 Evarts Street, N.E., Washington 18, D. C.). By contrast with the macro technique, Scheidegger's method (see also Zimmerman and Kruger, 1959) requires as little as 0.5% as much antigen solution and 1% as much antiserum. Electrophoresis takes only about 45 minutes, and immunodiffusion development requires only one or two days. The technique is as follows.

A glass microscope slide, previously coated with agar dried in the usual manner, is covered with 2 ml. of 2% agar to form a layer about 1 mm. thick. A cutter can be made by forcing two large gauge (10 or 13) hypodermic needles through the center area of large cork stopper about 7 mm. apart from each other and inserting, midway between these, two razor blades, so that the blades will be separated from each other by 1 mm. and extend out from the cork holder the same distance as each of the needles after the latter have had their points filed off. This cutter is lowered carefully onto the solidified agar gel, and agar is aspirated through the needles from the holes that they punch while the agar between the two slides simultaneously cut by the parallel razor blades is left in place until after electrophoretic separation. The slide so prepared is used as a bridge between two buffer vessels containing the electrodes, being connected at each end by filter paper dangling into buffer (Fig. II-4). Perhaps the most vulnerable part of this set-up is the filter paper connection between agar and buffer, which if it carries excessive current will tend to dry, carry more current, and cause irregular results. This vulnerability can be eliminated by the technique shown in Figs. V-15 and V-16. After electrophoresis (satisfactorily completed by Scheidegger's original procedure in 45 minutes) the band of agar between the slits previously cut by the razor blades of the cork cutter is removed, most conveniently by aspiration, and the trough resulting is charged with antiserum. The slide is allowed to develop precipitin reactions in a humid atmosphere, and these then are observed and photographed. These reactions can be permanently preserved on their microscope slides by one of the simple washing and staining procedures mentioned below.

A simplified microslide technique is to apply the sample to be electrophoresed to a thin layer of gel on a microscope slide by soaking some

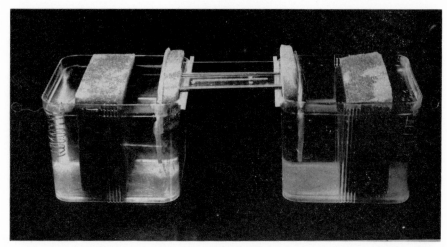

Fig. V-15. Simple micro immunoelectrophoresis set-up consisting of (from left to right) buffer vessel, electrode in first compartment, sponge to prevent electrolysis products from changing pH of second compartment of buffer vessel, second compartment, sponge connector, microscope slides on which electrophoresis takes place. The uppermost slide is covered simply with a layer of gel (procedure used for preparing Figs. V-1, V-2, V-3), while the lower slide is covered with Plexiglass template (used for preparing Frontispiece). Close-up view of slides and connector sponges is shown in Fig. V-16.

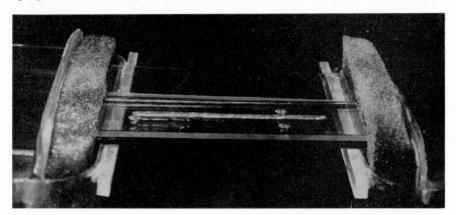

Fig. V-16. Close-up photograph of microscope slides and connector sponges used in simplified micro immunoelectrophoresis apparatus shown in Fig. V-15.

up into a small square of filter paper and allowing this to rest on a suitable area of the gel for 20 minutes (Wunderly, 1958a). Then, this small piece of filter paper is removed and discarded and electrophoresis is carried out as shown in Figs. V-15 and V-16. Finally, long narrow strips of filter paper soaked in indicator reactant are laid upon the gel on either side of the plane of electrophoretic fractionation, and precipitin bands are allowed to develop in the usual way in a humidified atmosphere. This is the method that was used to prepare Figs. V-1, V-2, and V-3 illustrating immunoelectrophoresis in three different kinds of gels. Its advantages are outstanding simplicity and elimination of a hole origin; its principle disadvantage is that it is rather wasteful of both antigen and antiserum by comparison with two other commonly used microimmunoelectrophoretic techniques.

Microscope slide immunoelectrophoresis can be further refined and improved by employing a Plexiglas template on top of agar on the slide (Crowle, 1960b; Fig. V-7:13). This permits use of very thin strips of agar and practically unlimited quantities of indicator reactant; it prevents drying of agar during electrophoresis or later immunodiffusion and eliminates the necessity for paper wick connectors between agar and buffer vessels. The technique is applied in the following manner.

To the long sides of a glass microscope slide are applied 3- to 5-layer strips of waterproof tape, each about 2 mm. wide. After these tapes have been applied, the uncovered part of the slide is polished very lightly with a water-repellent grease (a silicone, for example). This procedure is used in preference to precoating the glass slides with agar, as generally employed previously in this writer's and others' laboratories, because better electrophoretic fractionation is obtained (Crowle and Lueker, unpublished).* After this has been done, about 1.3 ml. of 1% agar melted in the electrolyte to be used is pipetted hot between the tapes, and while this is still molten the previously also siliconed plastic template is lowered upon the tapes. Connection between the agar, in the template-slide sandwich, and buffer vessels is made by placing the slide between two fine-pore synthetic sponges which dip into the buffer solution (Crowle, 1956), so that buffer makes direct contact with agar under conditions preventing any evaporation of water from the agar or connections between it and the electrode vessels (Figs. V-15 and V-16).

The template used in this technique is a rectangle of 3 mm. (⅛ inch) thick Plexiglas slightly smaller in length and width than a microscope slide, and in which have been cut (1) a central trough down nearly its full length, (2) two funnel-shaped holes on either side of his trough but at different distances from it, and near the center of the template, and (3) another funnel-shaped hole in a corner at one end of the template (Fig. V-7:13).

---

* Alternatively, the glass slide can be siliconed before application of the tapes with a product such as water-soluble "Siliclad" produced by Clay-Adams, Inc., of New York. Such treatment yields more reproducible results than are obtained simply by "greasing" the slides.

Reactant to be electrophoresed is placed in the agar gel through the two central holes on either side of the trough. The very thin disc of agar directly beneath each of these holes is cut free from surrounding agar with a very thin glass rod and aspirated, and then it is replaced by liquid reactant making a layer no thicker than that of the removed disc. This usually requires a volume of 0.0015 milliliter. Agar under the template corner hole is charged similarly with a weak solution (0.01%) of thiazine red dye made up in the same buffer as used for electrophoresis. Then, all three holes and the central trough are covered with individual portions of tape (e.g., the same kind as used between template and glass slide) to prevent evaporation and agar shrinkage during electrophoresis. A flexible sealant simply against evaporation, such as mineral oil, will not do. The sandwich slide is placed between its supporting sponges in their respective buffer vessels, and electrophoresis is carried out for about 45 minutes (depending upon various conditions, this can be as short as 15 minutes or as long as 2 hours). The extent of electrophoresis is indicated by the distance that thiazine red has moved from its corner well from cathode toward anode. After electrophoresis, the tape covering the central trough is removed without dislodging the template, and this trough is filled with indicator reactant.* Finally, the sandwich slide is held in a humid atmosphere for from 1 to 3 days, depending upon various conditions, for precipitin bands to develop. These can be examined from time to time through the plastic matrix. The final reading is made upon the glass slide and attached agar after the Plexiglas template has been pried off with a razor blade, and is followed by washing, staining, and drying.

Adjunct Techniques in Immunoelectrophoresis

Very small quantities of fluids or even of tissues can be submitted to agar electrophoresis by placing these in minute slits cut as origins in the agar and lightly blotting away any overflow (Wieme, 1958, 1959a). The pH or ionicity of an electrophoresis solution required for optimal fractionation of a given antigen may be unfavorable for antigen-antibody precipitation. This can be remedied by soaking agar in which electrophoresis has taken place and in which antigen-antibody reactions are to develop in the buffer of suitable pH and ionicity for a few minutes (Grabar, 1959a), carrying out electrophoresis in columns of agar which later are extruded and embedded in gel made up in acceptable buffer alongside troughs cast at the same time to later receive indicator reactant (Crowle, 1956), or arranging indicator reactant pH and elec-

---

* Sometimes it is desirable to scoop out agar in the trough and then, to seal it, fill the trough in quick succession with hot 1% agar solution, and empty it.

trolyte content so that compensatory changes will accompany its diffusion into adjoining agar gel.

Other media, such as paper, cellulose acetate membrane, and starch, have characteristics which permit them to yield electrophoretic separation of some materials which cannot be obtained as satisfactorily in agar gel (Moretti *et al.*, 1959). Hybrid immunoelectrophoretic techniques have been devised in which one medium is utilized for electrophoretic separation and another for immunoprecipitation. Serum can be electrophoresed in starch gel, a column of this gel containing the separated fractions overlaid with agar gel, and the latter in turn covered with indicator reactant, so that precipitin arcs form in the intervening agar (Poulik, 1956, 1959; Slater, 1955). The same can be done with paper (Poulik, 1952), or paper on which some mixture has been fractionated simply can be laid upon the surface of a thin agar gel next to and parallel to another strip of filter paper soaked with indicator reactant (Scheiffarth *et al.*, 1957). The same technique has been employed with cellulose acetate strips in place of filter paper (Kohn, 1958). A more sophisticated technique using cellulose acetate requires that the antigen be electrophoresed through a strip of this membrane, and then that indicator reactant be streaked alongside the path of separation so that precipitin reactions develop in the cellulose acetate itself rather than in agar (Consden and Kohn, 1959); agar is not used at all. Immunoelectrophoresis also can be carried out using Cyanogum 41 gel or gelatin in place of agar (Crowle, unpublished; Figs. V-1 and V-3).

Variations in basic agar immunoelectrophoresis techniques and auxiliary methods are employed for special purposes. The fraction in a given section of agar responsible for a precipitin band often can be identified chemically by cutting duplicate electrophoresis agar columns into small sections, and then analyzing those from one column chemically and those from the other serologically in some form of double diffusion plate test (Crouch, 1958; Crowle, 1956; Smith, 1956).

If electrophoresis has been carried out in an agar slab in preparation for subsequent immunoprecipitation analysis in the same slab, holes can be cut in series within the plane of separation in the agar and charged with indicator reactant (antibody). Then the trough usually charged with indicator reactant is charged with the same reactant that has been electrophoresed (antigen). If antibody happens to have been placed in an area of the agar containing a reactive antigen, this will combine with the antibody and prevent it from diffusing away from its well to react with the corresponding antigen diffusing toward it from the trough. Hence, that particular area will specifically lack a precipitin band formed elsewhere by the trough antigen and the series of wells con-

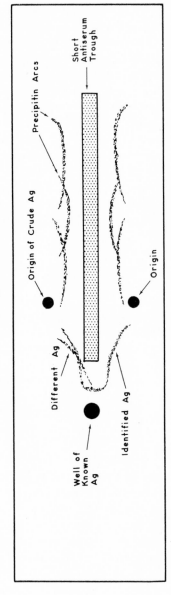

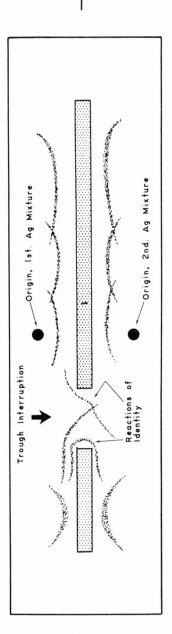

taining antibody (Kořínek and Paluska, 1959). This method can be used to identify individual precipitin bands in a complex double diffusion pattern. Moreover, cores of agar removed in this procedure to form the holes to be charged with antibody can be used in separate double diffusion counter-identifying tests as mentioned previously. A variation of this method which works upon already completed precipitin bands rather than on their formation consists of cutting a small well adjacent to a formed precipitate and charging it with a strong concentration of antigen suspected of having formed it. If the antigen placed in this small supplementary well and that forming the precipitate are immunologically closely related, and the specific precipitate is at least moderately sensitive to dissolution by antigen excess, then a portion of this band will be displaced or dissolved corresponding to the radial diffusion of the excess antigen (Gitlin et al., 1956). Unfortunately, many antigen-antibody precipitates are too insoluble, particularly when submitted to this method, to yield to the dissociating action of antigen excess, so that often this technique cannot be used.

If, among a complex series of antigens, one is to be identified with a separate, reasonably pure preparation of it, the "short trough" method of immunoelectrophoresis can be employed (Lévy and Polonovski, 1958; Fig. V-17). For example, if the subject for study is a serum α_2-globulin, then the trough usually cut in Scheidegger's microscope slide technique nearly as long as the slide purposely now is made shorter; it will not face the entire spectrum of serum proteins electrophoresed but only those on one side or the other of the area where this globulin is expected to come to rest after electrophoresis. Then, after electrophoresis of a serum sample on either side of the short trough, a hole is punched in line with the trough and ahead of this and is filled with purified α_2-globulin. Under optimal conditions, a precipitin band forming among the many which usually appear when whole serum is analyzed will be identified by its coalescence with that forming between the hole and the head of the trough and another analogous to it but forming on the opposite side of the trough. On this second side, one may alternatively have electrophoresed a partially purified antigen mixture instead of whole serum, intending to test it for its relative α_2-globulin content. A technique similar to this has been devised to compare individual fractions in different crude antigen mixtures electrophoresed simultaneously in the same agar and tested against the same indicator reactant (Clausen

---

Fig. V-17. Schematic representations of "short trough" and "interrupted trough" immunoelectrophoresis techniques used to identify individual precipitin band antigens.

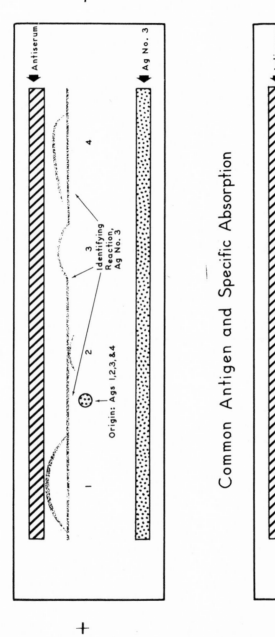

Common Antigen

Common Antigen and Specific Absorption

and Heremans, 1960). In this, there is an "interrupted trough," that is, a trough set between the two planes of electrophoretic separation but interrupted at a plane in the agar where the fractions of interest are expected to be after electrophoresis (Fig. V-17). Results obtained with this technique are similar to those of the short trough method, except that since a trough of antibody replaces the circular well of purified antigen, one must be certain to use sufficient antigen on either side of the troughs to encourage precipitin lines to grow sufficiently long through the interrupting gap between the tips of the troughs to coalesce with or cross each other, so that their respective relationships can be appreciated.

A given precipitin band formed by a particular antigen can be so identified by another method which depends on the appearance of a reaction of identity between one of the arcs formed by this antigen in a crude mixture of antigens and a straight band formed by antigen diffusing across the path through which electrophoresis took place (Osserman, 1959). The antigen mixture is electrophoresed through agar by one of the usual methods, and a trough on one side of the plane of separation and parallel to it is charged with antiserum (Fig. V-18). However, an identical trough on the other side of this plane is charged with supplementary antigen, preferably purified to contain principally the constituent to be identified. Antiserum diffusing against the fractionated antigens forms the usual spectrum of precipitin arcs, while with the supplementary antigen diffusing against it across the path of electrophoresis it forms a straight band, since the latter like the antiserum is diffusing from a trough. However, this straight band will be interrupted somewhere along its length by a bulge toward the antiserum trough, where the local concentration of separated antigen from the original crude mixture identical with the supplementary antigen is added to its own concentration; the otherwise discrete arc which would have been formed by the electrophoresed antigen alone has blended into and become part of the long band now formed cooperatively by the separated antigen and supplementary antigen. An advantage of this technique is that with it one also can compare directly and simultaneously antigen constituents of all electrophoretic mobilities in two crude mixtures (e.g., urine and serum), within the limits of precipitin band resolution for the particular technique employed for immunoelectrophoresis.

Several years ago Macheboeuf and co-workers (1953) showed that if

---

FIG. V-18. Schematic representations of immunoelectrophoretic methods employing the additive or absorptive effects of antigens to identify precipitin arcs formed by the same antigens in crude mixtures (see text for complete explanation).

antigen solution were streaked across the width of a strip of filter paper at one place and antiserum at another, so that upon subsequent electrophoresis antigen and antibody would cross each other, they would complex and become fixed to the paper. Other antigens and antiserum constituents not entering into this reaction remained soluble and could be washed from the paper strip leaving only the fixed aggregate demonstrable by later staining. A procedure resembling this but capable of locating electrophoresed agglutinins or antibodies which react only with insoluble antigens, which cannot be used in routine immunoelectrophoresis, consists of electrophoresing an antiserum on a slip of paper and then spraying antigen suspension onto the strip (Bustamante, 1957; Buttery, 1959). As in Macheboeuf's technique, antigen and antibody form fixed, insoluble, stainable complexes. Macheboeuf's technique of causing antibody to cross antigen during electrophoresis and precipitate it also has been used in agar gel. Tuberculoprotein, with an affinity for the anode, was placed in a column of agar in a glass tube behind its antiserum. During electrophoresis, the protein migrated toward the anode and the antibody toward the cathode, both invisibly, and upon meeting they formed a heavy, immobile precipitin band between their respective origins and nearest the antiserum origin (Crowle, 1956). This reaction was complete within about 20 minutes. The practical uses of this technique have not yet been explored, although Bussard and Huet (1959) point out, on the basis of similar experiments which they carried out, that its forceful acceleration of immunodiffusion reactions may be useful when heavy molecular weight antigens and antibodies are used, cutting the time required for them to diffuse and precipitate from days to minutes. The technique's greatest shortcoming is that several antigens in a crude mixture might migrate in the same direction as antibody and therefore not ever encounter it. Libich (1959) independently has developed this kind of technique into a method for demonstrating graphically, and in one experiment, precipitation under optimal reactant ratios as well as the breadth of the optimal reaction range. He believes that his method can be used advantageously to study the nature of antigen-antibody reactions. Conceivably, the basic technique of causing antigen to migrate electrophoretically across antibody might be used in other media, particularly in starch gels in which immunodiffusion reactions so far have not been demonstrated, perhaps because reactant diffusibility is so low in this medium.

Immunoelectrophoresis has been concerned nearly entirely with precipitins, that is, antibodies which precipitate soluble antigens, because soluble antigens have had to be used if they were to diffuse through semisolid media. From what just has been mentioned above, however,

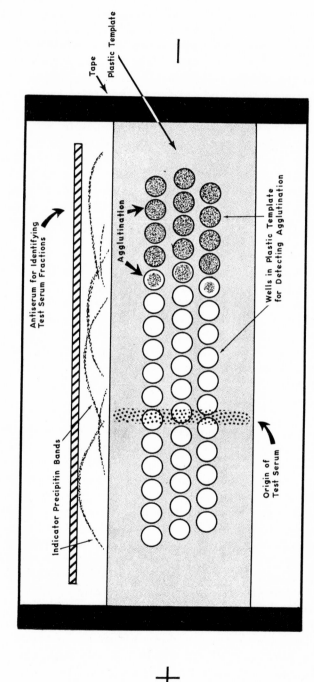

Fig. V-19. An immunoelectrophoretic method developed by Hanson and colleagues (1960) for determining the immunoelectrophoretic mobility of agglutinins. Tapes and plastic template are positioned after preliminary electrophoresis of test serum, for the second stage of the experiment in which agglutinins are located as to their electrophoretic positions in the agar gel under the template. See text for details.

it should be evident that other forms of antigen-antibody reaction might be employed in immunoelectrophoresis and immunodiffusion. This notion is supported by recent description of an immunoelectrophoretic method for determining electrophoretic mobilities in agar gels of hemagglutinins (Hanson *et al.*, 1960). A wide slab of agar is used for electrophoresis of a human antiserum, and parallel to the axis of fractionation there is the usual trough to receive indicator reactant (antiserum to human serum) after electrophoresis. However, the origin for the human antiserum being electrophoresed is wider than usual so that separated fractions will spread over a wide area of agar (Fig. V-19). After electrophoresis, a Plexiglas template is laid upon the agar, and each of numerous wells drilled through it in two long, parallel rows corresponding to the axis of electrophoresis is charged with antigen (e.g., red blood cells). The trough, meanwhile, is charged with antiserum to human serum in order to identify, by the usual precipitin arcs seen in immunoelectrophoresis, the separated constituents of antiserum. If hemagglutinins happen to be in the agar under a given template hole, they diffuse up into the small quantity of saline placed in this hole in a special short pre-incubation period and agglutinate the red blood cells that have been added to the hole after this pre-incubation. By correlating the location of wells showing hemagglutination with the analytic immunoelectrophoretic pattern which identifies antiserum fractions under any particular well, one can determine which antiserum fraction is responsible for hemagglutinating activity.

Conditions Affecting Immunoelectrophoresis

Conditions for satisfactory immunoelectrophoresis can be summarized as follows. Although a purified agar (or other gelling agent) is desirable to lower both electroosmosis and the quantity of nonbuffering but current-carrying salts, the agar should be selected primarily for adequate fractionation of the mixture being examined. Preference should be given, for example, to a batch in which no major antigen is located at the origin after electrophoresis. Ionicity, pH, and type of salts used in the buffer have to be selected rather empirically. Low ionicity speeds movement of fractions but also tends to broaden their zones, lowering resolution; high ionicity slows them, increases current and heat problems, and, if excessive, also lowers resolution by permitting inordinate diffusion. Generally, for agar and other negatively charged media, a pH should be selected which maintains all antigenic constituents that are charged in a negative charge state, to prevent their adsorption to the gelling medium; thus, the pH nearly always will be alkaline. Barbital buffers usually are employed for serum fractionations, but other buffers may give better results in certain circumstances or media and should not be overlooked; for other antigens, experimentation will lead to choice of the most suitable buffer.

A general rule for electrophoretic separation preceding immuno-precipitation is to use the highest voltage and most rapid separation of constituents compatible with maintaining the agar reasonably cool, that is, cool enough not to denature antigens being separated, or to melt the agar or dry it too much. To achieve this, one must take precautions to preserve the integrity of connections between the agar and buffer in the buffer vessels. Efficient cooling must be achieved, and it is ascertained by maintenance at a given voltage of a level of current not exceeding that measured at the beginning of electrophoresis; the current will rise if the agar warms, whereupon it conducts more electricity. Cooling can be intensified or reduced, as the need is indicated by a milliammeter. If no efficient means are available for closely regulating the temperature of agar during electrophoresis, one will have to use a sufficiently low voltage or ionicity or both, so that natural cooling can dissipate the heat generated during a run and a relatively constant current can be main-tained. Clever rather specialized ways for obtaining maximum speed of separation and resolution in agar by using very efficient cooling methods have been described fully by Wieme (1959a). For consistency from one electrophoretic run to another, one should include in the agar for each run some indicator of electrophoretic migration (see below).

Optimal conditions for immunoprecipitation following electrophoresis are the same as those of double diffusion plate tests. One difference peculiar to immunoelectrophoresis is that electrophoresis can cause some antigens soluble in mixture with others to become insoluble when grossly separated from them, and that the resulting precipitate may confusingly resemble one produced by antigen-antibody interaction. Another differ-ence is that the shapes of precipitin arcs in immunoelectrophoresis are governed by more factors than are those in double diffusion plates and must be interpreted in the light of all of these (e.g., mobility, electro-phoretic heterogeneity, electrophoretic dissimilarity-antigenic identity). A third is that a dual antigen may be split by electrophoresis into two while this may not occur in immunodiffusion tests, or it can be de-natured during electrophoresis.

Complications in Immunodiffusion

A minor complication in an immunodiffusion test can cause a major misinterpretation or arrest the trend of a certain line of research. Often, a supplementary or auxiliary technique can overcome this complication or otherwise improve immunodiffusion tests to make them more meaningful or more incisive. Such complications and auxiliary techniques often are mentioned only in passing by their users or discoverers, although knowledge of them can be very helpful to other workers. The following sections discuss some of these.

Reactant Stability

Among the most subtle difficulties in immunodiffusion and immuno-electrophoresis tests are protein-protein interactions. These are exempli-fied by the complexing of hemoglobin with haptoglobin. The resulting complex has a mobility differing from that of either original antigen (Hirschfeld, 1959b). Such complexing also could occur between immuno-globulins. such as β_2-globulin and abnormal γ-globulin found in myeloma sera (Grabar *et al.*, 1956a). Sometimes this phenomenon can be detected using double diffusion analysis to complement immunoelectrophoresis (Hanson and Johansson, 1959b). The opposite effect, dissociation, also can confuse analyses (Kleczkowski, 1957). Thus, dissociation, whatever its primary cause, probably plays a role in such observations as the splitting of sperm plasma from 8 fractions into 10 when the plasma is left standing for two days (Hermann, 1959). Aging may transmute one serum constituent to another. Thus, β_{1A}-globulin is not detectable in fresh serum, but β_{1C} is; if the serum is stored at $1°C$. for 4 to 6 weeks, the latter component is converted into the former, and at intermediate times both coexist (Müller-Eberhard *et al.*, 1960a). False precipitates have been observed to form in double diffusion plates left standing for a long time (Scanu *et al.*, 1958), although their occurrence is uncommon. Since not all true precipitin bands will take up any given protein stain (Crowle, unpublished), these artifacts cannot be identified with certainty simply if they cannot be stained. Electrophoretic analyses of human serum albumin may yield different results if the albumin is allowed to stand at different temperatures for different periods of time (Schultze, 1958). Moreover, patterns obtained when individual serum constituents are recombined may differ from those obtained with their original crude mixture in whole serum (Schultze, 1958).

Related to these dissociation-association changes are deterioration of certain antigens, their separation from others on which their solubility may depend, or their precipitation by newly added agents. Haptoglobin is not stable in phosphate buffer solution even when kept refrigerated (Burtin *et al.*, 1954). In agar immunoelectrophoresis, the principle serum lipoprotein, β-lipoprotein by paper electrophoresis, partly because of its poor solubility in agar gels, will be located among α_2-globulins and hence is called α_2-lipoprotein (Wieme, 1959a). This lipoprotein also actually interacts with agar gel (Wieme, 1959a). Hence, its true agar electrophoretic mobility is elusive, and its apparent mobility is concentration-dependent; the greater its concentration is, the lower is its apparent mobility (Uriel and Grabar, 1956b; Wieme, 1959a). Precipitation of serum lipoproteins in the agar is particularly marked with some sera from patients with liver maladies (Hartmann *et al.*, 1956). The immunoelectrophoretic α_2-lipoprotein may well account primarily for the nonspecific halos of precipitate seen in double diffusion tests when human serum is tested in agar dissolved in barbital buffer. As has been noted above, using phosphate buffer instead of barbital or using a high concentration of glycine as an additive apparently prevents such precipitation.

Medium

Commercial agar contains a factor which precipitates some serum proteins, although this effect is minimized at alkaline pH (Wieme, 1959a). Some antigens such a lysozyme, tend to combine with agar, and hence their mobilities cannot be determined at all by immunoelectrophoresis (Kaminski, 1955a). The mobility of C-reactive protein appears difficult to determine by agar immunoelectrophoresis, since the final location of this antigen with regard to its electrophoretic origin in the agar changes little in buffers of different pH ranging between 6.9 and 8.6, while other serum antigens tested simultaneously predictably change their apparent mobilities according to the pH of the solution employed (Fishel, personal communication). The absolute mobility of any antigen cannot be determined directly by immunoelectrophoresis, because various agar preparations differ in their degrees of electroosmosis (Fig. V-4). Rather, the mobility for such an antigen must be estimated by comparing it with that of an antigen whose mobility is known, such as serum albumin. Paradoxically, however, immunoelectrophoresis offers a far better final criterion for identifying and naming an antigen (e.g., β_{2M}-globulin) than other types of electrophoresis, which have generated lively and sometimes amusing controversies over whether a serum fraction is a fast γ- or a slow β-globulin, because serologic definition is far more precise than electrophoretic definition, and immunoelectrophoresis utilizes both.

Direct comparison of immunoelectrophoresis results obtained using different buffer salts at the same pH or ionicity or in different media is unreliable, as has already briefly been mentioned. Thus, β-lipoprotein found on paper is α_2-lipoprotein in agar gel (Scanu *et al.*, 1958). Barbital and borate buffers used in agar yield somewhat different patterns among the fast-moving serum proteins (Havez and Biserte, 1959a). Starch and agar electrophoresis give strikingly different results; the

β_{2A}-globulin of immunoelectrophoresis is Pre-albumin 1 of starch electrophoresis. The nature of an electrophoretic pattern obtained with starch depends upon such variables as the extent to which the starch has been hydrolyzed during its preparation (Poulik, 1959). Cellulose acetate strips hold so little buffer that serum being electrophoresed upon one can itself have a significant buffering effect which alters the electrophoretic pattern obtained (Bodman, 1959). Local aberrations in immunoelectrophoretic patterns and irregular results are likely to be obtained if the fluid to be

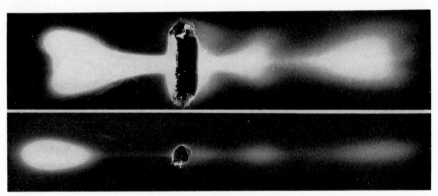

Fig. V-20. Photographs comparing effects of origin shape on electrophoresis of undiluted, undialyzed human serum in agar. Irregular ("bat wing") shape of fractions in slide with slot origin (top) apparently is due to the influence of serum electrolytes on current carried in unequal quantities through the origin at the beginning of electrophoresis. Circular origin is less affected because quantities of salts at its lateral edges are relatively small; excess electrolyte in center merely causes elongation of fractions into "tear-drop" shape. Electrophoresis above was carried out in BBL laboratory agar. Note greater electroosmosis than seen in Difco or "deionized" Difco agars, Fig. V-4.

electrophoresed is not first dialyzed to the ionicity and pH of the electrophoresis buffer (Wieme, 1959a). This is particularly a fault of techniques which employ an elongated origin as opposed to a circular origin (see Fig. V-20). It is minimized when a sample is applied by diffusion from a piece of filter paper (Wunderly's technique). The shape of a precipitin arc in immunoelectrophoresis can indicate something about the heterogeneity of an antigen forming it, but it must be interpreted taking into account such complications as tailing, antigen molecular weight, differences in the ratios of various forms of antigen present, and the possibility of serological false-identity reactions due to use of an improper antiserum (Hirschfeld, 1960a).

Antiserum

Using an indiscriminatory antiserum is a rather common fault in immunodiffusion tests, not necessarily because the user is unaware of this problem, but largely because the proper antiserum for an analysis cannot be obtained. For example, the most highly specific antiserum for discriminating between individual serum antigens in one species of animal can be prepared in either an animal of the same species (isologous antibody) or in animals of the species most closely related to it (Gengozian, 1959; Weigle, 1960). However, this is impossible when antigens to be analyzed are obtained from microorganisms. In such a situation, antiserum produced by one animal against antigen from one strain of bacterium, for example, might show what appears to be a reaction of complete identity with a similar antigen from another bacterial strain, while another animal of the same species or one of another species might produce antibodies which readily distinguish these two antigens. In this situation, trial and error seem to be the best guide. Hence, compared antigens only can be concluded to have a certain relationship relative to the antiserum used to compare them. For example, one is not justified in concluding that given antigens from two strains of bacteria are identical serologically if he has used only antiserum against one strain for comparing the two in a double diffusion test. He needs either a mixed antiserum against both or antiserum from an animal immunized with both. The analytic properties of an antiserum depend not only upon the species of animal producing it, but also upon the nature of the antigen injected into the animal (Kaminski, 1957a) and its route of injection (Crowle, 1960c). Some individual animals may respond to injection of a given antigen by forming antibodies which complex with but do not precipitate antigen and hence interfere with genuine precipitating antibodies produced by other animals of the same species and used in a common pool of antiserum (Gillert, 1958). Nonprecipitating antibodies also can have subtle effects upon visible precipitates (Goudie et al., 1959). Consequently, antisera should be tested and chosen carefully, and pooled only cautiously.

Physical Conditions

The physical conditions of an immunodiffusion test control the type of results which will be secured. For example, while periodic (secondary) precipitates do not develop visibly in single diffusion tube tests with rabbit antisera used in very low concentrations against high concentrations of various antigens, they do if higher concentrations of antibodies of H- rather than R-type are employed (Crowle, 1960c). Since such precipitin bands formed by H-type antiserum are not stationary, they are readily confused with primary precipitates. Secondary precipitin bands, most readily identifiable either by later dissolving (if horse antibody is used) or by not moving (if rabbit antibody is used), appear

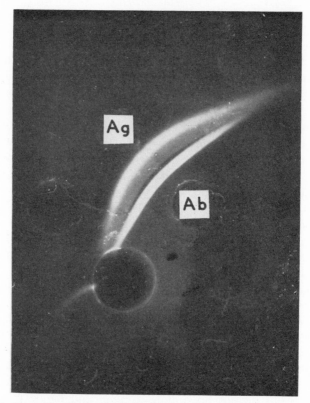

Fig. V-21. Example of secondary (Liesegang) precipitation in a double diffusion test due to excess reactant. In this instance, very strong mouse antibody (Ab) was used against a relatively weak solution of its antigen (Ag), ovalbumin, with the result that after primary precipitation (heavy band near Ab) despite the advantage of its low molecular weight, ovalbumin could not continue to diffuse fast enough to react with great excess of antibody rapidly built up in that area. Consequently, immediately beyond primary precipitate there is a gap where antibody excess completely prevented precipitation, followed by a broad area of poor precipitation which took place under the disadvantage of antibody excess, and finally by a heavy secondary precipitate (itself faintly split) where diffusion distance for antibody has tended to neutralize its initially overwhelming advantage over antigen, and a stable band forms. Note how tips of primary and secondary bands come together. This micro double diffusion test clearly shows that antibody is of R- rather than H-type, since primary precipitate strongly resisted dissolution in bath of excess antibody, as a precipitate formed by H-type antibody would not have done.

in single diffusion tubes subjected to sudden changes in temperature of as little as 2° or 3°C. during their incubation (Wilson, 1958). Similar artifacts are observed in double diffusion tests, although much less often (see Fig. V-21).

An unfavorable ratio of antigen to antibody in immunodiffusion experiments can cause bands to fail to appear, split, or appear and later disappear (Crowle, 1960c). False nonidentity reactions can develop in double diffusion plates in which identical antigens used in vastly different concentrations are tested side by side against the same antiserum (Feinberg, 1957). Prematurely reading immunodiffusion patterns may lead one to overlook some reactions that take a long time to develop visibly (Scheidegger, 1955). On the other hand, the prolonged incubation required to detect these reactions may permit dissolution, due to reactant excess, of bands originally present, particularly if H-type antibody is used. Hence, ideally, to detect the maximum number of possible reactions, one should make periodic readings. A sudden rise in the incubation temperature of a double diffusion plate has been observed to obliterate existing precipitin bands which had formed at refrigerator temperature, an effect attributed to the sudden increase in antigen diffusion rate and consequent local but maintained antigen excess (Rheins et al., 1956).

Miscellaneous difficulties arise in immunodiffusion experimentation. For example, although a precipitin zone's density is commonly accepted as proportional to the quantity of antibody forming it, this notion must be tempered by recent evidence showing that antigen quantity also influences it (Crowle, 1960c). Precipitin zone density also varies with the time of incubation and the presence of nonantibody antiserum constituents (Glenn, 1959a). A single immunodiffusion test may be highly informative, but any analysis is better accomplished if more than one test is set up using different ratios of reactants; two precipitating systems may produce two or more superimposed bands that appear to be single (Feinberg, 1957). This usually can be discovered by varying antigen-antibody ratios. Various nonspecific substances significantly can alter reactant diffusion rates, data particularly important in single diffusion analyses (Augustin and Hayward, 1955). Confusing effects of cross-reacting antigens upon each others' precipitin band formation in immunodiffusion tests already have been mentioned (see Fig. III-4). The slower of two diffusing antigens in a mixture may never be detected in single or double diffusion tests if it also happens to be the cross-reacting one (Franklin and Kunkel, 1957). It could be detected if specific antibodies for it could be procured and cross-reacting antibodies for the second antigen were removed by adsorption, and it could be demonstrated by immunoelectrophoresis if it happened to have a slightly different electrophoretic mobility from the second antigen. Although primarily, diffusion rates of cross-reacting antigens control the appearance or nonappearance of their precipitin bands in immunodiffusion tests, the ratios with antibody at which they precipitate also do, sufficiently so that on at least one recorded occasion an exception has been found to the rule that a cross-reacting antigen should not be detected if its concentration (and therefore diffusion rate) is lower than that of the homologous antigen (Wilson, 1958).

The number of precipitin lines produced by an antigen is likely to be less than its number of determinant groups, but on the other hand, and not widely enough recognized, if an antigen has more than one determinant group it can form more than one precipitin band (Crowle, 1960c). Interestingly, data recently reported by Finger and co-workers (1960) indicate that the appearance of two bands does not necessarily even mean that more than one determinant is present on an antigen molecule, let alone that more than one antigen has been detected. Their rather exceptional finding is that antibodies in certain human antisera to dextran, known by other tests which they performed as an antigen with only one combining site, produce two precipitin bands with this antigen. To explain their observation, they assume that certain individuals simultaneously form antibodies with two varieties of combining sites of distinctly different size and therefore sharply different avidities for antigen; this is contrasted to the usual course of antibody production, in which human beings produce a smoothly ranging spectrum of antibody varieties with equally varied avidities and with the capability of forming only one precipitin band.

Specific absorption is one of the most useful techniques in serological testing of any kind. For example, it can be used to increase the specificity of antibody by adding cross-reacting antigen to an antiserum to remove corresponding cross-reacting antibodies. When such a method is employed, enough absorbing reactant as well as its normally inactive complexes may remain in the absorbed fluid to affect a subsequent test in which it is used. For example, if absorbed antiserum is employed in a trough on one side and unabsorbed antiserum on the other side of a plane of electrophoretic separation of mixture of antigens in immunoelectrophoresis, residual soluble antigen used to absorb the first antiserum could diffuse across the path of the electrophoresed material and precipitate with antibodies in the unabsorbed antiserum diffusing from the second trough in the opposite direction. This complication can be avoided simply by cutting a narrow gap through the middle of the plane of electrophoretic separation to prevent diffusion of absorbing antigen across this area, but to leave side-by-side for comparison the developing immunoelectrophoretic patterns (Vaux Saint-Cyr et al., 1958).

General Auxiliary Methods

Sometimes, an original immunodiffusion technique has been improved to overcome some particular difficulty. Other times, improvements or auxiliary methods have been utilized to increase the value of an existing immunodiffusion procedure.

Specific Absorption

By using the auxiliary technique of specific absorption, just mentioned above, one can improve greatly the already respectable potentiality of immunodiffusion techniques in identifying antigen-antibody systems. Wishing to obtain an antiserum specific for precipitin band A, for example, among bands A, B, C, and D, one can fractionate the original crude antigen mixture to yield the last three and then treat with these antiserum produced against all four. This leaves in the antiserum only antibodies to antigen A and makes it a specific reagent for detecting this antigen in later analyses of crude antigen mixtures. Specific absorption has been used in immunodiffusion tests from the time of their first practical application (Oudin, 1947; see also Burtin *et al.*, 1954; Darcy, 1955; Franklin and Kunkel, 1957; Heremans *et al.*, 1959b; Jennings, 1953; Raynaud, 1958; Richter *et al.*, 1958; Scanu and Page, 1959; Vaux Saint-Cyr, 1959; Williams and Grabar, 1955a). One of the simplest specific absorption double diffusion plate techniques, and one which only several years after its first application (Björklund, 1952a) is beginning to see the use that it deserves, consists of incorporating the absorbent (e.g., antigen) in the agar gel to prevent specific reactant (antibody) from leaving its well to diffuse into intermediate agar where it can react with that antigen diffusing from an opposing well (see Fig. V-22). For example, if antigen mixture A + B is to be reacted with antiserum containing antibodies to both A and B, but one wishes to detect only reaction B, before the opposing wells are charged with their respective reactants both are filled with purified antigen A which is allowed to diffuse into the agar. Later, the wells are emptied of any liquid which may remain and are charged, respectively, with antigen and antibody. Diffusion of antigens A and B will occur into the pre-treated agar in normal fashion; antibody to B also will diffuse normally from its well. However, if the agar has been adequately pre-treated, antibody to A never will leave its well, since surrounding A antigen immediately binds it at its origin, and the result is that only precipitin band B will form (Björklund, 1956; Dray and Young, 1959; Feinberg, 1957; Harding and Perlmann, 1954). One variation of this technique is to mix purified

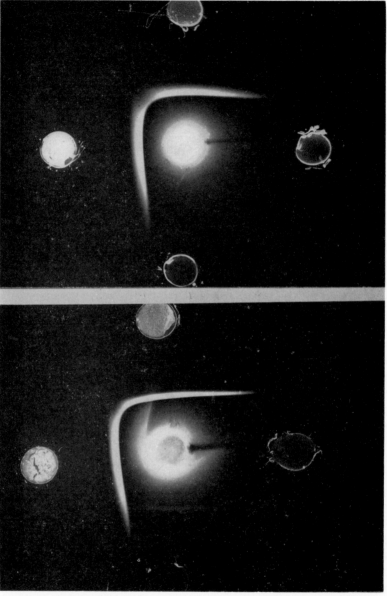

Fig. V-22. Micro double diffusion tests illustrating specific absorption of anti-body (against ovalbumin) from antiserum (to ovalbumin and bovine γ-globulin, placed in center depot). In lower photograph, two precipitin bands formed by ovalbumin solution (6 o'clock depot) are readily visible, one very near the central antiserum depot and the second midway between antigen and antibody depots. These bands fuse with similar bands formed by ovalbumin mixed with bovine

antigen A with the antiserum in its depot, for although by large antigen excess the antigen-antibody complexes which form as a result of this treatment may be soluble, they are too large to diffuse through agar gel into the reaction arena (Björklund, 1953b). Another variation is to incorporate the inhibiting reactant in melted and then cooled agar before it is poured (Oudin, 1955).

Incorporating the absorbing reactant in the agar either by pre-diffusion or by mixing with the melted agar is simple and in many instances works well. However, occasionally not enough can be used in this manner to effectively prevent diffusion of the reactant which one intends to absorb (Korngold, 1957; Oudin, 1955). On such an occasion the reactant must be pre-treated in liquid form by standard absorption procedures (Björklund and Björklund, 1957; Korngold, 1957). For example, antigen solution is mixed with antiserum at different proportions until maximum precipitation is attained; this precipitate is centrifuged out and discarded and the supernate of absorbed antiserum is ready for use. An alternative method is to percolate antiserum through a column of antigen rendered insoluble by denaturation which has been gentle enough not to injure its specific determinant groups, or by adsorption to insoluble particles such as of an anion exchange resin (Ishizaka *et al.*, 1960; see also Isliker, 1953, 1957).

Partial absorption of a reactant or a bolstering of its concentration can be used as identifying techniques, occasionally more efficiently than total absorption. When only partial purification of an absorbent has been achieved or when complex systems are being analyzed by absorption with only slightly less complex mixtures, these may be methods of necessity. If an antigen is partially absorbed from its mixture with other antigens, the precipitin band that it produces in a single diffusion tube appears to migrate down the tube through antibody-charged gel more slowly than it did before part of it was removed, because after its absorption it is less concentrated (Oudin, 1952, 1955). Conversely, if this particular antigen is present in a test mixture added to a standard one, this antigen's total concentration is raised and movement of its precipitin band is accelerated. In either instance, the movement of other bands is not affected unless they are formed by cross-reacting antigens or unless antigens forming them also coincidentally are bolstered or absorbed.

γ-globulin (9 o'clock depot). The latter antigen forms one very strong band and a second very faint one, both when it is mixed with ovalbumin (9 o'clock depot) and when it is used alone (12 o'clock). Buffer alone (3 o'clock), of course, forms no bands. Agar in second test (upper photograph) was mixed with ovalbumin before pouring to specifically prevent formation of ovalbumin precipitin bands. Note that these are absent, while formation of bands by bovine γ-globulin remains unaffected.

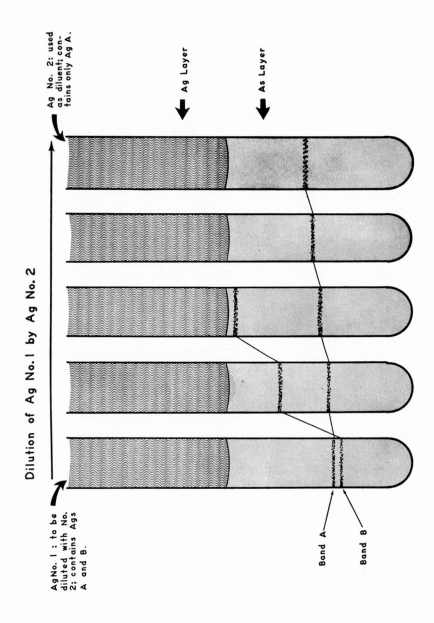

This technique can be applied to analyses of either antigen or antibody.

A variation of this analytic method consists of mutually diluting reactants (Oudin, 1955). For example, if two antigen solutions are used for mutual dilution, one containing antigens A and B and the other only A, and if the first is diluted with increasing quantities of the second, the rate of antigen A diffusion might drop at first, assuming that the first solution contains more of A than the second, but in succeeding series of solutions this drop would become progressively less to finally approach the rate shown by A antigen in the second solution alone (see Fig. V-23). The diffusion rate of the B band, on the other hand, falls off rapidly as its concentration becomes progressively weaker because it is diluted with a solution of A alone, exactly as it would if it were diluted with an inert solvent (Telfer, 1953).

The analytic technique in immunoelectrophoresis described independently by Heremans and co-workers (1959b) and by Osserman (1959) of charging a trough on one side of the plane of antigen electrophoresis in agar with antiserum and a trough on the opposite side with purified antigen has been mentioned above. Heremans and his coworkers improve somewhat on this basic method by charging the first trough with antiserum, as usual, but charging the second not with purified antigen alone, but rather with a mixture of excess antigen and the same antiserum as placed in the first trough (Fig. V-18). As a result, not only will a given precipitin arc be identified on the side of the first trough by its coalescence with a straight precipitin band formed by antigen diffusing from the second trough, but also its electrophoretic position will be evident by its conspicuous absence in the otherwise complete pattern of arcs produced between antiserum in the second trough and the electrophoresed mixture of antigens; antibody in this antiserum, which would have formed it, has been absorbed by mixture with excess specific antigen.

Substitution

The technique for identifying a precipitin band with the antigen responsible for its formation by punching a small hole in agar adjacent to it and then charging the hole with this antigen to see if the existing

---

FIG. V-23. Schematic representation of mutual dilution single diffusion tube technique for identifying an antigen. Antigen B is present in both antigen mixtures (1 and 2), and hence its position at a given interval of incubation is approximately same in series of tubes. Antigen A, on the other hand, is found only in antigen mixture No. 1, and being diluted by mixture No. 2 as though this were some indifferent buffer solution shows progressively less precipitin band migration in succeeding tubes, all observed after same incubation time.

band dissolves under the local influence of antigen excess (Oudin, 1955) has been used for unusual purposes by Korngold and van Leeuwen (1959b). They carried out double diffusion plate tests using large excesses of one or another reactant to find whether a specific precipitate always forms an immunologically specific barrier to diffusion of a reactant used in great excess. By punching small holes on the distal sides of such precipitin bands, charging them with fresh opposing reactant and noting the appearance of subsidiary precipitin bands forming in front of them, they showed that reactant in large excess truly can diffuse in serologically active form beyond the precipitin band which it at first formed with the much weaker complementary reactant.

Suspected superposition of precipitin bands formed by different antigens in a single diffusion tube test can be proved by removing the original solution of the two antigens, replacing it with a solution of one or the other of these, and noting subsequently whether the existing band splits into two, one migrating on downward and the other one remaining behind relatively immobile (Munoz and Becker, 1950). When large differences in the molecular weights of two antigens which appear to be immunologically related prevents their adequate comparison by the usual double diffusion plate techniques, special ones can be devised. A pattern is made in agar of four holes as corners of an imaginary square with a fifth in the square's center as in Fig. V-6:17. A pair of the opposite outer holes are charged with the two different antigens and the other pair with antiserum, and then precipitin reactions are allowed to develop. Following this, the central fifth hole is charged with one of the two antigens and the antibody wells are refilled. The relationships between originally and newly developed precipitin lines may provide the kind of comparative information desired (Franklin and Kunkel, 1957).

Enhancement

Some methods for increasing the potential sensitivity of immunodiffusion tests already have been mentioned. These enhancing methods include pre-concentrating the antiserum (Kaminski, 1957c), recharging the antiserum depot with fresh antiserum (Parlett and Reher, 1959) or with antiserum of known activity but used below the threshold of precipitation itself (Parlett, personal communication), using a positive serum adjacent to a weak antiserum suspected of having antibodies but unable by itself to produce a visible precipitate with an antigen (Heiner, 1958), enhancing precipitation or initiating visible antigen-antibody aggregation from otherwise invisible complexes by using specifically-acting cations (Crowle, 1958a, 1960a), enhancing by exposure of agar gel to hydrochloric acid fumes (Goudie *et al.*, 1959), using coprecipitating antibodies (Goudie *et al.*, 1959), and intensifying bands after unreacted proteins have been washed from the agar by treating the agar with protein precipitants such as picric acid, acetic acid, or trichloracetic acid (Bergrahm, 1960; Grabar, 1959a). Staining, as well as simply soaking agar in physiologic saline, sometimes reveals precipitin bands not previously visible in already incubated double diffusion plates (Crowle, 1958c; unpublished). The presence of minor antibody constituents in an antiserum probably is most reliably detected by using a "reversed" Oudin single diffusion tube test, that is, one in which antiserum is layered in high concentration over dilute antigen (Augustin, 1957). R-type antibodies generally are preferable to H-type for detecting minor antigens in crude mixtures, because precipitin bands that they form are not so readily dissociated by reactant excesses (Grabar *et al.*, 1958).

Utilization of barbital buffer in place of unbuffered saline or saline buffered with phosphate or citrate salts often has been found to increase the sensitivity of immunodiffusion tests (Crowle and Lueker, unpublished).

Secondary Auxiliary Methods

Secondary aids for immunodiffusion and immunoelectrophoresis tests include those not directly affecting electrophoresis or antigen-antibody reactions. They encompass methods for measuring electroosmosis, for judging the constancy of electrophoretic runs, for grossly locating electrophoresed fractions in agar without disturbing them, and for identifying particular antigens. They include also methods for photographing and staining precipitin bands, but these will be considered in their own right in an independent section below.

Electroosmosis through agar can be measured accurately by observing the movement during electrophoresis of inert particles such as uncharged polysaccharides like dextran (Wieme, 1959a; Wunderly, 1958a) or glucose (Bussard and Perrin, 1955). The location of such inert carbohydrates can be detected after electrophoresis by precipitation or some color reaction. Precipitation is the easiest, requiring only that the agar be treated with 70% ethanol and 5% acetic acid (Wieme, 1959a). This type of fixation is compatible with subsequent staining procedures in simple agar electrophoresis. Dextran can be colored before electrophoresis with such an agent as *o*-nitroaniline (Wunderly, 1958a). To simply establish whether the conditions of electrophoresis from one test to another are equivalent, one can deposit a weak solution of some acid dye at its own origin near the cathode end of a slide and then record its final location at the end of an electrophoretic run. In any two runs, the electrophoretic movement of a given antigen in one kind of gel can be assumed the same if similar electrophoretic conditions have been used and the acid dye has reached the same location (Crowle, 1956). To

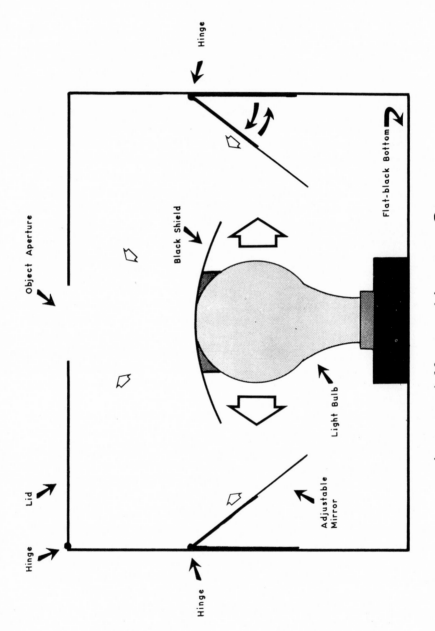

Immunodiffusion Viewing Box

locate and identify antigens grossly after their electrophoresis in agar, one can lay a thin strip of filter paper on the surface of the agar, allow it to soak up small quantities of each fraction from the agar surface for a few minutes, and then fix and stain the absorbed fraction on the filter paper just as is done in filter paper electrophoresis (Wieme, 1959a).

An antigen taking part in an immunodiffusion reaction can be identified in several ways. Aside from specific stains, one can take advantage of special properties of the antigen. For example, if it is an enzyme which can be detected in agar gel by spraying the gel with its substrate which it hydrolyses to produce some color (Oudin, 1952), one can show in the double diffusion plate test that this antigen is distributed on one side of its specific precipitate zone but not on the other, and that other precipitate zones produced by simultaneously present but different antigens offer no barrier to its passage by diffusion. The precipitin band due to this enzyme, then, can be specifically identified. Some antigens, like the hemolysins, have identifying characteristics which become evident when they are allowed to diffuse through agar containing red blood cells; their precipitin bands can be readily demonstrated as limiting zones of their specific type of hemolytic activity. Other antigens such as hemoglobin (Naylor and Adair, 1959) and horse ferritin (Easty and Mercer, 1958) have sufficient color of their own to identify themselves in precipitin bands. Still others can be discerned because they combine specifically with some other substance; haptoglobins, for example, combine with hemoglobin (Wieme, 1955).

Reading and Recording Results

Immunodiffusion tests can be no better than the methods used to read and record their results. Hence, this section is included to describe not only methods for observing immunodiffusion precipitates, but also techniques for recording them photographically. Methods for staining precipitin bands are detailed in the section following this one.

Illumination

Dark-field illumination is required for best visualization of precipitin bands in their gel background. Light should be directed through the

---

Fig. V-24. Diagram of a simple and inexpensive viewing box for immunodiffusion reactions which also serves as an excellent dark-field illuminator for immunodiffusion photography. Object aperture is made to fit size of most often used cell. Preferably, bottom of box and shield resting upon light bulb should be covered with black velvet cloth, although nearly comparable nonreflecting black background is obtained if both are painted with a "flat" black paint. Inside of box also should be so painted.

gel from below at an acute angle from the immunodiffusion cell, the cell should be surrounded by a mask slightly larger than itself to prevent any of this light from falling upon the observer's eye or the camera's lens, and below the cell should be a flat-black surface such as black velvet— the black background against which the white precipitin bands will be seen. Lighting apparatus of varying degrees of complexity and flexibility have been constructed just for this purpose (Lawson, 1957; Ouchterlony, 1958; Reed, 1960; Relyveld *et al.*, 1954; Schutz, 1958). However, a simple, yet fully adequate and versatile apparatus both for viewing and for photographing immunodiffusion results can be constructed as shown in Fig. V-24. This apparatus can be converted to a transmitted-light illuminator for stained slides simply by covering its aperture with a plate of opalescent "milk" glass or ground glass. The opening in this box is made to just accommodate a 4.5 cm. Petri dish, but it can be covered with appropriately cut cardboard masks with apertures of sizes and shapes suitable for critically viewing smaller objects, or it can be cut larger to accommodate 9 cm. Petri dishes.

Photometry

For many purposes, a rough sketch of the precipitin bands as seen with the aid of a viewer is sufficient record. However, more exact data are obtained on the number, form, and interrelationships of precipitin bands with the aid of photometry, microscopy, and photography. Photometry has proved particularly valuable for immunodiffusion tests set up in tubes. Glenn and his colleagues (cf. Glenn, 1956b,c, 1960; Glenn and Garner, 1957) have developed and used a completely automatic photometric tube scanner which records not only the number of precipitin bands and their positions in a tube, but also their densities and boundary characteristics.[*] Less complex and expensive ways of photometrically recording tube immunodiffusion results have been employed (Oudin, 1947, 1948a, 1952), although not usually with the precision obtainable with the Glenn apparatus. For example, the precipitin pattern can be photographed, and the negative itself can be scanned photometrically (Ouchterlony, 1958). Vyazov and co-workers (1959) describe a rather simple way of adapting a microscope for scanning immunodiffusion bands that appear in capillary tubing in double diffusion tests. The microscope stage is adapted to moving these tubes across its field of vision under precise control, a slit aperture is placed in the ocular perpendicular to the long axis of the capillary tube, and the photoelectric cell of a photometer is placed upon this ocular. To avoid excessive light

---

[*] This very useful apparatus is available commercially from the American Instrument Company, Inc., 8030 Georgia Ave., Silver Spring, Maryland.

scatter, the capillary tube is mounted on a microscope slide in immersion oil and covered with a cover slip.

Interferometry

Photometry is most useful for quantitative analyses. For qualitative analyses, for studies on the characteristics of antigen-antibody precipitation, in the comparison of two antigen mixtures, and for similar purposes, interferometry and macrophotography are more satisfactory. The former technique has not yet been widely used, apparently having been applied only in one laboratory (Ambrose and Easty, 1953; Easty and Ambrose, 1957). Since apparatus required for it is rather complicated, the reader is referred to the original articles for its description. Light transmitted through a clear gel and up the microscope described by these workers appears to the observer as a series of regularly alternating, straight, parallel light and dark bands extending across his field of vision. Accumulation in some plane of the gel of a band of antigen-antibody complexes, even though this may not be visible, causes a sharp linear deformity in the alternating dark-white pattern (Fig. V-14). Interferometry can be used for studying subvisible antigen-antibody aggregates, and their formation and dissolution under varying circumstances.

Photography

The most common means of reporting qualitative immunodiffusion analyses probably is photography which, if carefully applied, can reveal more precipitin bands in a test than are readily visible to the eye. Basically, there are four ways in which precipitin bands can be registered on photosensitive materials. One is to place the cell containing the precipitin bands directly upon photosensitive paper or film and then to shine light through it, so that precipitin bands are registered by the shadows that they cast to make a contact print from the cell itself. A second method is to photograph the cells, illuminated by dark-field lighting if the precipitin bands have not been stained, or by direct light if they have been. For the third, a dried film of agar containing stained precipitin bands can be placed directly upon photosensitive material to make a contact print or, for best results, inserted in a photographic enlarger or in a projector to make an enlarged projection print (see Frontispiece). The fourth method depends upon radioactive emanation rather than light to register the bands as photographic images. Antigen is labeled with some radioactive element, unreacted antigen is washed from the reaction medium, and the medium is dried to a thin film. Then it is placed in close contact with photosensitive film, whereupon the radioactivity from the tagged precipitated antigen registers the image of its precipitin band. Of these methods, the first (often called shadow-graphy) is the most difficult to use satisfactorily and generally is the least sensitive, but it also is the method requiring the least equipment. The second requires a camera capable of taking a close-up photograph in sharp focus; with proper lighting it can give excellent results. The third seems to be the best in combining simplicity with high sensitivity and resolution. The fourth requires special procedures which cannot be carried out in many laboratories, but potentially it is the most sensitive.

From several descriptions (Darcy, 1957; Dike, 1960; Grabar, 1959a; Grabar and Williams, 1955; Leone et al., 1955; Pernot, 1956; Wilson, 1958), one can summarize ideal conditions for shadowgraphic recording of precipitin bands as follows. Exposure must be carried out in a dark-room. High contrast photographic paper or film (see below) is immersed in water and the subject to be shadowgraphed is placed directly upon it, precautions being taken not to interpose bubbles between the two. This immersion in water prevents optical imperfections in the immunodiffu-sion cell from being recorded and increases the fidelity of the printing by minimizing light refraction. Optimal rendition is obtained if light rays can be focused upon the photosensitive material such as, for ex-ample, from a focused condenser-type photographic enlarger. The water used for immersion should have the same ionicity and pH as the gel which it covers, and it should be of the same temperature. Some unusual technical modifications in shadowgraphy have been reported. Darcy (1957) used ultraviolet light rather than visible light to make prints. To obtain maximum contrast between the precipitin bands and their clear agar background, Leone and co-workers (1955) incorporated blue dyes in their agar. Presumably, these function by more efficiently exposing the blue-sensitive photographic paper employed wherever there are no precipitin bands in an agar gel. Orange dyes also have been used in agar shadowgraphed on blue-sensitive film (Wilson, 1958), although apparently primarily for enhanced visual dark-field examination, since they should decrease the contrast between agar and precipitates in shadowgraphy rather than increase it.

Since photography of precipitin bands lighted by a dark field viewer using blue- or blue-green-sensitive (orthochromatic, as opposed to panchromatic) material depends upon deflection of light by the pre-cipitin bands into the camera lens and a minimizing of stray deflection by the background gel, it is an advantage to include a red or orange dye in the gel. For example, 0.003% methyl orange has been used (Björklund, 1952a). The prime essential for satisfactory photography, however, is proper lighting; only light reflected by precipitin bands should reach the lens. Once this is attained, photography can be carried out with any of various types of camera (preferably a view camera, single-lens reflex camera, or copying enlarger) on photosensitive paper or film by common photographic techniques.

A method for obtaining high quality photographic prints of precipitin reactions in agar is by projecting the actual stained image of these bands upon photosensitive material using an enlarger (Crowle, 1958c; Dike, 1960; Gell, 1955a; Poulik, 1959). This is especially convenient when microscope slides are used to support the agar in which reactions are carried out. After the precipitin bands have been stained and the agar has been dried to a thin transparent film, the slide is placed in the negative carrier of an enlarger, preferably surrounded by a close-fitting black paper mask, so as to limit passage of light through only the area covered by agar, and the enlarger is turned on to print the enlarged precipitin band image on photosensitive material held in an easel or similar holder. For maximum contrast, resolution, and sensitivity, one should use blue- or blue-green-sensitive photographic paper or film and have the precipitin bands stained red. To these photographic materials, insensitive to red light, even the faintest precipitin bands will appear to be black, while if a green or blue dye were employed such lines would appear to these materials actually lighter than they are visually.

Since exposure of photosensitive material by radioactive antigens in precipitates usually takes from several days to weeks, the principle precautions to be observed in autoradiography of immunodiffusion reactions should be to employ thoroughly washed agar so that radioactivity is limited only to the tagged precipitates, to obtain closest possible contact between the agar film and the photosensitive material, to use the thinnest possible agar for precipitin reactions, to avoid such influences as might cause nonspecific fogging of the film (heat, abrasion, stray light, uneven surface pressure, etc.), and to use high contrast, high resolution film. Essentially, procedures for immunodiffusion autoradiography are the same as those used in histology. For examples of autoradiographic recording of immunodiffusion reactions, the reader is referred to Bussard, 1958; Hirschfeld and Söderberg, 1960; O'Connor, 1957b; Perlmann and Hultin, 1958; Perlmann et al., 1959; Rejnek and Bednarik, 1960; Roitt and Doniach, 1958b.

Photosensitive Materials

In all of these methods, the use of a darkroom is to be preferred. However, for the second and fourth methods, a photographic "changing bag" is a good substitute. The aim of each method is to reproduce or slightly increase the contrast seen under optimal lighting conditions between the background gel and precipitin bands. Lack of contrast or an excess of it both result in loss of photographic fidelity. Hence, the selection of photographic materials plays no small part in the successful recording of precipitin bands.

Two types of photosensitive materials can be employed: film or paper. The former is more versatile and its variations in contrast more controllable, and it can be used later to produce enlargements on paper. However, it is inconvenient for study because it must be viewed by transmitted light. The latter, paper, is far cheaper as a routine recording medium and has the advantage that it can be examined by reflected light, but photographic reproductions for publication are difficult to make from paper negatives and processing controls are more limited than they are with films. The characteristics of a film or paper are the chief factors governing the amount of contrast between light and dark areas obtainable with it. Useful high-contrast films widely available include Contrast Process Ortho,* for cut film cameras and copying enlargers, glass Contrast Latern Slide Plates,* for copying cameras where possible film shrinkage needs to be avoided and Micro-File* roll film for 35 mm. cameras. These films can increase the visible contrast between precipitin bands and their agar background by a factor of 2 to 5 depending upon development procedures, they have high resolution and low graininess, and none are sensitive to red light. Hence, they can be handled in a darkroom under red light, and red dyes can be used to stain antigen-antibody precipitates to enhance their effectiveness. If these films or their high contrast equivalents do not happen to be available to a laboratory, ordinary film can be employed with appropriate light filters and high contrast development to give fairly good results.

Photographic paper can be used to record precipitin band images exactly as film is, except that being considerably less sensitive it will require several times as much exposure. Enlarging or projection printing paper is the most sensitive, and its glossy surface variety can be purchased in various contrast grades from grade 2, normal contrast, through grades 3, 4, and 5, the last giving 2 to 3 times normal contrast. Since the contrast of these paper materials cannot be varied much by development procedures, as that of film can, it must be predetermined by selection of the proper contrast grade. If a photograph of precipitin bands has been taken on high contrast film, and then this film is used to produce an enlarged projection print on paper, normal or near-normal contrast paper should be utilized, because multiplying the high contrast first obtained on the film by that yielded by high contrast paper results in excessive contrast and considerable loss in fidelity, as mentioned above.

* Products of Eastman Kodak Company, Rochester, New York.

Enlarging paper, economically available in convenient 8 by 10 inch sheets which can be cut to smaller sizes, suitable for recording precipitin reactions directly is exemplified by Kodabromide* F-4 or F-5, the numbers designating contrast grades and the letters the type of surface (glossy) and the weight of the paper (single weight).

Developers

The degree of contrast obtainable with films can be varied considerably by employing various developers for different development times. Their formulas can be found in any of several photographic handbooks or in other handbooks such as the *Handbook of Chemistry and Physics* (Chemical Rubber Publishing Co.) and therefore are not described here.

Usually, the highest possible increase in contrast should be sought in photographing immunodiffusion tests; it is easier later to tone down high contrast in making a print from such a negative than to increase it, and better photographs are secured. Maximum contrast with high contrast film is obtained with potent developers such as D-8, D-11, D-19, and D-76, listed in order of decreasing potency. The contrast produced by any developer can be increased somewhat by using it on a film longer than its recommended developing time (not practical with D-8, however), and conversely it can be decreased by shortening developing time. Nevertheless, since extreme overdevelopment can cause fogging and underdevelopment mottling of the film, one is best advised to control development of contrast by using the available range of different developers rather than using one beyond its limits. If normal contrast film has to be used, it can be developed to maximum contrast with such a developer as D-19 used for one and a half times the length of its recommended developing time, although such film still will not show so much contrast as can be attained with high contrast film developed even in D-76. Developers have been formulated for obtaining various degrees of contrast on one contrast grade of photographic paper, but they are more troublesome to employ than using the various contrast grades of paper and a single standard paper developer such as D-72.

Fixing, Washing, and Staining

The value of being able to preserve permanently an original immunodiffusion test itself cannot be questioned, despite the utility of photographs as permanent records. Fixing, washing, and staining procedures although developed relatively recently have become simple enough not only to make this possible but also highly desirable. Moreover, the

* Product of Eastman Kodak Company, Rochester, New York.

stained slide or plate sometimes reveals precipitates not visible before staining, and various color reactions employed for staining antigen-antibody precipitates often aid in defining the antigen forming a particular band. The following section is devoted to the technology of this subject.

Fixation

If some substance in a semisolid medium is to be stained specifically, similar substances which might also take the stain must be washed from the medium, the subject itself must be fixed in the medium so that it is not washed out, and the indicator or stain which is employed must combine or react with the test substance less reversibly than with the background medium so that its excess can be removed from the latter without removing it from the former.

In simple agar electrophoresis, fractions must be fixed by some outside agent, such as acetic acid for proteins; in immunodiffusion tests no fixation is required, since antigen and antibody mutually fix each other in the agar gel by combining to form a precipitate. Chemical fixation should be as mild as possible so as to do the least damage to substances being fixed which later must react with the indicator. For serum proteins, a 2% aqueous solution of acetic acid appears to be entirely satisfactory if it is applied long enough (Uriel, 1958a). However, some proteins not so readily precipitable as serum proteins may require the following stronger fixatives: 1.2% acetic acid in 40% ethanol (Grabar *et al.*, 1956b), 2% acetic acid in 60% ethanol, picric acid (Wieme, 1959a), a staining-fixing mixture of 5% trichloracetic acid, 1% acetic acid, 25% ethanol and a dye (Crowle, unpublished), or strong denaturants such as 1% mercuric chloride in 1% acetic acid (Burtin *et al.*, 1955a; Crowle, 1956). When, as in agar electrophoresis, fractions to be stained are localized, no washing preceding staining is needed to remove substances which might otherwise be stained, thus coloring the background. Many workers prefer to dry an agar gel before staining it, a procedure which is preferable when the gel is thick or when water-insoluble stains, such as for lipids, are to be applied. In this instance, fixation is carried out, if necessary, and then nonvolatile salts are washed out, or if no fixation is needed, washing is applied immediately. The agar does not have to be washed after fixation if entirely volatile fixatives such as ethanol, acetic acid, or trichloracetic acid are used.

Soaking time in denaturant required for fixing proteins or other substances in a gel depends upon how deep this is and therefore how much time passes before the denaturing agent penetrates the gel's full depth. This may be several hours for agar several millimeters thick or only 10 or 15 minutes for agar only a fraction of a millimeter thick.

So far, proteins have been the most commonly analyzed antigens, and these are fixed in several different ways, as mentioned earlier. However, some varieties of protein with special properties must be fixed with denaturants which do not destroy these properties, if they are important to an analysis. Thus, to permit detection of catalase and peroxidase activities of hemoglobin after electrophoresis in agar, an acid fixative must be avoided, since it will partially destroy peroxidase activity. Rather, zinc acetate dissolved in 50% ethanol is employed (Uriel, 1958b). Lipoproteins apparently can be more adequately fixed for special analyses if 10% calcium chloride is included in the fixative (Uriel and Scheidegger, 1955), although for routine serum analyses this is not necessary. Polysaccharide antigens are precipitated in gels with strong aqueous solutions of ethanol. Some lipids, whatever they might be attached to for mobility in agar, often can be precipitated by cadmium salt solutions.

Washing and Drying

Several procedures are used to wash and dry agar gels in which precipitin reactions have taken place (Fig. V-25). Antigen solution constituents and serum which have not been fixed by specific reaction can be leached from agar gel by soaking it in physiologic saline, preferably at a slightly alkaline pH (e.g., pH 7.4). Anywhere from one day to one week will be required, depending upon the thickness of the gel. This washing should precede drying of thick agar gels, such as are used in Petri dish tests. However, thin gels, like those employed in microscope slide varieties of immunodiffusion tests, can be dried directly without preliminary washing (Hartmann and Toilliez, 1957). The thin gel is covered with filter paper of the same size and then dried in a dry-air warm incubator. Both the fluid and the nonvolatile salts are soaked up from the agar by the filter paper leaving under it a completely dry sheet of transparent gel. The thicker gels even after washing should be dried in contact with filter paper to prevent their crinkling, cracking, or lateral shrinking (Grabar, 1959a). In addition to the optional procedures just mentioned of washing and then drying agar, or of drying it without first washing it, there is a third of washing the agar but not drying it before it is stained. An obvious criterion for choosing whether to stain a dried agar film or the moist gel is convenience; thick gels (more than 1 mm.) simply require too much time to stain and destain and should be dried to films first. Among techniques using thin gel layers, differences in time are negligible. Another criterion is whether a particular stain is most effective on gels or on dried films. Lipid stains popularly have been applied to dried agar, because their coloring agents usually have been dissolved in alcoholic rather than aqueous solutions.

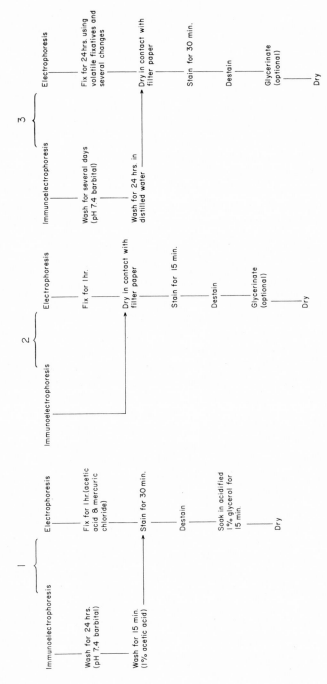

Fig. V-25. Flow diagrams outlining steps in three different techniques for washing, drying, and staining immunoelectrophoresis and agar electrophoresis slides. Procedures 1 and 2 should be applied only to agar slabs 1 mm. or less in thickness. Soaking agar in glycerol solution before it is dried often is used as an alternative to covering gel with filter paper during drying, a purpose for both being to prevent gel cracking, curling, or excess shrinkage. However, when thin agar has been used for an experiment, it can be dried at room temperature into a sturdy, intact film without either aid. This is important, since glycerol solutions sometimes tend to dissolve important features in these tests.

The composition of a wash bath depends on its purpose. To remove untreated antigen and serum constituents, one uses a slightly alkaline physiologic saline, such as a solvent equivalent to that originally used to dissolve the agar. Salts from this bath in turn should be removed before staining by a soaking in distilled water acidified with 1% acetic acid. A bath preceding final drying and storage usually should contain glycerine but no other nonvolatile substance. Flow diagrams illustrating the three principal fixing, washing, and drying procedures most commonly used in immunodiffusion experiments are presented in Fig. V-25.

Some points need to be made regarding drying an agar gel in direct contact with paper. If this gel is very thin and if it does not adhere very well to its glass support (as when this has been treated to be made water-repellent) it can be torn off its support and become impractical to separate from the filter paper. When the gel is thick enough that filter paper can be used without risking this difficulty, it may come off the gel spontaneously, or if not it usually can be stripped off after being moistened with some distilled water. When filter paper cannot be used and yet lateral shrinkage of the agar tends to cause distortion (e.g., tearing of an immunoelectrophoresis trough), the gel can be soaked in a solution of glycerol (1% to 10%, as required) before it is dried. Slow drying such as at room temperature, often eliminates the need of glycerol as well as for filter paper. Should the glycerol interfere with subsequent manipulations of the agar, it can be washed out of the dried film with ethanol or water. A filter paper should be selected for drying agar which is sturdy and lint-free. It also should have a relatively patternless surface.

When agar gels are to be dried for the last time before they are stored, they should be soaked in 1% or 2% glycerol and then dried; glycerol keeps the agar film from becoming brittle and, indeed, if used in larger quantities makes it pliable enough that it can be removed from its rigid support and stored like a piece of cellophane (Hayward and Augustin, 1957; Uriel, 1958a). Dried agar also has been preserved under a coating of clear plastic (Rondle and Carman, 1956).

Cellulose acetate as a medium for immunodiffusion tests does not require much different treatment than agar (Kohn, 1958). It is washed in physiologic saline and then in distilled water, stained with or without preliminary drying, washed again to remove excess stain, and dried between compressed sheets of filter paper as on a photographic print dryer. No dye solvents can be used which distort or dissolve the cellulose acetate (alcohols, esters, ketones). The cellulose acetate can be made transparent, after staining and complete desiccation, by soaking it in mineral oil (Consden and Kohn, 1959).

Cyanogum gel can be washed and dried in much the same way as agar. However, since its dried film regains water so readily, drying preliminary to aqueous staining is rather a hindrance than a help. This gum should not be dried in contact with filter paper because it sticks to it.

Staining

Staining immunodiffusion reactions is a relatively recently accepted innovation popularized by new improvements in technique; it has become an essential part of immunodiffusion research. Not only does it provide permanent records of original reactions and usually permit improved photographic recording, but also it aids in identification of antigens involved in specific precipitation. The choice of stains which can be applied is wide, and also likely to be somewhat confusing. Hence, a short discussion of the purposes and nature of immunodiffusion staining reactions will precede descriptions of staining techniques themselves.

As a general rule, any stain used in histology and histochemistry can also be applied to the thin sheet of agar containing precipitin bands or to the strip of cellulose acetate in which antigen-antibody reactions have occurred. Stains for proteins are the most frequently used, since antibody and usually antigen constituting precipitin bands are proteins. Any of several acid dyes dissolved in acidified water can be utilized, although some are considerably more satisfactory than others (Crowle, 1958a; Uriel and Grabar, 1956a). The stain most often employed (Goudie et al., 1959; Grabar, 1959a; Grabar et al., 1956b; Grasset et al., 1958; Havez and Biserte, 1959a; Kohn, 1958; Scheidegger, 1955; Uriel and Grabar, 1956a; Uriel and Scheidegger, 1955; Wieme, 1959a,b; Wunderly, 1957) is a dark blue dye with a confusing variety of names: amidoschwarz 10B, amidoblack 10B, buffalo black NBR, naphthol blue-black, naphthol black 12B, wool black. Other blue dyes which have been employed include indigo carmine (Grabar, 1959a; Smithies, 1955; Uriel, 1958a), bromphenol blue (Bird and Jackson, 1959; Grasset et al., 1958; Hayward and Augustin, 1957; Smithies, 1955; Uriel and Grabar, 1956a; Uriel and Scheidegger, 1955), bromthymol blue (Uriel and Grabar, 1956a), and water-soluble nigrosin (Consden and Kohn, 1959; Kohn, 1958; Wieme, 1959a), which is nearly black. One green dye has been reported useful: light green SF (Crowle, 1956; Kohn, 1958). A number of red dyes are employed, the most popular being azocarmine B (Grabar, 1959a; Grasset et al., 1958; Kohn, 1957, 1958; Scheidegger, 1955; Uriel, 1958a; Uriel and Grabar, 1956a; Uriel and Scheidegger, 1955). Among a large series of red acid dyes tested in the author's laboratory, thiazine red R and crocein scarlet MOO proved to be superior for staining specific precipitates in gels on microscope slides (Crowle, 1958c). Azocarmine G (Crowle, 1958c), ponceau S (Consden and Kohn, 1959; Kohn, 1958), ponceau fuchsin, Masson (Kohn, 1957) are other red dyes which have been utilized. Selection of any one among these various protein stains is partly arbitrary. Photographically, red dyes are preferable. Some dyes seem better suited than others for particular staining jobs. For example, some workers believe that azocarmine B stains specific precipitates formed by horse antiserum better than amido-schwarz 10B or indigo carmine, while these latter two stain rabbit antibody precipitates better than azocarmine B (Grabar, 1959a). Water-soluble nigrosin is reported to stain weak precipitin bands on cellulose acetate strips better than ponceau S; apparently it is too intense for use on stronger precipitates (Consden and Kohn, 1959). In agar it is not superior to amidoschwarz (Wieme, 1959a). Some proteins, such as insulin, do not give a stable dye-protein complex with amidoschwarz but will take up bromphenol blue (Smithies, 1955). Thiazine red R appears to stain a somewhat greater variety of human serum constituents in agar than amidoschwarz (Crowle, unpublished). To compensate for known or suspected deficiencies in the staining abilities of any single dye, mixtures of them can be used. For example, the three dyes amidoschwarz 10B, light green SF, and thiazine red R, each with somewhat different affinities for serum proteins electrophoresed in agar, can be used in common solution as a simultaneous triple stain (Crowle and Lueker, unpublished).

Some selected formulas for protein stains and procedures for using them are gathered for convenient reference in Appendix IV. Others can be obtained from references mentioned above. Most of the dyes described will be suitable for any of various immunodiffusion media, but one stain, nigrosin, appears to have particular application to cellulose acetate medium and is so indicated. Details for various techniques differ according to their individual applications. For example, the time required for adequately staining an agar gel varies with the thickness of the agar or the inclusion in the staining solution of surface tension depressants such as ethanol, and hence it should be ascertained in a given instance, for which there is no previous information, by trial. Dried agar films and agar gels less than 1 mm. thick usually require between 15 to 60 minutes of staining in 0.1% aqueous solutions of a dye, while thicker gels may require several hours. Destaining (or differentiation) is by inspection, the destaining solution being replaced periodically whenever it has accumulated nearly as much stain as appears to remain in the medium being destained, and destaining continuing until no more

dye can be extracted from the medium. The common basis for all pro-
tein-staining formulas so far used in immunodiffusion is that they contain an acid dye dissolved in a distinctly acid solution of pH around 3.
The wash baths usually are composed of the same solvent as used for
the dye, although when nonvolatile substances are included in the
dyeing bath these are excluded from the wash. Since the principle for
staining proteins in agar is to have the negatively-charged dye combine
with the positively-charged protein but not with the negatively-charged
agar gel, any significant alkalinity in the gel will interfere with this
combination, and soaking agar in which proteins have already been
stained in an alkaline solution will dissociate the dye-protein complex.
The alkaline dyes commonly used in bacteriology cannot be used, because under conditions that they require for staining proteins they also
would stain the agar.

Lipids generally are stained with water-insoluble dyes used as saturated ethanolic solutions. Sudan black B is the most popular dye (Korngold and Lipari, 1955a; Larkey and Belko, 1959; McDonald and Rebeiro,
1959; Uriel and Scheidegger, 1955; Wieme, 1959a), but oil red O seems
to be equally useful (Korngold and Lipari, 1955a; Uriel, 1958a; Uriel
and Scheidegger, 1955), and Sudan IV (Geigy scarlet R) has been employed (Uriel and Grabar, 1956a). Nile blue A, contrary to the three
just mentioned, is a water-soluble lipophilic dye and has been used
successfully in aqueous solution to stain immunoelectrophoresis patterns
(Crowle, unpublished). It probably is safe to assume, as has proved
true in other instances, that any of numerous lipid stains used in histochemistry could be applied with excellent results to immunodiffusion
and immunoelectrophoresis patterns.

The basic principle for staining lipids is that these lipids more readily
dissolve a given dye than the solvent in which it is presented to the
lipid and therefore incorporate it to become colored. Hence, one should
strive to apply the stain in as physically unstable a solution as possible,
and then to remove excess stain from the background medium (e.g.,
agar gel) using an even less efficient solvent than was originally employed to make the stain.

No special fixing methods have appeared to be necessary to devise for
serum lipoproteins, although research in the future with other mixtures
containing lipids may reveal a need for such. Although staining of pre-
dried films rather than agar gels is preferable when ethanolic solutions
of dye are used (Uriel, 1958a), it is not absolutely necessary if the
moist agar is brought to the same concentration of ethanol used to dissolve the stain. Neither is it required if Nile blue A is employed. When
saturated dye solutions are employed, their instability requires that

special precautions must be taken to prevent the dye from precipitating upon the material being stained. Insurance against this can be obtained by filtering the dye solution just before it is used, and by resting the slide upside down upon two glass rods in the staining solution during staining, and by keeping the bath enclosed and at a constant temperature to prevent solvent evaporation (Grabar, 1959a; Uriel and Grabar, 1956a). Staining time for lipids varies with the subject and with the dye. For example, desiccated agar films require one-twelfth as much time with Sudan black as with Sudan IV; under these conditions, Sudan black requires between 30 and 60 minutes. If the dye solvent is 60% ethanol, usually the differentiating bath will be a slightly weaker alcohol solution, e.g., about 50%. Nile blue A as a water-soluble lipid stain is destained with an aqueous rather than ethanolic bath. This dye tends to produce a metachromatic stain, some lipids staining with a reddish hue and others simply blue. Formulas for some lipid stains which have been used primarily on electrophoresed serum proteins and procedures for applying them are given in Appendix V. The formula for Sudan black B calls for optional addition of sodium hydroxide solution to the dye solution; some commercial Sudan black preparations contain an impurity which slightly colors the agar in acid or neutral medium (Uriel and Grabar, 1956b). This option apparently need not be taken for the certified dye produced in the United States (Crowle, unpublished). A choice among presently available lipid-staining procedures is so limited as not to be difficult. Photographically, oil red O is preferable for reasons mentioned previously. Nile blue A remains to be fully evaluated, presently owing its chief utility to being uniquely soluble in water.

Sometimes it may be possible to facilitate staining of lipids in a material to be electrophoresed by a pre-staining process; that is, a lipid stain is applied to the sample before it is submitted to separation so that the lipids become fully stained. Their movement can be seen during agar electrophoresis, and later staining is not necessary. This technique has not yet been applied either to agar electrophoresis or to immunodiffusion. Consequently, it is mentioned here primarily because of its likely usefulness. It is applied in paper electrophoresis with Sudan black B (Larkey and Belko, 1959; McDonald and Rebeiro, 1959).

Double stains have been used in agar- and immuno-electrophoresis for lipids and proteins, and for proteins alone in agar or on cellulose acetate (Consden and Kohn, 1959; Crowle, unpublished; Uriel, 1958a; Uriel and Grabar, 1956b; Uriel and Scheidegger, 1955). The value of these double stains performed to detect two types of substance on a single sample by contrast to comparable single stains performed on separate samples is questionable, since one stain tends to obscure the other when both are deposited in the same area. A double stain for one substance alone (e.g., protein), however, can reveal fractions which are not revealed or only poorly so by a single stain (Consden and Kohn, 1959; Crowle, unpublished; see Frontispiece). Thus, heavy deposits of protein in precipitin bands on cellulose acetate strips are first stained with the relatively weak dye ponceau S; then, fainter bands are revealed by subsequent application of a very weak solution of nigrosin WS, a dye which apparently has a much greater capacity for staining proteins than ponceau S. This type of double stain is not so heavy as to blot out details of heavy and broad precipitin bands which tend to overstain, but on the other hand neither is it so weak that the faintest bands are not adequately stained (Consden and Kohn, 1959). A staining solution containing light green SF, thiazine red R, and amidoschwarz 10B tends to reveal more proteins in an agar electrophoresis strip than a solution of any one of these dyes alone. Procedures for applying some double stains are given in Appendix VI.

Stains for polysaccharides, glycoproteins, and mucopolysaccharides always have posed somewhat of a problem because agar, the most commonly used matrix for immunodiffusion tests, is itself a polysaccharide. Gelatin and Cyanogum 41, of course, are not, and hence should be readily adaptable to use with these stains. Several have been devised and include the Schiff reagent stain (Uriel and Grabar, 1956a), which is the most tedious to apply but also one whose mechanisms are understood, an α-naphthol-p-phenylenediamine color reaction (Grabar, 1959a; Uriel, 1958a), stains employing basic fuchsin or Mayer's mucicarmine (Björklund, 1954a), and alcian blue (Crowle, unpublished). The last two are technically the simplest. Mucicarmine detects serum mucoproteins (glycoproteins) better than it does mucopolysaccharides, while alcian blue is particularly well suited to the latter. Glycoproteins and mucopolysaccharides both are detected by the Schiff reagent or the α-naphthol test. Basic fuchsin has been used specifically to detect highly purified bacterial polysaccharides composing specific precipitates (Björklund, 1954a). Factors governing the use and mode of action of the Schiff reagent in detecting polysaccharides are too complex to be discussed here; the reader is referred to the discussion by Uriel and Grabar (1956a). Suffice it to say that the technique must be followed precisely as it has been described if satisfactory results are to be obtained.

Of the stains listed in Appendix VII for polysaccharides, the α-naphthol-p-phenylenediamine is the most likely to satisfy the average user of immunodiffusion techniques, for polysaccharides are vividly stained and background agar is not colored (see Frontispiece). The Schiff stain, properly applied, gives comparable results, but it is not as simple to use.

Among the other three stains listed, all can give good results, but the background agar is likely to be heavily stained unless the stains are applied to previously dried agar.

In simple electrophoresis, polysaccharides to be detected are not bound by antibody and must be fixed before staining. This presents no new problem when they are bound to proteins and are precipitated with them in the usual acid fixing solutions. If some are suspected not to be bound, however, then the fixing solution should include a substantial quantity of ethanol as precipitant.

Although protein, lipid, and polysaccharide stains have been the most commonly employed in agar electrophoresis, immunoelectrophoresis, and immunodiffusion techniques, other stains with greater specificity probably can be employed just as they are in histochemistry with some adaptions to fit them to their new use. For example, Uriel and Grabar (1956a) have described a stain specific for acetylphosphatides.

＊　　＊　　＊

The technology of immunodiffusion has advanced very rapidly during the past two years. More recently, this advance seems to have abated somewhat, although it certainly has not become static, as time is taken to apply the many newly devised techniques to specific research problems. This particular period in the history of immunodiffusion techniques therefore has seemed opportune to the writer as an interlude in which to consolidate knowledge which has been accumulated, even though it is not complete, as an aid to both the increasingly common first user of immunodiffusion and the more frequent user, who has found keeping up with the literature in this field difficult.

References

Abramson, H. A., Moyer, L. S., and Gorin, M. H. (1942). "Electrophoresis of Proteins," 341 pp. Reinhold, New York.

Adler, F. L. (1956a). *J. Immunol.* **76**, 217–227.

Adler, F. L. (1956b). *Federation Proc.* **15**, 580–581.

Affronti, L. F. (1959). *Am. Rev. Tuberc. Pulmonary Diseases* **79**, 284–295.

Aladjem, F., and Campbell, D. H. (1957). *Nature* **179**, 203–204.

Aladjem, F., and Lieberman, M. (1952). *J. Immunol.* **69**, 117–130.

Aladjem, F., Jaross, R. W., Paldino, R. L., and Lackner, J. A. (1959). *J. Immunol.* **83**, 221–231.

Alexander, A. E., and Johnson, P. (1949). "Colloid Science," Vol. II, pp. 556–837. Oxford Univ. Press, London, and New York.

Allison, A. C., and Humphrey, J. H. (1959). *Nature* **183**, 1590–1592.

Allison, A. C., and Humphrey, J. H. (1960). *Immunology* **3**, 95–106.

Ambrose, E. J., and Easty, G. C. (1953). *Nature* **172**, 811–813.

Arrhenius, S. (1907). "Immunochemistry," 309 pp. Macmillan, New York.

Augustin, R. (1955). *Quart. Rev. Allergy and Appl. Immunol.* **9**, 504–560.

Augustin, R. (1957). *Intern. Arch. Allergy Appl. Immunol.* **11**, 153–169.

Augustin, R. (1959a). *Immunology* **2**, 148–169.

Augustin, R. (1959b). *Immunology* **2**, 230–251.

Augustin, R., and Hayward, B. J. (1955). *Intern. Arch. Allergy Appl. Immunol.* **6**, 154–168.

Augustin, R., and Hayward, B. J. (1960). *Nature* **187**, 129–130.

Augustin, R., Hayward, B. J., and Spiers, J. A. (1958). *Immunology* **1**, 67–80.

Balbinder, E., and Preer, J. R., Jr. (1959). *J. Gen. Microbiol.* **21**, 156–167.

Baltimore Biological Laboratory, Inc. (1960). Brochure on "K Agar."

Barandun, S., Stampfli, K., Spengler, G. A., and Riba, G. (1959). *Helv. Med. Acta* **26**, 203–367.

Bargob, I., Cleve, H., and Hartmann, F. (1958). *Deut. Arch. klin. Med.* **204**, 708–720.

Bartel, A. H., and Campbell, D. H. (1959). *Arch. Biochem. Biophys.* **82**, 232–234.

Bechhold, H. (1905). *Z. physik. Chem.* **52**, 185–199.

Bechhold, H., and Ziegler, J. (1906). *Z. physik. Chem.* **56**, 105–121.

Becker, E. L. (1953). *Federation Proc.* **12**, 717–722.

Becker, E. L., and Munoz, J. (1949a). *J. Immunol.* **63**, 173–181.

Becker, E. L., and Munoz, J. (1949b). *Proc. Soc. Exptl. Biol. Med.* **72**, 287–289.

Becker, E. L., and Neff, J. C. (1958). *J. chim. phys.* **55**, 334–339.

Becker, E. L., and Neff, J. C. (1959). *J. Immunol.* **83**, 571–581.

Becker, E. L., Munoz, J., Lapresle, C., and LeBeau, L. J. (1951). *J. Immunol.* **67**, 501–511.

Beiser, S. M., Dworetzky, M., Smart, K. M., and Baldwin, H. S. (1958). *J. Allergy* **29**, 44–47.

Belicetta, V. F., Markham, A. E., Peniston, Q. P., and McCarthy, J. L. (1949). *J. Am. Chem. Soc.* **71**, 2879.

Belyavin, G., and Trotter, W. R. (1959). *Lancet* **i**, 648–652.

Bent, D. F., Rosen, H., Levenson, S. M., Lindberg, R. B., and Ajl, S. J. (1957). *Proc. Soc. Exptl. Biol. Med.* **95**, 178–181.

Bergdoll, M. S., Surgalla, M. J., and Dack, G. M. (1959). *J. Immunol.* **83**, 334–338.

Bergrahm, B. (1960). *Nature* **185**, 242–243.

Biguet, J., Havez, R., and Ky, T. V. (1959). *Compt. rend. acad. sci.* **249**, 895–897.

Bird, R., and Jackson, D. (1959). *J. Clin. Pathol.* **12**, 373–374.

Biserte, G., Havez, R., Hayem, A., and Laturaze, J. (1960). *Compt. rend. acad. sci.* **250**, 418–420.

Björklund, B. (1952a). *Proc. Soc. Exptl. Biol. Med.* **79**, 319–324.

Björklund, B. (1952b). *Proc. Soc. Exptl. Biol. Med.* **79**, 324–328.

Björklund, B. (1953a). *Atti congr. intern. microbiol., 6th Congr.* **2**, 344.

Björklund, B. (1953b). *Intern. Arch. Allergy Appl. Immunol.* **4**, 340–359.

Björklund, B. (1953c). *Intern. Arch. Allergy Appl. Immunol.* **4**, 379–414.

Björklund, B. (1954a). *Proc. Soc. Exptl. Biol. Med.* **85**, 438–441.

Björklund, B. (1954b). *Intern. Arch. Allergy Appl. Immunol.* **5**, 293–298.

Björklund, B. (1956). *Intern. Arch. Allergy Appl. Immunol.* **8**, 179–192.

Björklund, B., and Berengo, A. (1954). *Acta Pathol. Microbiol. Scand.* **34**, 79–86.

Björklund, B., and Björklund, V. (1957). *Intern. Arch. Allergy Appl. Immunol.* **10**, 153–184.

Block, R. J., Durrum, E. L., and Zweig, G. (1955). "Paper Chromatography and Paper Electrophoresis," 484 pp. Academic Press, New York.

Bodman, J. (1959). *Clin. Chim. Acta* **4**, 103–109.

Bodon, L. (1955). *Acta Vet. Acad. Sci. Hung.* **5**, 157–159.

Boerma, F. W. (1956). *J. Pathol. Bacteriol.* **72**, 515–518.

Boivin, P., Hartmann, L., and Fauvert, R. (1959). *Rev. franç. études clin. et biol.* **4**, 799–808.

Bowen, H. E. (1952). *J. Immunol.* **68**, 429.

Boyd, W. C. (1956). "Fundamentals of Immunology," 3rd ed., 776 pp. Interscience, New York.

Branham, S. E., Hiatt, C. W., Cooper, A. D., and Riggs, D. B. (1959). *J. Immunol.* **82**, 397–408.

Bridges, R. A., and Good, R. H. (1959). *J. Lab. Clin. Med.* **54**, 794.

Briner, W. W., Riddle, J. W., and Cornwell, D. G. (1959). *Proc. Soc. Exptl. Biol. Med.* **101**, 784–786.

Broberger, O., and Perlmann, P. (1959). *J. Exptl. Med.* **110**, 657–674.

Brown, R. (1940). *Proc. Soc. Exptl. Biol. Med.* **45**, 93–95.

Brown, F., and Crick, J. (1957). *Nature* **179**, 316–318.

Brown, F., and Crick, J. (1958). *Virology* **5**, 133–144.

Brown, F., and Crick, J. (1959). *J. Immunol.* **82**, 444–447.

Brown, F., and Graves, J. H. (1959). *Nature* **183**, 1688–1689.

Buchanan-Davidson, D. J., and Oudin, J. (1958). *J. Immunol.* **81**, 484–491.

Buchanan-Davidson, D. J., Dellert, D. J., Kornguth, E. E., and Stahmann, M. A. (1959a). *J. Immunol.* **83**, 543–551.

Buchanan-Davidson, D. J., Stahmann, M. A., Lapresle, C., and Grabar, P. (1959b). *J. Immunol.* **83**, 552–560.

Buchanan-Davidson, D. J., Stahmann, M. A., and Dellert, E. E. (1959c). *J. Immunol.* **83**, 561–570.

Bukantz, S. C., and Berns, A. W. (1959). *Intern. Arch. Allergy Appl. Immunol.* **15**, 1–15.

Burrell, R. G., and Rheins, M. S. (1957). *Intern. J. Leprosy* **25**, 223–230.

Burrell, R. G., Rheins, M., and Birkeland, J. M. (1956). *Am. Rev. Tuberc. Pulmonary Diseases* **74**, 239–244.

Burtin, P. (1954a). *Bull. soc. chim. biol.* **36**, 833–836.

Burtin, P. (1954b). *Bull. soc. chim. biol.* **36**, 1021–1028.

Burtin, P. (1954c). *Rev. intern. hépatol.* **4**, 641–650.

Burtin, P. (1955). *Bull. soc. chim. biol.* **37**, 977–994.

Burtin, P. (1957). *Semaine hôp.* **33–34**, 2177–2179.

Burtin, P. (1958). *Rev. franc. Et. clin. biol.* **3**, 62–70.

Burtin, P. (1959a). *Clin. Chim. Acta* **4**, 72–78.

Burtin, P. (1959b). *Ann. inst. Pasteur* **97**, 325–339.

Burtin, P., and Grabar, P. (1954). *Bull. soc. chim. biol.* **36**, 335–345.

Burtin, P., and Kourilsky, R. (1959). *Ann. inst. Pasteur* **97**, 148–170.

Burtin, P., and Pocidalo, J. (1954a). *Compt. rend. acad. sci.* **238**, 1628–1630.

Burtin, P., and Pocidalo, J. (1954b). *Presse méd.* **62**, 1072–1074.

Burtin, P., Grabar, P., Boussier, G., and Jayle, M. F. (1954). *Bull. soc. chim. biol.* **36**, 1029–1035.

Burtin, P., Hartmann, L., Fauvert, R., and Grabar, P. (1955a). *Compt. rend. acad. sci.* **241**, 339–341.

Burtin, P., Fauvert, R., and Grabar, P. (1955b). *Semaine hôp.* **31**, 1–2.

Burtin, P., Hartmann, L., Fauvert, R., and Grabar, P. (1956). *Rev. franç. études clin. et biol.* **1**, 17–28.

Burtin, P., Hartmann, L., Heremans, J., Scheidegger, J. J., Westendorp-Boerma, F., Wieme, R., Wunderly, Ch., Fauvert, R., and Grabar, P. (1957). *Rev. franç. études clin. et biol.* **2**, 161–177.

Bussard, A. (1954). *Compt. rend. acad. sci.* **239**, 1702–1704.

Bussard, A. (1958). *Résumé, VII⁰ Congr. intern. microbiol.*, p. 152.

Bussard, A., and Huet, J. (1959). *Biochim. et Biophys. Acta* **34**, 258–260.

Bussard, A., and Perrin, B. (1955). *J. Lab. Clin. Med.* **46**, 689–701.

Bustamante, V. (1957). *Bull. soc. chim. biol.* **39**, Suppl. I, 155–160.

Buttery, S. Nature (1959). **183**, 686–687.

Carpenter, P. L. (1956). "Immunology and Serology," 351 pp. Saunders, Philadelphia.

Carter, H. S., and Wilson, W. (1949). *Glasgow Med. J.* **30**, 43–48.

Caspary, A. A. (1956). *Biochem. J.* **62**, 13P.

Castañeda, M. R. (1950). *Proc. Soc. Exptl. Biol. Med.* **73**, 46–49.

Chahbasi, P. (1957). *Ann. inst. Pasteur* **92**, 239–256.

Chen, T. H., and Meyer, K. F. (1955). *J. Immunol.* **74**, 501–507.

Clausen, J., and Heremans, J. (1960). *J. Immunol.* **84**, 128–134.

Cleve, H. (1958). *Z. Rheumaforsch.* **17**, 350–361.

Cleve, H., and Hartmann, F. (1957a). *Verhandl. deut. Ges. inn. Med.* **63**, 637–641.

Cleve, H., and Hartmann, F. (1957b). *Klin. Wochschr.* **35**, 334–340.

Cleve, H., and Schwick, G. (1957). *Z. Naturforsch.* **12b**, 375–384.

Cluff, L. E. (1954). *J. Exptl. Med.* **100**, 391–403.

Croissile, Y. (1959). *Compt. rend. acad. sci.* **249**, 1712–1714.

Commoner, B., and Rodenberg, S. D. (1955). *J. Gen. Physiol.* **38**, 475–492.

Consden, R., and Kohn, J. (1959). *Nature* **183**, 1512–1513.

Cooper, R. S. (1950). *J. Exptl. Zool.* **114**, 403–420.

Crouch, D. J. (1958). "Immunochemical Studies of Cerebrospinal Fluid," M.A. Thesis, 40 pp. Stanford University, Stanford, California.

Crowle, A. J. (1956). Unpublished experiments.

Crowle, A. J. (1954). "A Study of the Immunizing Factors of the Tubercle Bacillus," Dissertation, 140 pp. Stanford University, Stanford, California.
Crowle, A. J. (1956). *J. Lab. Clin. Med.* 48, 642–648.
Crowle, A. J. (1958a). *J. Immunol.* 81, 194–198.
Crowle, A. J. (1958b). *Intern. Arch. Allergy Appl. Immunol.* 12, 215–222.
Crowle, A. J. (1958c). *J. Lab. Clin. Med.* 52, 784–787.
Crowle, A. J. (1960a). *Intern. Arch. Allergy Appl. Immunol.* 16, 113–125.
Crowle, A. J. (1960b). *J. Lab. Clin. Med.* 55, 593–604.
Crowle, A. J. (1960c). *Ann. Rev. Microbiol.* 14, 161–176.
Crowle, A. J., and Lueker, D. C. (1961). Unpublished experiments.
Crumpton, M. J., and Davies, D. A. L. (1956). *Proc. Roy. Soc.* 145, 109–134.
Cushing, J. E., and Campbell, D. H. (1957). "Principles of Immunology," 344 pp. McGraw-Hill, New York.
Darcy, D. A. (1955). *Nature* 176, 643–644.
Darcy, D. A. (1957). *Brit. J. Cancer* 11, 137–147.
Deicher, H. R. G., Holman, H. R., and Kunkel, H. G. (1959). *J. Exptl. Med.* 109, 97–114.
De Oliveira, H. L. (1958). *Intern. Arch. Allergy Appl. Immunol.* 12, 356–360.
Dike, G. W. R. (1960). *J. Clin. Pathol.* 13, 87–89.
Doniach, D., and Roitt, I. M. (1957). *J. Clin. Endocrinol. and Metabolism* 17, 1293–1304.
Doniach, D., and Roitt, I. M. (1959). "Immunopathology, 1st International Symposium, Basel/Seelisberg, 1958," pp. 168–179. Benno Schwabe & Co., Basel, Switzerland.
Dray, S. (1960). *Federation Proc.* 19, 205.
Dray, S., and Young, G. O. (1958). *J. Immunol.* 81, 142–149.
Dray, S., and Young, G. O. (1959). *Science* 129, 1023–1025.
Duclaux, J. (1936). *Actualités sci. et ind.* 350, 1–50.
Durieux, J., and Kaminski, M. (1956). *Bull. soc. chim. biol.* 38, 1445–1456.
Easty, G. C. (1954). *Discussions Faraday Soc.* 18, 364.
Easty, G. C., and Ambrose, E. J. (1957). *J. Exptl. Biol.* 34, 60–70.
Easty, G. C., and Mercer, E. H. (1958). *Immunology* 1, 353–364.
Ebel, D. (1955). *Intern. Arch. Allergy Appl. Immunol.* 7, 75–91.
Efford, R. J. (1952). "The Agar Precipitin Test," M.A. Thesis, 48 pp. Stanford University, Stanford, California.
Elek, S. D. (1948). *Brit. Med. J.* 1, 493–496.
Elek, S. D. (1949a). *Brit. J. Exptl. Pathol.* 30, 484–500.
Elek, S. D. (1949b). *J. Clin. Pathol.* 2, 250–258.
Elek, S. D., and Levy, E. (1950a). *J. Pathol. Bacteriol.* 62, 541–554.
Elek, S. D., and Levy, E. (1950b). *Brit. J. Exptl. Pathol.* 31, 358–368.
Engelberg, J. (1959). *J. Immunol.* 82, 467–470.
Fahey, J. L., and Horbett, A. P. (1959). *J. Biol. Chem.* 234, 2645–2651.
Fairbrother, F., and Mastin, H. (1923). *J. Chem. Soc.* 123, 1412–1424.
Fasella, P., Baglioni, C., and Turano, C. (1957). *Experientia* 13, 406–407.
Faure, R., Fine, J. M., Saint-Paul, M., Eyquem, A., and Grabar, P. (1955). *Bull. soc. chim. biol.* 37, 783–796.
Fayet, M. T., Mackowiak, C., Camand, R., and Leftheriotis, E. (1957). *Ann. inst. Pasteur* 92, 466–472.
Feinberg, J. G. (1956). *Nature* 178, 1406.
Feinberg, J. G. (1957). *Intern. Arch. Allergy Appl. Immunol.* 11, 129–152.

Feinberg, J. G. (1959). *Immunology* **4**, 346–350.

Feinberg, J. G., and Grant, R. A. (1957). *Biochem. J.* **65**, 40P.

Feinberg, J. G., and Grayson, H. (1959). *Nature* **183**, 987.

Filitti-Wurmser, S., Jugon, M. P., and Hartmann, L. (1958). *Rev. franç. études clin. et biol.* **3**, 1080–1083.

Fine, J. M., and Battistini, A. (1960). *Experientia* **16**, 57–59.

Finger, I., and Kabat, E. A. (1958). *J. Exptl. Med.* **108**, 453–474.

Finger, I., Kabat, E. A., Bezer, A. E., and Kidd, A. (1960). *J. Immunol.* **84**, 227–230.

Fishel, C. W. (1960). Personal communication.

Fishel, C. W. (1960). *Nature* **186**, 804–805.

Francq, J. -C., Eyguem, A., Podliachouk, L., and Jacqueline, F. (1959). *Ann. inst. Pasteur* **96**, 413–419.

Frandsen, V. A., and Samsøe-Jensen, T. (1955). *Acta Allergol.* **8**, 70–74.

Franklin, E. C., and Kunkel, H. G. (1957). *J. Immunol.* **78**, 11–18.

Freeman, V. J. (1950). *Public Health Repts.* (*U. S.*) **65**, 875–882.

Freimer, E. H., Krause, R. M., and McCarty, M. (1959). *J. Exptl. Med.* **110**, 853–874.

Frick, E., and Scheid-Seidel, L. (1957). *Z. ges. exptl. Med.* **129**, 221–246.

Fujio, H., Kishigushi, S., Noma, Y., Skinka, S., Saiki, Y., and Amano, T. (1958). *Biken's J.* **1**, 138–156.

Fujio, H., Nowa, Y., and Amano, T. (1959). *Biken's J.* **2**, 35–49.

Fuks, M. A. (1956). *Ann. Microbiol.* **4**, 61–68.

Fuks, M. A. (1958). "Studies on the Polysaccharide Antigens of *Mycobacterium tuberculosis*," Dissertation, 82 pp. University of Brazil, Rio de Janeiro.

Gard, S., Heller, L., and Weibull, C. (1955). *Acta Pathol Microbiol. Scand.* **36**, 30–38.

Gavrilesco, K., Courcon, J., Hillion, P., Uriel, J., Lesin, J., and Grabar, P. (1955). *Bull. soc. chim. biol.* **37**, 803–807.

Gell, P. G. H. (1955a). *J. Clin. Pathol.* **8**, 269–275.

Gell, P. G. H. (1955b). *Biochem. J.* **59**, viii.

Gell, P. G. H. (1957). *J. Clin. Pathol.* **10**, 67–71.

Gendon, I. Z. (1958). *J. Microbiol. Epidemiol. Immunobiol.* (*U.S.S.R.*) **29**, 416–423.

Gengozian, N. (1959). *J. Immunol.* **83**, 173–183.

Gillert, K. E. (1958). *Blut* **4**, 8–13.

Gispen, R. (1955). *J. Immunol.* **74**, 134–141.

Gitlin, D., Hitzig, W. H., and Janeway, C. A. (1956). *J. Clin. Invest.* **35**, 1199–1204.

Glasstone, S. (1950). "The Elements of Physical Chemistry," 695 pp. Van Nostrand, New York.

Glenn, W. G. (1956a). *School Aviation Med., USAF, Rept. No. 56-116.*

Glenn, W. G. (1956b). *J. Immunol.* **77**, 189–192.

Glenn, W. G. (1958a). *School Aviation Med., USAF, Rept. No. 58-133.*

Glenn, W. G. (1958b). *In* "Serological and Biochemical Comparisons of Proteins" (W. H. Cole, ed.), pp. 71–91. Rutger Univ. Press, New Brunswick, New Jersey.

Glenn, W. G. (1959a). *School Aviation Med., USAF, Rept. No. 58-134.*

Glenn, W. G. (1959b). *Aerospace Med.* **30**, 576–579.

Glenn, W. G. (1959c). *Med. Technicians Bull.* **10**, 101–104.

Glenn, W. G. (1960). *Federation Proc.* **19**, 204.

Glenn, W. G., and Garner, A. C. (1956). *School Aviation Med., USAF, Rept. No. 56-92.*

Glenn, W. G., and Garner, A. C. (1957). *J. Immunol.* **78**, 395–400.

Glenn, W. G., and Marable, I. W. (1957). *School Aviation Med., USAF, Report No. 58-10.*

Glenn, W. G., Lanchantin, G. F., Mitchell, R. B., and Marable, I. W. (1958a). *Texas Repts. Biol. and Med.* **16**, 320–332.

Glenn, W. G., Lanchantin, G. F., Mitchell, R. B., and Marable, I. W. (1958b). *School Aviation Med., USAF, Rept. No. 58-32.*

Glenn, W. G., King, A. H., and Marable, I. W. (1959). *School Aviation Med., USAF, Rept. No. 59-32.*

Goldfarb, A. R., Libretti, A., Kaplan, M., Abramson, H. A., and Aaronson, A. (1956). *Intern. Arch. Allergy Appl. Immunol.* **8**, 243–251.

Goldfarb, A. R., Bhattacharya, A. K., and Kaplan, M. (1959). *Intern. Arch. Allergy Appl. Immunol.* **15**, 165–171.

Goodman, M., and Wolfe, H. R. (1952). *J. Immunol.* **69**, 423–434.

Goodman, M., Wolfe, H. R., and Norton, S. (1951). *J. Immunol.* **66**, 225–236.

Goodman, M., Ramsey, D. S., Simpson, W. L., and Brennan, M. J. (1957). *J. Lab. Clin. Med.* **50**, 758–768.

Goodman, M., Newman, H. S., and Ramsey, D. S. (1958a). *J. Lab. Clin. Med.* **51**, 814–823.

Goodman, M., Ramsey, D. S., and Poulick, E. (1958b). *Federation Proc.* **17**, 514.

Gotschlich, E., and Stetson, C. A. (1960). *J. Exptl. Med.* **111**, 441–451.

Götz, H., and Scheiffarth, F. (1957). *Z. Immunitätsforsch.* **114**, 72–84.

Goudie, R. B., Anderson, J. R., and Gray, K. G. (1959). *Immunology* **4**, 309–321.

Grabar, P. (1954). *Bull. soc. chim. biol.* **36**, 65–77.

Grabar, P. (1955a). *Ann. Acad. Sci. Fennicae Ser. A. II* **60**, 401–405.

Grabar, P. (1955b). *Arch. sci. biol. (Bologna)* **39**, 589–592.

Grabar, P. (1955c). *Zentr. Bakteriol., Parasitenk. Abt. I Orig.* **164**, 15–24.

Grabar, P. (1957a). *Bull. soc. chim. biol.* **39**, Suppl. I, 3–9.

Grabar, P. (1957b). *Proc., European Brewery Convention,* pp. 147–154.

Grabar, P. (1957c). *Ann. N. Y. Acad. Sci.* **69**, 591–607.

Grabar, P. (1958). *Advances in Protein Chem.* **13**, 1–33.

Grabar, P. (1959a). *Methods of Biochem. Anal.* **7**, 1–38.

Grabar, P. (1959b). *Ann. inst. Pasteur* **97**, 613–625.

Grabar, P., and Burtin, P. (1955a). *Bull. soc. chim. biol.* **37**, 797–802.

Grabar, P., and Burtin, P. (1955b). *Presse méd.* **63**, 804–805.

Grabar, P., and Burtin, P. (1959). *Sang* **4**, 1–6.

Grabar, P., and Courcon, J. (1958). *Bull. soc. chim. biol.* **40**, 1993–2003.

Grabar, P., and Williams, C. A., Jr. (1953). *Biochim. et Biophys. Acta* **10**, 193–194.

Grabar, P., and Williams, C. A., Jr. (1955). *Biochim. et Biophys. Acta* **17**, 67–74.

Grabar, P., Séligmann, M., and Bernard, J. (1954). *Compt. rend. acad. sci.* **239**, 920–922.

Grabar, P., Séligmann, M., and Bernard, G. (1955a). *Ann. inst. Pasteur* **88**, 548–562.

Grabar, P., Fauvert, R., Burtin, P., and Hartmann, L. (1955b). *Compt. rend. acad. sci.* **241**, 262–264.

Grabar, P., Fauvert, R., Burtin, P., and Hartmann, L. (1956a). *Rev. franç. études clin. et biol.* **1**, 175–186.

Grabar, P., Nowinski, W. W., and Genereaux, B. D. (1956b). *Nature* **178**, 430.

Grabar, P., Burtin, P., and Seligmann, M. (1958). *Rev. franc. études clin. et biol.* **3**, 41–47.

Grant, G. H. (1959). *J. Clin. Pathol.* **12**, 510–517.

Grasset, E., Bonifas, V., and Pongratz, E. (1958). *Proc. Soc. Exptl. Biol. Med.* **97**, 72–77.

Grasset, E., Pongratz, E., and Brechbuhler, T. (1956). *Ann. inst. Pasteur* **91**, 162–186.

Grumbach, M. M., Kaplan, S. L., and Solomon, S. (1960). *Nature* **185**, 170–172.

Guillaumie, M., Kréguer, A., and Geoffroy, M. (1954). *Ann. inst. Pasteur* **87**, 522–533.

Gundersen, W. B. (1959). *Acta Pathol. Microbiol. Scand.* **47**, 65–74.

Halbert, S. P. (1958). *J. Exptl. Med.* **108**, 385–410.

Halbert, S. P., Swick, L., and Sonn, C. (1955a). *J. Exptl. Med.* **101**, 539–556.

Halbert, S. P., Swick, L., and Sonn, C. (1955b). *J. Exptl. Med.* **101**, 557–576.

Halick, P., and Seegers, W. H. (1956). *Am. J. Physiol.* **187**, 103–106.

Hanks, J. H. (1935). *J. Immunol.* **28**, 95–104.

Hanson, L. Å. (1959). *Intern. Arch. Allergy Appl. Immunol.* **14**, 279–290.

Hanson, L. Å., and Johansson, B. (1959a). *Intern. Arch. Allergy Appl. Immunol.* **15**, 245–256.

Hanson, L. Å., and Johansson, B. (1959b). *Intern. Arch. Allergy Appl. Immunol.* **15**, 257–269.

Hanson, L. Å., and Johansson, B. (1959c). *Experientia* **15**, 377.

Hanson, L. Å., Raunio, V., and Wadsworth, C. (1960). *Experientia* **16**, 327–329.

Harding, C. V., and Perlmann, P. (1954). *Exptl. Cell Research* **6**, 202–210.

Harris, T. N., Harris, S., and Ogburn, C. A. (1955). *Proc. Soc. Exptl. Biol. Med.* **90**, 39–45.

Hartman, R. J. (1947). "Colloid Chemistry," 2nd ed., 572 pp. Houghton Mifflin, Boston, Massachusetts.

Hartmann, L., and Toilliez, M. (1957). *Rev. franç. études clin. et biol.* **2**, 197–199.

Hartmann, L., Burtin, P., Grabar, P., and Fauvert, R. (1956). *Compt. rend. acad. sci.* **243**, 1937–1939.

Havez, R., and Biserte, G. (1959a). *Clin. Chim. Acta* **4**, 334–339.

Havez, R., and Biserte, G. (1959b). *Clin. Chim. Acta* **4**, 694–700.

Hayward, B. J., and Augustin, R. (1957). *Intern. Arch. Allergy Appl. Immunol.* **11**, 192–205.

Heiner, D. C. (1958). *Pediatrics* **22**, 616–627.

Heiner, D. C. (1959). *J. Diseases Children* **98**, 673–674.

Heiner, D. C., and Kevy, S. V. (1956). *New Engl. J. Med.* **254**, 629–636.

Heitefuss, R., Buchanan-Davidson, D. J., and Stahmann, M. A. (1959). *Arch. Biochem. Biophys.* **85**, 200–208.

Heller, P., Yakulis, V. J., and Zimmerman, H. J. (1959). *Proc. Soc. Exptl. Biol. Med.* **101**, 509–513.

Heremans, J. F. (1959). *Clin. Chim. Acta* **4**, 639–646.

Heremans, J., and Vaerman, J. P. (1958). *Clin. Chim. Acta* **3**, 430–434.

Heremans, M. -Th., Vaerman, J. P., and Heremans, J. F. (1959a). *Proc., 7th Colloq., Protides of the Biological Fluids, Bruges, Belgium*, pp. 396–403.

Heremans, J. F., Heremans, M. -Th., and Schultze, H. E. (1959b). *Clin. Chim. Acta* **4**, 96–102.

Hermann, G. (1959). *Clin. Chim. Acta* **4**, 116–123.

Heymann, W., Hackel, D. B., and Hunter, J. L. P. (1960). *Federation Proc.* **19,** 195.

Hirschfeld, J. (1959a). *Acta Pathol. Microbiol. Scand.* **47,** 160–168.

Hirschfeld, J. (1959b). *Acta Pathol. Microbiol. Scand.* **47,** 169–172.

Hirschfeld, J. (1959c). *Acta Pathol. Microbiol. Scand.* **46,** 229–238.

Hirschfeld, J. (1960a). *Nature* **187,** 164–165.

Hirschfeld, J. (1960b). *Acta Pathol. Microbiol. Scand.* **49,** 255–269.

Hirschfeld, J. (1960c). *Nature* **187,** 126–129.

Hirschfeld, J., and Söderberg, U. (1960). *Experientia* **16,** 198–199.

Hitzig, W. H., Scheidegger, J. J., Butler, R., Gugler, E., and Hässig, A. (1959). *Helv. Med. Acta* **26,** 142–151.

Hussels, H. (1955). *Zentr. Bakteriol., Parasitenk. Abt. I. Orig.* **162,** 67–71.

Hussels, H. (1958). *Röntgen- u. Laboratoriumpraxis* **11,** 181–186.

Inoue, T. (1957). *Ann. Tuberc. (Tenri, Japan)* **8,** 1–8.

Ishizaka, T., Campbell, D. H., and Ishizaka, K. (1960). *Proc. Soc. Exptl. Biol. Med.* **103,** 5–9.

Isliker, H. C. (1953). *Ann. N. Y. Acad. Sci.* **57,** 225.

Isliker, H. C. (1957). *Advances in Protein Chem.* **12,** 387–463.

Isojima, S., and Stepus, S. (1959). *Intern. Arch. Allergy Appl. Immunol.* **15,** 350–359.

Itano, A. (1933). *Ber. Ohara Inst. landwirtsch. Forsch. Japan* **6,** 59–72; from *Chem. Abstr.* (1934) **28,** 3846.

Jeener, R., Lemoine, P., and Lavand'homme, C. (1954). *Boichim. et Biophys. Acta* **14,** 321–334.

Jennings, R. K. (1953). *J. Immunol.* **70,** 181–186.

Jennings, R. K. (1954a). *J. Bacteriol.* **67,** 559–564.

Jennings, R. K. (1954b). *J. Bacteriol.* **67,** 565–570.

Jennings, R. K. (1956). *J. Immunol.* **77,** 156–164.

Jennings, R. K. (1958). *J. Lab. Clin. Med.* **51,** 152–162.

Jennings, R. K. (1959a). *J. Immunol.* **83,** 237–245.

Jennings, R. K. (1959b,c,d). Unpublished papers.

Jennings, R. K., and Malone, F. (1954). *J. Immunol.* **72,** 411–418.

Jennings, R. K., and Malone, F. (1955). *Brit. J. Exptl. Pathol.* **36,** 1–7.

Jensen, K. E., and Francis, T., Jr. (1953). *J. Immunol.* **70,** 321–325.

Jutisz, M., Cummins, T., and Legault-démare, J. (1957). *Biochim. et Biophys. Acta* **23,** 173–180.

Kabat, E. A. (1958). *In* "Serological and Biochemical Comparisons of Proteins" (W. H. Cole, ed.), pp. 92–112. Rutgers Univ. Press, New Brunswick, New Jersey.

Kagan, I. G. (1957). *J. Infectious Diseases* **101,** 11–19.

Kagan, I. G., and Bargai, U. (1956). *J. Parasitol.* **42,** 237–245.

Kagan, I. G., Jeska, E. L., and Gentzkow, C. J. (1958). *J. Immunol.* **80,** 400–406.

Kaminski, M. (1954a). *Bull. soc. chim. biol.* **36,** 279–288.

Kaminski, M. (1954b). *Bull. soc. chim. biol.* **36,** 289–293.

Kaminski, M. (1954c). *Biochim. et Biophys. Acta* **13,** 216–223.

Kaminski, M. (1954d). *Bull. soc. chim. biol.* **36,** 79–84.

Kaminski, M. (1955a). *J. Immunol.* **75,** 367–376.

Kaminski, M. (1955b). *Actes Colloq. Diffusion Montpellier* pp. 1–14.

Kaminski, M. (1957a). *Ann. inst. Pasteur* **93,** 102–122.

Kaminski, M. (1957b). *Ann. inst. Pasteur* **92,** 802–816.

Kaminski, M. (1957c). *Bull. soc. chim. biol.* **39,** Suppl. I, 85–104.

Kaminski, M. (1960). *Ann. inst. Pasteur* **98**, 51–60.
Kaminski, M., and Durieux, J. (1954). *Bull. soc. chim. biol.* **36**, 1037–1051.
Kaminski, M., and Durieux, J. (1956). *Exptl. Cell Research* **10**, 590–618.
Kaminski, M., and Nouvel, J. (1952). *Bull. soc. chim. biol.* **34**, 11–20.
Kaminski, M., and Ouchterlony, Ö. (1951). *Bull. soc. chim. biol.* **33**, 758–770.
Kaminski, M., and Tanner, C. E. (1959). *Biochim. et Biophys. Acta* **33**, 10–21.
Kantor, F. S., and Cole, R. M. (1959). *Proc. Soc. Exptl. Biol. Med.* **102**, 146–150.
Karjala, S. A., and Nakayama, Y. (1959). *Clin. Chim. Acta* **4**, 369–373.
Keutel, H. J., Hermann, G., and Licht, W. (1959). *Clin. Chim. Acta* **4**, 665–673.
Kniker, W. T. (1960). Personal communication.
King, E. P., Frobisher, M., Jr., and Parsons, E. I. (1949). *Am. J. Public Health*
    39, 1314–1320.
Kirkbride, M. B., and Cohen, S. M. (1934). *Am. J. Hyg.* **20**, 444–453.
Kistner, S. (1959). *Acta Chem. Scand.* **13**, 1149–1158.
Kleczkowski, A. (1957). *J. Exptl. Microbiol.* **16**, 405–417.
Kohn, J. (1957). *Nature* **180**, 986–987.
Kohn, J. (1958). *Clin. Chim. Acta* **3**, 450–454.
Komárková, A., and Kořínek, J. (1959). *J. Lab. Clin. Med.* **54**, 707–711.
Kořínek, J., and Paluska, E. (1959). *Z. Immunitätsforsch.* **117**, 60–69.
Korngold, L. (1956a). *J. Immunol.* **77**, 119–122.
Korngold, L. (1956b). *Federation Proc.* **15**, 597–598.
Korngold, L. (1957). *Ann. N. Y. Acad. Sci.* **69**, 681–697.
Korngold, L., and Lipari, R. (1955a). *Science* **121**, 170–171.
Korngold, L., and Lipari, R. (1955b). *Cancer Research* **15**, 159–161.
Korngold, L., and Lipari, R. (1956a). *Cancer* **9**, 183–192.
Korngold, L., and Lipari, R. (1956b). *Cancer* **9**, 262–272.
Korngold, L., and van Leeuwen, G. (1957a). *J. Exptl. Med.* **106**, 467–476.
Korngold, L., and van Leeuwen, G. (1957b). *J. Exptl. Med.* **106**, 477–484.
Korngold, L., and van Leeuwen, G. (1957c). *J. Immunol.* **78**, 172–177.
Korngold, L., and van Leeuwen, G. (1958). *Federation Proc.* **17**, 521.
Korngold, L., and van Leeuwen, G. (1959a). *J. Exptl. Med.* **110**, 1–8.
Korngold, L., and van Leeuwen, G. (1959b). *Intern. Arch. Allergy Appl. Immunol.*
    15, 278–290.
Korngold, L., van Leeuwen, G., and Brener, J. L. (1959). *J. Lab. Clin. Med.* **53**,
    517–524.
Kovaleva, V. V. (1958). *J. Microbiol. Epidemiol. Immunobiol.* (*U.S.S.R.*) **29**,
    129–132.
Kruyt, H. R. (1949). "Colloid Science," 753 pp. Elsevier, Rotterdam, 1949.
Kuhns, W. J. (1955). *J. Exptl. Med.* **101**, 109–117.
Kunkel, H. G. (1954). *Methods of Biochem. Anal.* **1**, 141–170.
Lacko, L., Kořínek, J., and Burger, M. (1959). *Clin. Chim. Acta* **4**, 800–806.
Lamanna, C., and Lowenthal, J. P. (1951). *J. Bacteriol.* **61**, 751–752.
Lapresle, C. (1955). *Ann. inst. Pasteur* **89**, 654–665.
Lapresle, C. (1959). *Ann. inst. Pasteur* **97**, 626–635.
Lapresle, C., and Durieux, J. (1957a). *Ann. inst. Pasteur* **92**, 62–73.
Lapresle, C., and Durieux, J. (1957b). *Bull. soc. chim. biol.* **39**, 833–841.
Lapresle, C., and Durieux, J. (1958). *Ann. inst. Pasteur* **94**, 38–48.
Lapresle, C., and Grabar, P. (1957). *Rev. franç. études clin. et biol.* **2**, 1025–1037.
Lapresle, C., Webb, T., Kaminski, M., and Campagne, M. (1959a). *Bull. soc.
    chim. biol.* **41**, 695–706.
Lapresle, C., Kaminski, M., and Tanner, C. E. (1959b). *J. Immunol.* **82**, 94–102.

Larkey, B. J., and Belko, J. S. (1959). *Clin. Chem.* 5, 566–568.

Larson, T. L., and Feinberg, R. (1954). *Science* 120, 426.

Lawson, D. F. (1957). *J. Photo. Sci.* 5, 1.

Lebedev, A. D., and Tsilinskii, I. I. (1958). *J. Microbiol. Epidemiol. Immunobiol.* (*U.S.S.R.*) 29, 685–693.

Le Boivier, G. L. (1957). *J. Exptl. Med.* 106, 661–675.

Lederer, M. (1955). "An Introduction to Paper Electrophoresis and Related Methods," 206 pp. Elsevier, New York.

Leone, C. A., Leonard, A. B., and Pryor, C. (1955). *Univ. Kansas Sci. Bull.* 37, 477–497.

Lester, W., and Colton, R. (1959). *Trans. 18th Conf. Chemotherapy of Tuberculosis, Veterans Administration-Armed Forces,* pp. 232–236.

Lévy, G., and Polonovski, J. (1958). *Bull. soc. chim. biol.* 40, 1293–1298.

Libich, M. (1959). *Folia Biol.* (*Prague*) 5, 71–81.

Libretti, A., Kaplan, M. A., and Goldin, M. (1955). *Proc. Soc. Exptl. Biol. Med.* 90, 481–484.

Lind, A. (1959). *Intern. Arch. Allergy Appl. Immunol.* 14, 264–278.

Liu, C. T., and McCrory, W. W. (1958). *J. Immunol.* 81, 492–498.

Lohss, F., and Kallee, E. (1959). *Clin. Chim. Acta* 4, 127–133.

Loriewicz, Z., Huianicka, E., and Weinrauder, H. (1957). *Acta Microbiol. Polon.* 6, 311–320.

McDonald, H. J. (1955). "Ionography," 268 pp. Year Book Publ., Chicago, Illinois.

McDonald, H. J., and Rebeiro, L. P. (1959). *Clin. Chim. Acta* 4, 458–459.

McDuffie, F. C., Kabat, E. A., Allen, P. Z., and Williams, C. A., Jr. (1959). *J. Immunol.* 81, 48–64.

Macheboeuf, M., Rebeyrotte, P., Dubert, J., and Brunerie, M. (1953). *Bull. soc. chim. biol.* 35, 334–345.

McIlwain, H. (1938). *Brit. J. Exptl. Pathol.* 19, 411–416.

McIvor, B. C., and Moon, H. D. (1959). *J. Immunol.* 82, 328–331.

Maegraith, B. G. (1933). *Brit. J. Exptl. Pathol.* 14, 227–235.

Maegraith, B. G., and Adelaide, M. B. (1934). *Lancet* i, 17–19.

Makinodan, T., Gengozian, H., and Canning, R. E. (1959). *Science* 130, 1419.

Mankiewicz, E. (1958). *Can. J. Microbiol.* 4, 565–570.

Marcuse, K., and Hussels, H. (1955). *Zentr. Bakteriol., Parasitenk. Abt. I* 162, 72–78.

Marquevielle, J. (1957). "Research on the Role Exercised by Serum Lipids on the Antigen-antibody Precipitation Reaction," 128 pp. E. Drouillard, Bordeaux, France.

Marsh, J., and Whereat, A. F. (1959). *J. Biol. Chem.* 234, 3196–3200.

Martin, E., Scheidegger, J. J., Grabar, P., and Williams, C. A., Jr. (1954). *Bull. acad. suisse sci. med.* 10, 193–198.

Martin du Pan, R., Scheidegger, J. J., Pongratz, E., and Roulet, H. (1955). *Arch. franç. pédiat.* 12, 243–250.

Martin du Pan, R., Wenger, P., Koechli, S., Scheidegger, J. J., and Roux, J. (1959). *Clin. Chim. Acta* 4, 110–115.

Matthews, P. R. J. (1958). *J. Med. Lab. Technol.* 15, 95–101.

Maurer, P. H., Subrahmanyam, D., Katchalski, E., and Blout, E. R. (1959). *J. Immunol.* 83, 193–197.

Miller, R. L., and Heckly, R. J. (1959). *J. Lab. Clin. Med.* 54, 333–334.

Mollaret, P., Delay, J., Burtin, P., and Lemperiere, T. (1956). *Arch. biol. med.* 14, 1–5.

Moretti, J., Boussier, G., Hugou, M., and Hartmann, L. (1959). *Bull. soc. chim. biol* **41**, 79–87.

Morton, J. I., and Deutsch, H. F. (1958). *J. Biol. Chem.* **231**, 1119–1127.

Muller, M., Fontaine, G., Muller, P., and Donazzan, M. (1958a). *Lille Med.* **3**, 218–223.

Muller, M., Fontaine, G., and Muller, P. (1958b). *Lille Med.* **3**, 773–776.

Muller, M., Fontaine, G., Muller, P. (1959). *Lillie Med.* **4**, 150–153.

Muller, W., Klein, N., and Matthes, M. (1958). *Z. Rheumaforsch.* **17**, 226–233.

Müller-Eberhard, H. J., and Nilsson, U. (1960). *J. Exptl. Med.* **111**, 217–234.

Müller-Eberhard, H. J., Nilsson, U., and Aronsson, T. (1960). *J. Exptl. Med.* **111**, 201–215.

Munoz, J. (1954). *In* "Serological Approaches to Studies of Protein Structures and Metabolism" (W. H. Cole, ed.), pp. 55–73. Rutgers Univ. Press, New Brunswick, New Jersey.

Munoz, J. (1959). *Anal. Chem.* **31**, 981–985.

Munoz, J., and Becker, E. L. (1950). *J. Immunol.* **65**, 47–58.

Munoz, J., and Becker, E. L. (1952). *J. Immunol.* **68**, 405–412.

Nachkov, D., and Nachkova, O. (1959). *Bull. soc. chim. biol.* **41**, 159–171.

Nakamura, S., Hosoda, T., and Ueta, T. (1959a). *Proc. Japan. Acad.* **34**, 742–746.

Nakamura, S., Takeo, K., Katuno, A., and Tominaga, S. (1959b). *Clin. Chim. Acta.* **4**, 893–900.

Naylor, G. R. E., and Adair, M. E. (1959). *Nature* **184**, 1854–1855.

Neff, J. C., and Becker, E. L. (1956). *Walter Reed Army Inst. Research, Rept.* **147–56**, 12 pp.

Neff, J. C., and Becker, E. L. (1957a). *Federation Proc.* **16**, 427.

Neff, J. C., and Becker, E. L. (1957b). *J. Immunol.* **78**, 5–10.

Newton, J. W., and Levine, L. (1959). *Arch. Biochem. Biophys.* **83**, 456–471.

Nicolle, M., Cesari, E., and Debains, E. (1920). *Ann. inst. Pasteur* **34**, 596–599.

Oakley, C. L. (1954). *Discussions Faraday Soc.* **18**, 358–364.

Oakley, C. L., and Fulthorpe, A. J. (1953). *J. Pathol. Bacteriol.* **65**, 49–60.

O'Connor, G. R. (1957a). *A.M.A. Arch. Ophthalmol.* **57**, 52–57.

O'Connor, G. R. (1957b). *Am. J. Ophthalmol.* **44**, 75–85.

Oeding, P. (1959). *Acta Pathol. Microbiol. Scand.* **47**, 53–64.

Olitzki, A. L., and Sulitzeanu, A. (1959). *J. Bacteriol.* **77**, 264–269.

Ormsbee, R. A., and Larson, C. L. (1955). *J. Immunol.* **74**, 359–370.

Osserman, E. F. (1959). *J. Immunol.* **84**, 93–97.

Ouchterlony, Ö. (1948a). *Arkiv Kemi Mineral. Geol.* **26B**, 1–9.

Ouchterlony, Ö. (1948b). *Acta Pathol. Microbiol. Scand.* **25**, 186–191.

Ouchterlony, Ö. (1949a). *Acta Pathol. Microbiol. Scand.* **26**, 516–524.

Ouchterlony, Ö. (1949b). *Lancet* **i**, 346–348.

Ouchterlony, Ö. (1949c). *Acta Pathol. Microbiol. Scand.* **26**, 507–515.

Ouchterlony, Ö. (1949d). *Arkiv Kemi* **1**, 43–48.

Ouchterlony, Ö. (1949e). *Arkiv Kemi* **1**, 55–59.

Ouchterlony, Ö. (1953). *Acta Pathol. Microbiol. Scand.* **32**, 231–240.

Ouchterlony, Ö. (1958). *Progr. in Allergy* **5**, 1–78.

Ouchterlony, Ö. (1959). *Recent Progr. in Microbiol.* **7**, 163–169.

Ouchterlony, Ö., Ericsson, H., and Neumuller, C. (1950). *Acta Med. Scand.* **138**, 76–79.

Oudin, J. (1946). *Compt. rend. acad. sci.* **222**, 115–116.

Oudin, J. (1947). *Bull. soc. chim. biol.* **29**, 140–148.

Oudin, J. (1948a). *Ann. inst. Pasteur* **75**, 30–51.

Oudin, J. (1948b). *Ann. inst. Pasteur* **75**, 109–129.

Oudin, J. (1949). *Compt. rend. acad. sci.* **228**, 1890–1892.

Oudin, J. (1952). *Methods in Med. Research* **5**, 335–378.

Oudin, J. (1954). *Faraday Soc. Discussions* **18**, 351–357.

Oudin, J. (1955). *Ann. inst. Pasteur* **89**, 531–555.

Oudin, J. (1956a). *Compt. rend. acad. sci.* **242**, 2489–2490.

Oudin, J. (1956b). *Compt. rend. acad. sci.* **242**, 2606–2608.

Oudin, J. (1957). *In* "Symposium on Protein Structure" (A. Neuberger, ed.), pp. 298–301. Methuen, London.

Oudin, J. (1958a). *VII Congr. Intern. Microbiol., Stockholm.*

Oudin, J. (1958b). *J. Immunol.* **81**, 376–388.

Oudin, J. (1960a). *Compt. rend. acad. sci.* **250**, 770–772.

Oudin, J. (1960b). *J. Immunol.* **84**, 143–151.

Paluska, E., and Kořínek, J. (1960). *Z. Immunitätsforsch.* **119**, 244–257.

Parlett, R. C., and Reher, C. A. (1959). *Am. Rev. Resp. Diseases* **80**, 886–894.

Parlett, R. C., and Youmans, G. P. (1956). *Am. Rev. Tuberc. Pulmonary Diseases* **73**, 637–649.

Parlettt, R. C., and Youmans, G. P. (1958). *Am. Rev. Tuberc. Pulmonary Diseases* **77**, 450–461.

Parlett, R. C., and Youmans, G. (1959). *Am. Rev. Tuberc. Pulmonary Diseases* **80**, 153–166.

Parlett, R. C., Youmans, G. P., Reher, C., and Lester, W. (1958). *Am. Rev. Tuberc. Pulmonary Diseases* **77**, 462–472.

Paton, A. M. (1959). *Nature* **183**, 1812–1813.

Peetoom, F., Rose, N., Ruddy, S., Micheli, A., and Grabar, P. (1960). *Ann. inst. Pasteur* **98**, 252–260.

Pepys, J., Riddell, R. W., and Clayton, Y. M. (1959a). *Nature* **184**, 1328–1329.

Pepys, J., Augustin, R., and Paterson, A. B. (1959b). *Tubercle* **40**, 163–172.

Pereira, H. G., Allison, A. C., and Farthing, C. P. (1959). *Nature* **183**, 895–896.

Perlmann, P. (1953). *Exptl. Cell Research* **5**, 394–399.

Perlmann, P. (1957). *Exptl. Cell Research* **13**, 365–390.

Perlmann, P. (1959). *Experientia* **15**, 41–52.

Perlmann, P., and D'Amelio, V. (1958). *Nature* **181**, 491–492.

Perlmann, P., and Hulton, T. (1958). *Nature* **182**, 1530–1531.

Perlmann, P., and Kaltenbach, J. C. (1957). *Exptl. Cell Research* **12**, 185–188.

Perlmann, P., and Perlmann, H. (1957). *Exptl. Cell Research* **13**, 454–474.

Perlmann, P., Hulton, T., D'Amelio, V., and Morgan, W. S. (1959). *Exptl. Cell Research Suppl.* **7**, 279–295.

Pernot, E. (1956). *Bull. soc. chim. biol.* **38**, 1041–1054.

Pernot, E., and Szumowski, P. (1958). *Bull. soc. chim. biol.* **40**, 1423–1434.

Petrie, G. F. (1923). *Brit. J. Exptl. Pathol.* **13**, 380–394.

Petrie, G. F., and Steabben, D. (1943). *Brit. Med. J.* I, 377–379.

Pierce, W. A., Jr. (1959). *J. Bacteriol.* **77**, 726–732.

Pittman, M., Branham, S. E., and Sockrider, E. M. (1938). *Public Health Repts.* (*U.S.*) **53**, 1400–1408.

Polonovski, J., Lévy, G., and Wald, R. (1958). *Bull. soc. chim. biol.* **40**, 1319–1324.

Polonovski, J., Lévy, G., and Wald, R. (1959). *Ann. inst. Pasteur* **97**, 466–472.

Polson, A. (1958). *Sci. Tools* **5**, 17–20.

Pope, C. G., and Stevens, M. F. (1958a). *Brit. J. Exptl. Pathol.* **39**, 139–149.

Pope, C. G., and Stevens, M. F. (1958b). *Brit. J. Exptl. Pathol.* **39**, 150–157.

Pope, C. G., and Stevens, M. F. (1959). *Brit. J. Exptl. Pathol.* **40**, 410–416.

Pope, C. G., Stevens, M. F., Caspary, E. A., and Fenton, E. L. (1951). *Brit. J. Exptl. Pathol.* **32**, 246–258.

Popovich, B. I. (1935). *Russ.* **44**, 289; from *Chem. Abstr.* (1938) **32**, 3061.

Porter, R. R. (1957). *Biochem. J.* **66**, 677–686.

Poulik, M. D. (1952). *Can. J. Med. Sci.* **30**, 417–419.

Poulik, M. D. (1953). *Can. J. Med. Sci.* **31**, 485–492.

Poulik, M. D. (1956). *Nature* **177**, 982–983.

Poulik, M. D. (1959). *J. Immunol.* **82**, 502–515.

Poulik, M. D., and Poulik, E. (1958). *Nature* **181**, 354–355.

Preer, J. R., Jr. (1956). *J. Immunol.* **77**, 52–60.

Preer, J. R., Jr., and Telfer, W. H. (1957). *J. Immunol.* **79**, 288–293.

Pressman, D., James, A. W., Yagi, Y., Hiramoto, R., Woernley, D., and Maxwell, W. T. (1957). *Proc. Soc. Exptl. Biol. Med.* **96**, 773–777.

Pruzansky, J. J., Feinberg, S. M., and Wojcik, N. (1960). *Federation Proc.* **19**, 203.

Rafyi, A., Chamsy, H. M., and Delsal, J. L. (1954). *Rev. immunol.* **18**, 391–398.

Randall, J. E. (1958). "Elements of Biophysics," 333 pp. Year Book Publ., Chicago, Illinois.

Ransom, J. P., Quan, S. F., Omi, G., and Hoggan, M. D. (1955). *J. Immunol.* **75**, 265–268.

Rao, S. S., Kulkarni, N. E., Cooper, S. N., and Radhakrishman, M. R. (1955). *Brit. J. Ophthalmol.* **39**, 163–169.

Raymond, S., and Wang, Y. (1959). "Cyanogum 41 Gelling Agent," 8 pp. Brochure, American Cyanamid Company, New York, N.Y.

Raymond, S., and Weintraub, L. (1959). *Science* **130**, 711.

Raynaud, M. (1958). *In* "Mechanisms of Hypersensitivity," International Symposium, pp. 27–46. Little, Brown, Boston, Massachusetts.

Raynaud, M., and Relyveld, E. H. (1959). *Ann. inst. Pasteur* **97**, 636–678.

Raynaud, M., Relyveld, E. H., Girard, O., and Corvazier, R. (1959a). *Ann. inst. Pasteur* **96**, 129–139.

Raynaud, M., Turpin, A., Relyveld, E. H., Corvazier, R., and Girard, O. (1959b). *Ann. inst. Pasteur* **96**, 649–658.

Reed, F. C. (1960). *Am. J. Clin. Pathol.* **33**, 363–366.

Reiner, L., and Kopp, M. (1927). *Kolloid-Z.* **42**, 335.

Rejnek, J., and Bednarik, T. (1960). *Clin. Chim. Acta* **5**, 250–258.

Relyveld, E. H., and Efraim, S. B. (1959). *Ann. inst. Pasteur* **97**, 697–717.

Relyveld, E. H., and Raynaud, M. (1957). *Ann. inst. Pasteur* **93**, 246–250.

Relyveld, E. H., and Raynaud, M. (1958). *In* Proceedings of the 5th Colloqium on "Protides of the Biologic Fluids," pages 147–153. Elsevier Publishing Co., Amsterdam.

Relyveld, E. H., and Raynaud, M. (1959). *Ann. inst. Pasteur* **96**, 537–547.

Relyveld, E. H., Turpin, A., Laffaille, A., Paris, C., and Raynaud, M. (1954). *Ann. inst. Pasteur* **87**, 301–313.

Relyveld, E. H., Grabar, P., Raynaud, M., and Williams, C. A., Jr. (1956). *Ann. inst. Pasteur* **90**, 688–696.

Relyveld, E. H., Girard, O., Corvazier, R., and Raynaud, M. (1957). *Ann. inst. Pasteur* **92**, 631–641.

Relyveld, E. H., van Triet, A. J., and Raynaud, M. (1959). *J. Microbiol. Serol.* **25**, 369–402.

Rheins, M., Burrell, R. G., and Birkeland, J. M. (1956). *Am. Rev. Tuberc. Pulmonary Diseases* **74**, 229–238.

Richou, R., Velu, H., and Kourilsky, R. (1959). *Rev. immunol.* **23**, 354–358.

Richter, M., Rose, B., and Sehon, A. H. (1958). *Can. J. Biochem. and Physiol.* 36, 1105–1113.

Riley, C. M. (1960). Personal communication.

Robert, B., Vaux St. Cyr, C., Robert, L., and Grabar, P. (1959). *Clin. Chim. Acta* 4, 828–840.

Roitt, I. M., and Doniach, D. (1958a). *Lancet* **ii**, 1027–1033.

Roitt, I. M., and Doniach, D. (1958b). In "Mechanisms of Hypersensitivity," International Symposium, pp. 325–348. Little, Brown, Boston, Massachusetts.

Roitt, I. M., Campbell, P. N., and Doniach, D. (1958). *Biochem. J.* 69, 248–256.

Rondle, C. J. M., and Carman, B. J. (1956). *Experientia* 12, 443–447.

Rose, N. R., and Arbesman, C. E. (1960). *Federation Proc.* 19, 212.

Rose, H. R., and Witebsky, E. (1959). *J. Immunol.* 83, 34–40.

Rubinstein, H. M. (1954). *J. Immunol.* 73, 322–330.

Rybak, M. (1959). *Clin. Chim. Acta* 4, 310–312.

Salmon, J. (1959). *Clin. Chim. Acta* 4, 767–775.

Salvinien, J. (1957). *Bull. soc. chim. biol.* 39, Suppl. 1, 11–44.

Salvinien, J., and Kaminski, M. (1955a). *Compt. rend. acad. sci.* 240, 257–258.

Salvinien, J., and Kaminski, M. (1955b). *Compt. rend. acad. sci.* 240, 377–378.

Sandor, G., and Sandor, M. (1960). *Compt. rend. acad. sci.* 250, 767–769.

Sang, J. H., and Sobey, W. R. (1954). *J. Immunol.* 72, 52–65.

Scanu, A., and Page, I. H. (1959). *J. Exptl. Med.* 109, 239–256.

Scanu, A., Lewis, L. A., and Page, I. H. (1958). *J. Exptl. Med.* 108, 185–196.

Scheidegger, J. J. (1955). *Intern. Arch. Allergy Appl. Immunol.* 7, 103–110.

Scheidegger, J. J. (1956). *Semaine Hôp.* 32, 2119–2127.

Scheidegger, J. J. (1957). *Bull. soc. chim. biol.* 39, Suppl. 1, 45–63.

Scheidegger, J. J., and Roulet, H. (1955). *Praxis* 44, 73–76.

Scheidegger, J. J., Martin, E., and Riotton, G. (1956). *Schweiz. med. Wochschr.* 86, 224–225.

Scheidegger, J. J., Weber, R., and Hässig, A. (1958). *Helv. Med. Acta* 25, 25–40.

Scheiffarth, F., and Götz, H. (1960). *Intern. Arch. Allergy Appl. Immunol.* 16, 61–92.

Scheiffarth, F., Götz, H., and Soergel, K. (1957a). *Intern. Arch. Allergy Appl. Immunol.* 10, 82–99.

Scheiffarth, F., Berg, G. Götz, H., and Trabulsi, L. R. (1957b). *Intern. Arch. Allergy Appl. Immunol.* 10, 276–284.

Scheiffarth, F., Götz, H., and Soergel, K. (1958a). *Klin. Wochschr.* 36, 82–86.

Scheiffarth, F., Frenger, W., and Götz, H. (1958b). *Klin. Wochschr.* 36, 367–369.

Scheiffarth, F., Götz, H., and Warnatz, H. (1958c). *Clin. Chim. Acta* 3, 535–547.

Schiottt, C. R. (1953). *Acta Pathol. Microbiol. Scand.* 32, 251–257.

Schmid, K., and Macnair, M. B. (1956). *J. Clin. Invest.* 35, 814–824.

Schmidt, W. C. (1957). *J. Immunol.* 78, 178–184.

Schuchardt, L. F., Munoz, J., and Verwey, W. F. (1958). *J. Immunol.* 80, 237–242.

Schultze, H. E. (1958). *Clin. Chim. Acta* 3, 24–33.

Schultze, H. E., and Schwick, G. (1959). *Clin. Chim. Acta* 4, 15–25.

Schultze, H. E., Schönenberger, M., and Schwick, G. (1956). *Biochem. Z.* 328, 267–284.

Schutz, J. N. (1958). *J. Biol. Photo. Assoc.* 26, 159–164.

Schwick, G., and Schultze, H. E. (1959). *Clin. Chim. Acta* 4, 26–35.

Seeliger, H. (1955). *Z. Hyg. Infektionskrankh.* 141, 110–121.

Seeliger, H. P. R., and Sulzbacher, F. (1956). *Can. J. Microbiol.* 2, 220–231.

Seibert, F. B., and Soto-Figueroa, E. (1957). *Am. Rev. Tuberc. Pulmonary Diseases* **75**, 601–607.

Seligmann, M. (1956). *Compt. rend. acad. sci.* **243**, 531–534.

Seligmann, M. (1957a). *Compt. rend. acad. sci.* **244**, 2192–2194.

Seligmann, M. (1957b). *Vox Sanguinis* **2**, 270–282.

Seligmann, M. (1958). *Rev. franc. Et. clin. biol.* **3**, 558–580.

Seligmann, M. (1959). *In* "Proceedings of the 1st International Symposium, Immuno pathology," Basel/Seelisberg, 1958 pp. 402–415. Benno Schwabe, Basel, Switzerland.

Seligmann, M., and Grabar, P. (1958). *Rev. franç. études clin. et biol.* **3**, 1073–1075.

Seligmann, M., and Hanau, C. (1958). *Rev. hématol.* **13**, 239–248.

Seligmann, M., Grabar, P., and Bernard, G. (1955). *Sang* **26**, 52–70.

Serre, H., and Jaffiol, C. (1958). *Presse méd.* **66**, 2044–2047.

Shandon Scientific Co., Ltd. (1959). "Feinberg Agar Gel Cutters," Data Sheet No. AG/559. Cromwell Place, London.

Sia, R. H. P., and Chung, S. F. (1932). *Proc. Soc. Exptl. Biol. Med.* **29**, 792–795.

Singer, S. J. (1957). *J. Cellular Comp. Physiol.* **50**, Suppl. 1, 51–78.

Slater, R. J. (1955). *Arch. Biochem. Biophys.* **59**, 33–44.

Slater, R. J., Ward, S. M., and Kunkel, H. G. (1955). *J. Exptl. Med.* **101**, 85–108.

Smith, C. D. (1956). "An Immunoelectrophoretic Study of Tuberculous Sera," 46 pp. M.A. Thesis, Stanford University, Stanford, California.

Smith, D. C., and Murchison, W. (1959). *J. Med. Lab. Tech.* **16**, 197–200.

Smith, E. L., and Jager, B. V. (1952). *Ann. Rev. Microbiol.* **6**, 207–228.

Smithies, O. (1955). *Biochem. J.* **61**, 629–641.

Spalding, D. H., and Metcalf, T. G. (1954). *J. Bacteriol.* **68**, 160–166.

Spiers, J. A., and Augustin, R. (1958). *Trans. Faraday Soc.* **54**, 287–295.

Spuhler, V., Moosbrugger, G. A., and Meter, K. (1958). *Schweiz. Arch. Tierheilk.* **100**, 610–615.

Stahmann, M. A., Buchanan-Davidson, D. J., Lapresle, C., and Grabar, P. (1959a). *Nature* **184**, 549–550.

Stahmann, M. A., Tsuyuki, H., Weinke, K., Lapresle, C., and Grabar, P. (1955). *Compt. rend. acad. sci.* **241**, 1528–1529.

Stahmann, M. A., Lapresle, C., Buchanan-Davidson, D. J., and Grabar, P. (1959b). *J. Immunol.* **83**, 534–542.

Stanworth, D. R. (1957a). *Biochem. J. Appl. Immunol.* **65**, 582–598.

Stanworth, D. R. (1957b). *Intern. Arch. Allergy Appl. Immunol.* **11**, 170–191.

Staub, A. M., and Pon, G. (1956). *Ann. inst. Pasteur* **90**, 441–457.

Stern, K. H. (1954). *Chem. Revs.* **54**, 79–100.

Subrahmanyam, D., and Maurer, P. H. (1959). *J. Immunol.* **83**, 327–333.

Sulitzeanu, D. (1958). *Brit. J. Exptl. Pathol.* **39**, 267–275.

Surgalla, M. J., Bergdoll, M. S., and Dack, G. M. (1952). *J. Immunol.* **69**, 357–365.

Surgalla, M. J., Bergdoll, M. S., and Dack, G. M. (1954). *J. Immunol.* **72**, 398–403.

Telfer, W. H. (1953). *Federation Proc.* **12**, 734–738.

Telfer, W. H., and Williams, C. M. (1953). *J. Gen. Physiol.* **36**, 389–413.

Toda, Y. (1957). *Ann. Tuberc.* (*Nara, Japan*) **8**, 20–24.

Tunevall, G. (1953). *Acta Pathol. Microbiol. Scand.* **32**, 193–197.

Turpin, A., and Raynaud, M. (1959). *Ann. inst. Pasteur* **97**, 718–732.

Turpin, A., Relyveld, E. H., Pillet, J., and Raynaud, M. (1954). *Ann. inst. Pasteur* **87**, 185–193.

Uriel, J. (1957). *Bull. soc. chim. biol.* **39**, Suppl. 1, 105–118.

Uriel, J. (1958a). *Bull. soc. chim. biol.* **40**, 277–280.

Uriel, J. (1958b). *Clin. y Lab.* **65**, 89–94.

Uriel, J., and Grabar, P. (1956a). *Ann. inst. Pasteur* **90**, 427–440.

Uriel, J., and Grabar, P. (1956b). *Bull. soc. chim. biol.* **38**, 1253–1269.

Uriel, J., and Scheidegger, J. J. (1955). *Bull. soc. chim. biol.* **37**, 165–168.

Uriel, J., Götz, H., and Grabar, P. (1957). *Schweiz. med. Wochschr.* **87**, 431–434.

Uyeu, F., and Pavageau, D. (1956). *Ann. inst. Pasteur* **90**, 482–488.

van Oss, C. H. (1959). *Science* **129**, 1365–1366.

van Regenmortel, M. H. V. (1959). *Biochim. et Biophys. Acta* **34**, 553–554.

van Slogteren, E., and van Slogteren, D. H. M. (1957). *Ann. Rev. Microbiol.* **11**, 149–164.

Vaughan, J. H., and Kabat, E. A. (1953). *J. Exptl. Med.* **97**, 821–844.

Vaughan, J. H., and Kabat, E. A. (1954a). *J. Immunol.* **73**, 205–211.

Vaughan, J. H., and Kabat, E. A. (1954b). *J. Allergy* **25**, 387–394.

Vaux Saint-Cyr, C. (1959). *Compt. rend. acad. sci.* **248**, 2818–2820.

Vaux Saint-Cyr, C., Courcon, J., and Grabar, P. (1958). *Bull. soc. chim. biol.* **40**, 579–590.

von Muralt, G., and Gugler, E. (1959). *Helv. Med. Acta* **26**, 410–423.

Vyazov, O. E., Konyukhov, B. V., and Lishtvan, L. L. (1959). *Bull. Exptl. Biol. Med.* **47**, 646–649.

Wadsworth, C. (1957). *Intern. Arch. Allergy Appl. Immunol.* **10**, 355–360.

Weigle, W. O. (1960). *Federation Proc.* **19**, 205.

Weil, A. J., and Finkler, A. E. (1959). *Proc. Soc. Exptl. Biol. Med.* **102**, 624–626.

Went, H., and Mazia, D. (1959). *Exptl. Cell Research* **18**, Suppl. 7, 200–218.

Weyzen, W. W. H., and Vos, O. (1957). *Nature* **180**, 288–289.

Whiteside, R. E., and Baker, E. E. (1960). *J. Immunol.* **84**, 221–226.

Wieme, R. J. (1955). *Bull. soc. chim. biol.* **37**, 995–997.

Wieme, R. J. (1958). *Behringwerk. Mitt.* **34**, 27–37.

Wieme, R. J. (1959a). "Studies on Agar Gel Electrophoresis; Techniques—Applications," 531 pp. Arscia Uitgaven N. V. Publ., Brussels.

Wieme, R. J. (1959b). *Clin. Chim. Acta* **4**, 317–321.

Wieme, R. J., and Kaminski, M. (1955). *Bull. soc. chim. biol.* **37**, 247–253.

Williams, C. A., Jr. (1960). *Sci. Am.* **202**, 130–140.

Williams, C. A., Jr., and Grabar, P. (1955a). *J. Immunol.* **74**, 158–168.

Williams, C. A., Jr., and Grabar, P. (1955b). *J. Immunol.* **74**, 397–403.

Wilson, G. S., and Miles, A. A. (1955). "Topley and Wilson's Principles of Bacteriology and Immunity," 4th ed., 2331 pp. Williams & Wilkins Co., Baltimore, Maryland.

Wilson, M. W. (1958). *J. Immunol.* **81**, 317–330.

Wilson, M. W., and Pringle, B. H. (1954). *J. Immunol.* **73**, 232–243.

Wilson, M. W., and Pringle, B. H. (1955). *J. Immunol.* **75**, 460–469.

Wilson, M. W., and Pringle, B. H. (1956). *J. Immunol.* **77**, 324–331.

Witebsky, E., and Rose, N. R. (1959). *J. Immunol.* **83**, 41–48.

Wodehouse, R. P. (1953). *Ann. Allergy* **11**, 720–731.

Wodehouse, R. P. (1954a). *Ann. Allergy* **12**, 363–374.

Wodehouse, R. P. (1954b). *Intern. Arch. Allergy Appl. Immunol.* **5**, 337–366.

Wodehouse, R. P. (1954c). *Intern. Arch. Allergy Appl. Immunol.* **5**, 425–433.

Wodehouse, R. P. (1955a). *Ann. Allergy* **13**, 39–52.

Wodehouse, R. P. (1955b). *Intern. Arch. Allergy Appl. Immunol.* **6**, 65–79.

Wodehouse, R. P. (1956a). *Ann. Allergy* **14**, 96–113.

Wodehouse, R. P. (1956b). *Ann. Allergy* **14**, 121–138.

Wodehouse, R. P. (1957). *Ann. Allergy* **15**, 527–536.

Wolstenholme, G. E. W., and Millar, E. C. P. (eds.) (1956). "Ciba Foundation Symposium on Paper Electrophoresis," 224 pp. Little, Brown, Boston, Massachusetts.

Woodin, A. M. (1959). *Biochem. J.* **73**, 225–237.

Wright, S. T. C. (1959). *Nature* **183**, 1282–1283.

Wunderly, C. (1957). *Experientia* **13**, 421–464.

Wunderly, C. (1958a). *Clin. Chim. Acta* **3**, 298–299.

Wunderly, C. (1958b). *Deut. med. Wochschr.* **83**, 407–410.

Wunderly, C. (1959). *Naturwissenschaften* **46**, 107–108.

Yamaguchi, K. (1955). *Ann. Tuberc.* (*Nara, Japan*) **6**, 56–63.

Zach, J., and Zimmermann, K. (1959). *Klin. Wochschr.* **37**, 160–161.

Zalta, J. P., and Khouvine, Y. (1956). *Compt. rend. Soc. biol.* **150**, 339–342.

Zimmermann, G., and Kruger, K. (1959). *Pharmazie* **14**, 222–223.

Glossary

Absorben: antigen used to absorb its complementary antibodies from an antiserum. The term also can be applied to antibodies used to absorb complementary antigen.

Aggregation: the bridging of antigen-antibody complexes to form aggregates, in the second stage of antigen-antibody precipitation.

Anodic: adjective describing fractions appearing after electrophoretic separation on the anode side of their pre-electrophoresis origin.

Arc: in immunoelectrophoresis, the curved precipitin band formed by the indicator reactant diffusing in a straight front against a separated fraction.

Cathodic: the opposite of anodic and indicative of a fraction appearing after electrophoresis on the cathode side of its origin.

Coalescence: complete joining or fusion of two precipitin bands produced respectively by two compared reactants with a reference reactant and suggesting their immunologic identity; the reaction of fusion or identity.

Compared reactants: antigens reacted simultaneously with an antiserum or reference reactant in examination of their potential immunologic relationships; antisera similarly compared using a reference antigen.

Complex system: a mixture of two cross-reacting but not identical antigens reacted with antiserum specific for one of them but able also to react to a minor extent with the other.

Deviation: in the double diffusion plate test, deviation of a precipitin band from its expected course of precipitation by its growth into an area containing reactant cross-reacting with one of those forming it. Deviation often precedes coalescence.

Differentiation: in the staining of electrophoresis patterns, this is the process of removing stain from the background, that is, stain which is not fixed to the substance being stained. The word "de-stain" often is used as a substitute.

Double diffusion: an immunodiffusion test in which both antigen and antibody must diffuse more than a few microns before entering into the precipitin reaction, a test in which the diffusion of both reactants is required for precipitation to take place.

Double diffusion gradient test: a form of double diffusion test in which the paths of examined and indicator reactants cross each other, usually at right angles.

Electroosmosis: the flow of electrolyte fluid caused by passage of electric current through it while it is held within a charged gel or matrix. When the gel is agar and an alkaline buffer is employed, electroosmotic flow is strongly cathodic.

Electrophorese: a verb, coined from the noun electrophoresis, which has come into popular usage in place of such a phrase as "to submit something to electrophoresis."

Equivalence: in immunodiffusion tests this is the ratio between initial antigen and antibody concentrations at which their precipitin band is formed by their diffusion into it at immunologically equivalent rates. A band formed in the double diffusion test under these conditions would be sharp and immobile. This equivalence is not necessarily the same as an equivalence in liquid medium in a serial dilution test.

External reactant: in the single diffusion test this is the reactant, usually the antigen, which by its excess diffuses to form the specific precipitate in a matrix charged with the other (internal) reactant, usually antibody.

Flocculating antibody: the type of antibody, most commonly produced by the horse injected with protein antigens, which forms specific precipitates with its antigen which dissolve readily in either antigen or antibody excess. Since it is typified by horse antibody, often it is called "H-type antibody."

Fusion: see *Coalescence.*

Gap: when R-type antibody is used in the single diffusion test, antigen diffusing through it forms a precipitin band sharp in front but trailing out to the rear. A sudden change in incubation temperature may cause the ordinarily continuous formation of precipitate at the band's front, under given steady conditions, to be interrupted, so that, temporarily, precipitate is formed at a different rate at the band front. Precipitation fails in a narrow portion of the agar leaving a gap in the otherwise regular precipitate trail behind the moving band front. Gaps can form with H-type antibody, but are likely to disappear again quickly. An opposite condition results in temporary intensification of precipitation at the band front, so that when the front moves on down the tube it leaves behind an area of intensified precipitation commonly called a *stria.* Striae formed by H-type antibody also may be only temporary. Often, a gap will form just below a stria, or vice versa.

H-type antibody: see flocculating antibody.

Immunodiffusion: a word recently introduced by several authors to describe serologic tests occurring in or on media of restricted fluidity, and in which reactants mix solely by diffusion. For example, this term conveniently replaces the confusing phrase "agar diffusion precipitin test."

Immunoelectropherogram: a term sometimes used in place of the phrase "immunoelectrophoresis separation pattern" and similar expressions. Occasionally, this has been shortened to the word "immunogram" which, however, more properly would refer to the precipitate band pattern produced in single or double diffusion patterns in which electrophoresis has not been used.

Immunoelectrophoresis: a technique in which instead of stains the precipitin reaction (that is, immunodiffusion) is employed to reveal electrophoretically separated fractions. Generally, *immunoelectrophoresis* refers only to tests in which both electrophoresis and subsequent immunodiffusion occur in the same medium, but it also can be applied to techniques in which a substance is electrophoresed in one medium and the separated constituents are allowed to diffuse directly from this medium into another for precipitin reactions to take place.

Immunogram: this word has been used to refer to the precipitate band pattern produced in immunodiffusion tests not employing electrophoresis; see *Immunoelectropherogram.*

Indicator reactant: the reactant used to detect and indicate electrophoresed fractions in immunoelectrophoresis by its reaction with these to form specific precipitate arcs corresponding to each of these.

Interference phenomenon: in immunodiffusion, the reaction responsible for coalescence or fusion (cf.), in which, within a moderate range of reactant equivalence, the specific precipitate band acts as an immunologic barrier to both reactants but not to incompletely cross-reacting substances. Thus, there is an interference with diffusion of either reactant which may be manifested in any of several ways.

Internal reactant: the reactant in the single diffusion test of serologically lower concentration, usually the antibody, into which the external reactant (cf.), usually antigen, diffuses to produce a precipitin band.

Ionicity: a shortened term for ionic strength (cf.).

Ionic strength: an expression for the conductivity of an electrolyte solution; it is one-half the sum of the molality of all electrolyte ions present in the solution times the square of each one's valence. Since this value often is difficult to calculate because dissociation of salts, acids, and bases (particularly weak ones) varies considerably with their concentration, the pH of the solution, its temperature, and other factors, conductivity actually determined for the solution being used relative to some standard should be more valuable in a report of an immunoelectrophoretic experiment than anything short of giving the formula for the electrolyte employed.

Liesegang phenomenon: a type of secondary antigen-antibody precipitate formed usually when reactant quantities are large, and one is excessive relative to the other. It is most readily seen in single diffusion tests. The phenomenon sometimes is referred to as periodic precipitation. Originally, *Liesegang phenomenon* referred solely to periodic precipitation between two inorganic solutions, but recent evidence and theories suggest that its application to periodic antigen-antibody precipitation is logical.

Looping: a term meaning the same as fusion or coalescence (see the latter).

Matrix: can have two meanings. It can be the gel or supporting medium in which an immunodiffusion reaction is carried out, or, less preferably, it can be used as an alternate for *template* to designate a device in which there are several holes to receive reactants and which is laid upon the gel so as to feed these into the gel in the same pattern as used in the hole arrangement.

Multiple system: one in which antigen antibody systems acting independently of each other form precipitin bands which have no influence on each others' shape, position, or aggregation.

Nonspecific substances: often abbreviated n.s.s., this term designates substances of no specific serologic activity such as salts, carbohydrates, or proteins unrelated to antigen-antibody systems being studied, but which physically may affect the activity of one or more of these systems, such as in the rate of precipitin band migration in single diffusion tests or a band's optical density.

Pattern of fusion: is formed between two immunologically identical antigens reacting with an antibody in any comparator cell or plate immunodiffusion test. The bands formed by each antigen independently on approaching each other at their respective tips tend to bend toward each other by the interference phenomenon and finally fuse or coalesce.

Pattern of intersection: the pattern produced when two unrelated antigens reacting in any comparator cell or plate with antiserum containing antibodies to both of them form precipitin bands indifferently crossing each other, or a similar pattern produced on comparison of two different species of antibodies against a single mixture of their respective antigens.

Pattern of partial intersection: the pattern produced when partially related antigens are compared using a single antiserum, their bands extending beyond the point of crossing being acutely curved and distinctly fainter than they were before the point of crossing.

Precipitating antibody: often used to indicate a precipitin typified by those produced by rabbits which forms a precipitate with its antigen practically insoluble in antibody excess and often not readily soluble in antigen excess. Often it is called rabbit-type or "R"-type antibody, although other commonly used laboratory animals preferentially form this antibody rather than the flocculating or H-type antibody.

Precipitin: antibody capable of forming a precipitate with its antigen; it may be of either the R-type or H-type.

Precipitinogen: antigen stimulating precipitin formation on injection into an animal.

Printing off: the process of laying a strip of filter paper upon agar gel over the plane of electrophoresis, so that the paper absorbs from the gel's surface small quantities of the separated fractions. This strip then is removed and stained and serves as a convenient gross detector of fraction positions without affecting the original electropherogram.

R-type antibody: see *Precipitating antibody.*

React: a verb recently appearing in written reports in transitive or intransitive form to replace such a phrase as "antigen and antibody were allowed to react" with "antigen and antibody were reacted."

Reaction of identity: see *Pattern of fusion.*

Reaction of nonidentity: see *Pattern of intersection.*

Reaction of partial identity: see *Pattern of partial intersection.* These three terms are older and therefore have been used more frequently than the *pattern* terms, but they can be misleading, since a pattern of fusion can be given by nonidentical antigens.

Simple diffusion: derived from the same term used in French by J. Oudin, describes an immunodiffusion test in which diffusion of one reactant, the internal reactant, is insignificant by comparison with diffusion of the other, the external reactant. The term *single diffusion* means the same, and it is preferable in English usage.

Simple system: an antigen-antibody system in an immunodiffusion test producing only one precipitin band; hence, also a *single system.*

Single diffusion: see *Simple diffusion.* This term is more descriptive than *simple diffusion* and by the context in which the French term, *diffusion simple,* originally was used probably is more correct than the presently more frequently used English translation, *simple diffusion.*

Specific precipitation: in immunodiffusion this term designates antigen-antibody precipitation as opposed to precipitation of antigen or antibody by something other than its serologic counterpart.

Spur: an extension of a precipitin band beyond a point of partial fusion between it and another band growing into it; the weaker, acutely curved band seen in the pattern of partial intersection (cf.).

Stria (*pl. striae*): an area or band of increased optical density in the trailing edge of a precipitin band moving in the single diffusion test through the internal reactant and caused by temporary build-up of specific precipitate at the front of the moving band. This in turn has been brought on by a sudden change in the external reactant's diffusion rate, such as by sudden temperature change. This name can be applied to such a band sometimes observed in any of various other types of immunodiffusion tests. Often it is associated with a gap (cf.).

Template: a form, usually made of stiff, transparent plastic, in which are drilled holes to serve as holders of reactant solutions in immunodiffusion tests. The template is laid directly upon the medium in which precipitation is to occur and feeds the reactants into this medium.

APPENDIX I

Freund's Adjuvant

1. Incomplete type (without mycobacteria), two formulas.
   a. 3 parts light mineral oil U.S.P.
      1 part Aquaphore, Falba, or anhydrous lanolin
      4 parts physiologic phosphate buffer
   b. 4 parts n-hexadecane
      1 part glycerol monooleate (Myverol®, Distillation Products, Inc.)
      10 parts physiologic phosphate buffer
2. Complete type (with mycobacteria).

Add mycobacteria (living avirulent tubercle bacilli, heat-killed virulent tubercle bacilli, *Mycobacterium butyricum*, or *M. smegmatis*) to make a final concentration by moist weight of 10 mg. per ml. of water-in-oil emulsion. The same final concentration of any particular antigen can be used. Bacilli and antigen should be suspended in the aqueous phase before emulsification.

3. Emulsification.

Emulsifier (e.g., glycerol monooleate) is dissolved in oil, and oil is layered upon water. Water-in-oil emulsions are obtained by mixing these two phases together vigorously with a syringe and large gauge needle, vibrator, high speed stirrer, or other such instrument. For example, one can employ a high-speed engraving tool in which is chucked a 2½ inch box nail as impeller. With this nail rotating at high speed (e.g., 15,000 r.p.m. or more), its head slowly is lowered into the mixture causing emulsification to proceed from top to bottom. The stability of a water-in-oil emulsion can be tested by dropping some on cold water; the drop should remain intact.

APPENDIX II

Selected Immunodiffusion Electrolyte Solutions

(All formulas are made up to 1 liter)

1. Isotonic sodium chloride, ionicity 0.15, pH variable.
   8.8 gm. sodium chloride
2. Barbital, ionicity 0.15,* pH 7.4.
   6.98 gm. sodium barbital
   6.0 gm. sodium chloride
   2.7 ml. 1 N hydrochloric acid
3. Phosphate, ionicity 0.15*, pH 7.4.
   12.8 gm. Na_2HPO_4
   2.62 gm. $NaH_2PO_4 \cdot H_2O$
4. TRIS, ionicity 0.15*, pH 7.4.
   9.3 gm. 2-amino-2-(hydroxymethyl)-1,3-propanediol
   74 ml. 1 N hydrochloric acid
   7.0 gm. sodium chloride
5. Ethylenediamine-acetic acid, ionicity 0.15*, pH 7.4
   15.8 gm. ethylenediamine
   23.8 gm. glacial acetic acid

Allow to stand for 24 hours to permit maximum electrolyte dissociation.

* Ionic strengths have been determined by electric conductivity in comparison with isotonic sodium chloride.

APPENDIX III

Selected Immunoelectrophoresis Buffers

(All formulas are made up to 1 liter*)

1. Barbital, ionicity 0.1, pH 8.2.
   15.85 gm. sodium barbital
   770 ml. distilled water
   230 ml. 0.1 N hydrochloric acid
2. Barbital-acetate, ionicity 0.05,† pH 8.6.
   5.4 gm. sodium barbital
   4.3 gm. sodium acetate · $3H_2O$
   58.2 ml. 0.1 N hydrochloric acid
3. Borate, ionicity 0.05,† pH 8.6.
   6.7 gm. boric acid
   13.4 gm. sodium borate · $10H_2O$
4. Ethylenediamine-acetic acid, ionicity 0.05,† pH 8.2.
   2.5 gm. ethylenediamine
   2.4 gm. glacial acetic acid

Allow to stand for 24 hours before using to permit maximum electrolyte dissociation.

5. Phosphate, ionicity 0.05,† pH 7.4.
   6.4 gm. Na_2HPO_4
   1.3 gm. NaH_2PO_4 · H_2O

* As a preservative, 100 mg. of thimerosal (Merthiolate®, Lilly) can be added to the liter of each of these buffers; in buffer No. 3, the borate itself acts as a preservative.

† Ionic strengths have been determined by electric conductivity in comparison with sodium chloride solution.

APPENDIX IV

Selected Protein Stains

1. Thiazine red R (Crowle, 1958c).
   0.1 gm. thiazine red R
   100 ml. 1% acetic acid

Differentiate in 70% ethanol containing 1% acetic acid.

2. Crocein scarlet MOO (Crowle, unpublished).
   0.3 gm. crocein scarlet MOO
   5 gm. trichloracetic acid
   25 ml. 95% ethanol
   75 ml. 1% acetic acid

Differentiate in 70% ethanol containing 1% acetic acid. Crocein scarlet MOO can be replaced with the dyes amidoschwarz 10B, light green SF, or azocarmine G.

3. Amidoschwarz (Uriel, 1958a).
   0.1 gm. amidoschwarz 10B
   45 ml. 12% acetic acid
   45 ml. 1.6% sodium acetate
   10 ml. glycerol

Differentiate in 2% acetic acid.

4. Azocarmine B, for cellulose acetate (Kohn, 1957).
   0.05 gm. azocarmine B
   100 ml. 2% acetic acid

Differentiate in 2% acetic acid.

5. Nigrosin, for cellulose acetate (Kohn, 1958).
   5 mg. nigrosin, water-soluble
   100 ml. 2% acetic acid

Wash cellulose acetate matrix free of unreacted antigen and antibody. Soak in stain for one hour; differentiate with 2% acetic acid. Dry strip between filter paper under pressure.

6. Bromphenol blue (Hayward and Augustin, 1957).
   0.1 gm. bromphenol blue
   100 ml. 90% ethanol

Bring agar to 90% ethanol before staining. Differentiate in 90% ethanol. Soak in dilute glycerine, dry agar, and expose it to ammonia vapor.

NOTE: The above stains can be applied to agar gels either before or after they have been dried, preferably after. In either event, they should be free of most alkaline salts before they are stained. Staining time will vary with the dye and the thickness of the agar from about 15 minutes for the agar used in microscope slide techniques or dried agar to several hours in macro techniques employing agar several millimeters thick that has not been dried.

APPENDIX V

Selected Lipid Stains

1. Sudan black B (Grabar, 1959a; Uriel, 1958a; Uriel and Grabar, 1956a).
   100 ml. 60% ethanol
   sufficient Sudan black B to saturate this ethanol at 37°C

Cool solution to room temperature and filter. Just before use, filter again and add 0.1 ml. of 25% sodium hydroxide solution for every 50 ml. of dye. Stain from a few minutes (micro techniques) to 2 or more hours (macro techniques); differentiate with 50% ethanol. Preferably apply to dried agar.

2. Oil red O (Grabar, 1959a; Uriel, 1958a; Uriel and Grabar, 1956a).
   100 ml. 60% ethanol
   sufficient oil red O to saturate this ethanol at 37°C

Cool solution to room temperature and filter. Filter again just before use. Stain for 30–60 minutes (micro techniques) or for several hours (macro techniques). Differentiate with 50% ethanol. Preferably apply to dried agar.

3. Nile blue A (Crowle, unpublished).
   0.1 gm. Nile blue A
   100 ml. 1% sulfuric acid

Boil for 5 minutes, cool before using. Stain as required (15–20 minutes for micro techniques), and differentiate with 1% sulfuric acid. Wash, before drying, with distilled water and then distilled water containing 1% glycerol.

APPENDIX VI

Selected Double Stains

1. For protein and lipid (Uriel and Scheidegger, 1955)
   50 mg. bromphenol blue or amidoschwarz 10B
   2 ml. acetic acid
   100 ml. 60% ethanol saturated with oil red O

   Stain pre-dried agar as required. Differentiate with 50% ethanol containing 1% acetic acid. If bromphenol blue version is used, expose dried slide to ammonia vapor.

2. For protein and lipid (Uriel and Scheidegger, 1955)
   50 mg. azocarmine B
   2 ml. acetic acid
   100 ml. 60% ethanol saturated with Sudan black B

   Stain pre-dried agar as required. Differentiate with 50% ethanol containing 1% acetic acid.

3. For protein on cellulose acetate strips (Consden and Kohn, 1959)
   a. 150 mg. Ponceau S
      3 gm. trichloracetic acid
      100 ml. distilled water
   b. 2.5 mg. nigrosin WS
      2 gm. acetic acid
      100 ml. distilled water

   Stain first with solution *a* and then with solution *b*, both for about 30 minutes. Differentiate in 2% acetic acid.

4. For protein (Crowle, unpublished)
   a. 1 gm. light green SF
      1 gm. acetic acid
      100 ml. distilled water
   b. 0.1 gm. thiazine red R
      1 gm. acetic acid
      100 ml. distilled water

   Stain with solution *a*, differentiate with 1% acetic acid; stain with solution *b*, differentiate with 1% acetic acid. Staining time for micro tests is about 15 minutes for each stain.

5. For protein, triple stain (Crowle, unpublished)
   0.1 gm. thiazine red R
   0.1 gm. amidoswarz 10B
   0.1 gm. light green SF
   2 gm. acetic acid
   0.1 gm. mercuric chloride
   100 ml. distilled water

Stain as required (15 minutes for micro tests); differentiate with 2% acetic acid.

APPENDIX VII

Selected Polysaccharide Stains

(To be used on pre-dried agar)

1. Schiff reagent (Uriel and Grabar, 1956a)
   A. Solutions
      a. 1.5 gm. basic fuchsin
        500 ml. boiling distilled water
        Filter at 55°C and cool to 40°C. Add
        25 ml. 2 N hydrochloric acid
        3.75 gm. $Na_2S_2O_5$
        Agitate to ensure rapid solution. Allow to stand stoppered in refrigerator for 6 hours. Add
        1.2 gm. animal charcoal

Mix vigorously for 50 seconds and filter rapidly, filtration time not exceeding 2–3 minutes. Store stoppered in refrigerator.

   b. 1.0 gm. periodic acid
     0.82 gm. anhydrous sodium acetate
     100 ml. distilled water
   c. 0.54 gm. acetic acid
     0.89 gm. anhydrous sodium acetate
     10 gm. hydroxylamine hydrochloride
     100 ml. distilled water
   d. 5 ml. 10% $Na_2S_2O_5$
     5 ml. 2 N hydrochloric acid
     90 ml. distilled water

Solution d should be made just before it is used. This also serves as the final wash bath when it contains 20% glycerol.

B. Procedure
   Soak pre-dried agar in c for 15 minutes.
   Wash in running water for 15 minutes.
   Soak in b for 10 minutes.
   Wash in running water for 10 minutes.
   Soak in a, diluted immediately before use with an equal volume of distilled water, for 3 minutes.
   Wash 3 times for 2 minutes each in d.
   Wash 3 times for 1 hour each in glycerinated d.
   Dry agar in warm air oven.

2. *p*-Phenylenediamine oxidation reaction (Grabar, 1959a; Uriel, 1958a)
A. Solutions
   a. 1 gm. periodic acid
     1.64 gm. anhydrous sodium acetate
     100 ml. 50% ethanol
   b. 144 mg. α naphthol
     100 ml. distilled water
     Dissolve with heat and then cool.
   c. 108 mg. *p*-phenylenediamine
     100 ml. distilled water
     Prepared immediately before using.
   d. 10% hydrogen peroxide
B. Procedure
   Soak pre-dried agar for 15 minutes in *a*.
   Wash for 10 minutes in running water for 5 minutes in distilled water.
   Soak for 5–10 minutes in solutions of *b:c:d* = 5:5:1, freshly mixed.
   Wash for 10 minutes in running water and finally in distilled water.
   Air-dry in warm oven.
3. Alcian blue (adapted from Heremans and Vaerman, 1958)
   0.1 gm. alcian blue
   10 gm. acetic acid
   100 ml. distilled water

Stain as required (15 minutes or more for micro tests). Differentiate with 1% acetic acid.

4. Mayer's mucicarmine (adapted from Björklund, 1954a)
   0.1 gm. Mayer's mucicarmine
   100 ml. 50% ethanol

Stain as required (15 minutes or more for micro tests). Differentiate with 50% ethanol.

5. Basic fuchsin (Björklund, 1954a)
   0.4 gm. basic fuchsin
   1 ml. acetic acid
   100 ml. 70% ethanol

Stain as required (2 hours or less in Petri dish double diffusion tests). Differentiate with 70% ethanol.

Subject Index

A

Absorben, uses of, 250, 251, 253, 295

Acetic acid, 257, 267

Acetone, use in agar purification, 195

Acetylphosphatides, stain for, 275

Acid dyes, protein staining with, 270

Acid fumes, test enhancement with, 228, 257

Acids
  in gel swelling and shrinkage, 22
  test enhancement with, 228, 257

Acquired hemolytic anemia, hapto-globins in, 120

Acrylamide gels, see Cyanogum 41

Addition of specific reactant, for precipitin band identification, 253

Additives for gel solvents, *193*
  effects of, 23, 194
  gelatin, 92
  glycine, 92
  as pH indicators, 194
  purposes of, 92, 194

Adenovirus, cytotoxin of, 139, 151, 163

Adjuvants, 186, 301

Adrenal gland, antigens of, 108

Affinity, antigen for antibody, 175

Agammaglobulinemia, 110, 128

Agar, *21*
  calcium salt of, 195
  chemical alteration to potassium salt, 195
  combination with lysozyme, 245
  deionization of, 196
  depression of lipoprotein solubility by, 244
  destaining of, 272
  differences from other gel media, 245
  drying of, 243
  impurity of, precipitating serum protein, 245
  properties of, 22, 195, 196
  purification of, 195, 196

selection of, for immunoelectrophoresis, 242

use with other media for immunoelectrophoresis, 201–202

Agar coating, for glass surfaces, 204, 207

Agar concentration, effect on diffusion rates, 45

Agar cutters, 204, 214

Agar gel
  effects on immunodiffusion tests, 24, 34, 42, 45, 191
  gelling-melting cycles, effects on, 45, 196
  maximum usable concentration, 159
  mixture with absorben, 253
  monovalent ion form, 195
  properties of, 21–22, 24

Agar punches, 204

Agglutination, 11, 124

Agglutinin(s), 242
  cold, in diagnosis, 126
  erythrocyte, immunoelectrophoretic mobility of, 166

Aggregates, antigen-antibody, subvisible, 82, 86, 176, 261

Aggregation, antigen-antibody, 15, 169–170, 295

Aging, as a cause of antigen changes and reactant transmutation, 99, 101, 244

Alastrim virus, identification of, 132

Albumin
  bovine serum, 153–154, 158, 161–162, 168, 176, 185
  human serum, 99, 102, 103, 104, 116, 153, 158, 173
  human, placental, 103

Albuminoids, chemistry of, *153*

Albumins, diffusion coefficient determinations of, 157

Alcian blue, polysaccharide stain, 274, 310

311

uses and procedures, 5, 183, 202–203, 207–208, 218

varieties of, 204

Small animals, useful for antiserum production, 184

Smallpox virus, identification of, 132

Snake serum, *see Vipera aspis*

Snakes, taxonomy, *133*

Sodium azide, electrolyte and preservative, 189, 193

Sodium barbital, solvent buffer, 189

Sodium bicarbonate, solvent buffer, 189

Sodium borate, solvent buffer and preservative, 189

Sodium chloride, buffer electrolyte and additive, 30, 189, 194

Sodium citrate, solvent buffer, 189

Sodium dodecyl sulfate, reversal of antigen-antibody aggregation with, 177

Sodium ethylenediaminetetracetate, chelator for calcium, 193

Sodium hydroxide, special use with Sudan black solutions, 273

Sodium phosphate, solvent buffer, 189

Soluble antigen-antibody complexes, 169, 173

Special uses, for various species of antisera, 185–186

Specific absorption, 250, *251*, 253, 255

Specific dissolution, use for band identification, 237

Specific gravity, convection currents caused by, 43

Specific ions, in antigen-antibody precipitation, *170*

Specificity

of antibody, 17, 174–176, 177

maximum, 188

of precipitin reaction, both stages, 12–13

Sperm antigens, 108, 140

Sperm plasma antigens, 104, 244

Spleen antigens, 108, 240

Sporotrichum, taxonomy, 132

Spray, antigen, to detect electrophoresed antibody, 202

Spur, conditions for formation and interpretation of, 71–74, 135, 299

Spurious precipitin band formation, 69, 223

Spurring, effects of antigenic determinants on, 74

Sputum, in pathology, *120*

SSS, 4

Stability of reactants, *244*

Stability of specific precipitate, 13, 171, 175

Stabilization of reactants, with gelatin, 198

Stainability, lack of, as complication, 244

Staining, purposes and procedures for, 201, 269, 270–273

Stains, *see also* individual stains and substances stained

double, value of, 273

for increasing test sensitivity, 228, 257

negative and positive, 8

special, 200

Staphylococcus, 143

antigens, 6, 143–144, 151, 163, 170, 184, 185

antibodies to, human, 125

infection, *123*

relationship to *Listeria,* 144

toxigenicity and virulence, 150

Starch gel

antigens electrophoresed in, 99–101

characteristics of, 21–22, 35, 246

immunoelectrophoresis performed with, 202, 235, 245

Stork, taxonomy, 135

Streptococcus, 130, 139, *144*

antigens of, 144–145, 163

antiserum to, 185

infection, diagnosis of, *123*

Streptolysin O, 123, 145, 163, 184

Streptomycin, use of as preservative, 193

Stress, physiological, detection of with single diffusion test, 102

Striae, 53–55, 186

Structural changes in antigen, induction and detection of, 156

Substitution technique, for band identification, 255–256

Subvisible antigen-antibody complexes, revelation of, 170

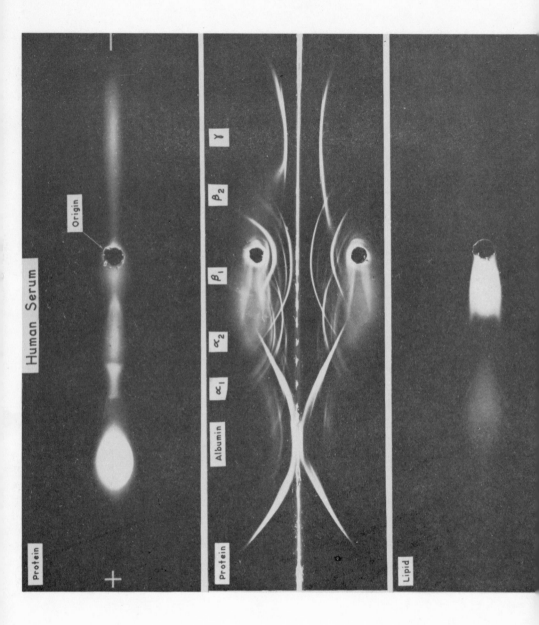

Frontispiece. Analysis of human serum by agar electrophoresis and immunoelectrophoresis and by use of specific stains for protein, lipid, and glycoprotein.
Electrophoresis was carried out on siliconized microscope slides under Plexiglass
templates in pH 8.2 barbital buffer of 0.1 ionic strength and at 70 volts for 90
minutes. Immunoprecipitation was continued for three of the slides under templates
feeding Pasteur Institute horse antiserum to human serum from a central slot into